ANIMAL WORLDS

Photographs by

Emil Schulthess

Fritz Goro

Eliot Porter

George Holton

Weldon King

Ylla

Sven Gillsater

Ron Church

and others

Drawings by Kenneth Gosner

A CHANTICLEER PRESS EDITION

ANIMAL WORLDS

by Marston Bates

RANDOM HOUSE, NEW YORK

Published, 1963, in New York by Random House, Inc.,

and simultaneously in Toronto, Canada,

by Random House of Canada, Limited

Planned and produced by Chanticleer Press, Inc., New York

Library of Congress Catalog Number: 63-14144

Manufactured in the United States of America

Special map credits: Page 196, left, based on a map from
"Migration of Birds" by Frederick C. Lincoln,
copyright 1939, Doubleday & Company, Inc.; right, adapted
from a map from "Birds of Arabia" by R. Meinertzhagen.

Contents

FOREWORD

This book might well have been called an animal natural history, but the term "natural history" is not so fashionable as it used to be. The current word is "ecology," which is defined as the study of the relations between organisms and their environments. Since other organisms are part of the environment of every individual, ecology necessarily includes the study of interactions among animals and of the behavior of animals and plants, though this is often neglected in ecology books.

Animal Worlds could be called ecological because it is an examination of some of the ways in which animals have adapted to the range of environments on the planetary surface, from ocean depths to mountain heights and from tropics to poles. Such a survey is necessarily selective, partly because no one author can master all of the materials, partly because it is impossible to cover the entire subject within reasonable space and still make it understandable in nontechnical terms. Our concern is with animals—from subvisible creatures to elephants and whales—but this whole animal system depends on plants, which have been given only incidental attention in the text.

As far as possible, I have tried to illustrate various points with descriptions of the behavior of particular animals—supplemented by the splendid photographs that the editors have collected. Thus, the coverage of the animal kingdom is hardly uniform, and the points often might equally well have been supported with quite different cases. I have not dealt with the problem of whether a given species truly represents its genus, family, order, class, or phylum, for my aim was to survey animal environments, not animals per se, which have been covered in many other books.

Among the million-odd kinds of animals, there is a curious species called *Homo sapiens* which has effected every part of the animal world in one way or another. The man-altered landscape is rapidly approaching domination of the planet and we urgently need to arrive at a better understanding of the meaning of this. For this reason, toward the end of the book, I have concentrated on the relationships between man and other animals.

The man-altered landscape is still only one of the many worlds of animal life— and all of them are fascinating. In surveying these worlds, it is logical to start with the seas, because the evidence indicates that life started there, and all living things can still be looked at as more or less modified packages of sea water adapted to the diverse conditions of the planetary surface. How animals have adapted to the swift currents of mountain brooks, the dryness of deserts, the cold of tundra, the remoteness of oceanic islands, the thin air of mountains, and finally how some animals have met the problem of getting along with man, is the main theme of the book. This adaptation involves structure, physiology and behavior; and the same problems have often been solved in quite different ways by different animals, even though the broad patterns of life remain similar everywhere.

But to perceive this we must look at the animals in their various worlds.

I

The Conditions
of Animal Life

Life—as we know it at any rate—is confined to the surface of our planet. It can be looked at as a sort of thin film spread over that surface and called the biosphere, lying between the atmosphere above and the solid lithosphere below. In the seas, living things occur from the surface to the greatest depths, so that the maximum thickness of that part of the biosphere is something like 35,800 feet. In the air, no organism can maintain itself indefinitely without support. Birds, to be sure, can fly to considerable heights; and various forms of life like insects, spores, and pollen can float with atmospheric currents; but always, in the end, they must return to the surface of the earth. On land, then, aside from these temporary excursions upward, the maximum thickness of the biosphere would correspond with the greatest height of forest trees. The tallest known trees are the redwoods of California, reaching up to 364 feet, and the eucalyptus of Australia, reaching 350 feet. We may add a few feet for the penetration of living things into the soil; but our biosphere remains a thin film indeed.

Life, of course, follows the contours of the mountains, reaching up to and beyond the line of permanent snow. It may also extend to considerable depths in caves and underground streams. But compared with the 4000-mile radius of the solid planet, or the upward extension of atmospheric gases for a hundred miles or so, this is still a narrow zone.

The biosphere is the world of life, the network of animals, plants, and subvisible organisms that envelops our planetary surface. In a real sense, it is one world, an interconnected system in which every part is related in some way, however remote, to every other part. Yet it is also many worlds—deserts, mountains, forests, streams, and open seas—each with its own types of inhabitants, its own kinds of patterns of living. Before looking at these many worlds, at the diversity of nature, we should look at the unity, at some of the general principles that characterize living systems.

The Beginnings of Life

There is not much use in trying to define life. We all think we know what we mean by the word, and ordinarily manage to use it without much difficulty. When we try to define it, trouble starts. The children ask whether the Christmas tree is dead, and we don't know what to answer. Out in the fields is was clearly alive; brown and dried out, it is clearly dead. I suppose the tree, as such, is dead as soon

as it is cut, although the tissues continue to function for a short while. If the Christmas tree happened to be a red cedar, a really skillful gardener could cut off pieces and start them growing again, though most conifers are difficult or impossible to propagate from cuttings.

Many kinds of plants grow easily from cuttings; some will even grow from fragments of leaves. In parts of the tropics one commonly sees fence posts sprouting branches, continuing to grow, to live. Most animals, of course, die if they are cut in pieces, though this is not true of some of the lower invertebrates like flatworms and earthworms. But there is no use in laboring the point that it is sometimes difficult to tell when life stops.

On the other hand, there is the question of when life starts. Life as we know it now is always a continuing process; living things always come from other living things. It must all have got started somewhere, sometime—but if we could go back and watch the beginnings, we would surely find it difficult to point to a precise stage at which we could say that the nonliving had come to life.

Most biologists today believe that life started on this earth under conditions very different from those prevailing now. The early atmosphere probably did not contain either oxygen or carbon dioxide. These gases, which we think of as essential to life, were in the first place consequences of life. The chief gases in the earth's early atmosphere may have been water vapor, methane, ammonia, and hydrogen. In 1953, S. L. Miller, working under Harold Urey at the University of Chicago, demonstrated that if these gases were circulated continuously in the presence of an electric spark, amino acids—the basic building blocks of living stuff—would be formed.

One can imagine that, in the turbulent early days of the earth, the seas slowly became a sort of thin, organic soup; and that somehow, in this soup, a kind of self-duplicating process got started. When both growth and self-reproduction had developed, life had clearly begun. But something like a billion years may have passed before this diffuse organic stuff had become the definitely organized animals and plants that we find as the earliest known fossils. The intermediate stages, slowly unfolding over this immensity of time, are hard to imagine. Our fragmentary record, then, covers only half of the presumed history of life.

Plants, animals, and microbes are present in a diversity of forms among the first fossils—life is already organized essentially as we find it today, and most of the major types of organisms have already evolved. To be sure, the early fossils are all marine, and as we follow the record over its hundreds of millions of years, we can glimpse the way life extended from the seas to the land and to inland waters. We can follow the evolution of many groups, including the flowering plants and the vertebrates that form such a conspicuous part of the living world today. We can see shifts in the relative importance of major organic types—mosses and ferns giving way to seed plants, reptiles to mammals and birds. We can watch an endless procession of species come and go. But the basic pattern of relationships among these organisms—the way in which the biological community is organized—does not change. It was already established before our record begins.

The Food Web

Community structure turns essentially on the question of who eats whom, with green plants—or rather, chlorophyll-bearing plants—always at the base of the eating

The animal community depends essentially on who eats whom. Here, a nephila spider prepares to devour a praying mantis. (Sven Gillsater)

system. In many algae and in some other plants, the green of the chlorophyll is masked by pigments of other colors, but the chlorophyll is there playing its part in the process of converting the radiant energy of the sun into the chemical energy of the sugars and starches that keep the rest of the system going.

One might call these chlorophyll-bearing plants the *producers* of the community. They themselves use part of the chemical energy that they build up for their own maintenance, growth, and reproduction; but they also pass the energy source on to the animals that eat them, the *consumers* of the community. The animals that live directly off the plants can be thought of as first-order consumers—or, in the phrase of the British ecologist Charles Elton, as "key-industry animals," since the economy of all of the other animals depends on them.

Animals live off each other in endlessly diverse ways, and it is difficult to make a general and comprehensive classification of their food habits. One way of dealing with this is to group animals according to the degree of their remoteness from the producing system as second-, third-, or fourth-order consumers. It is difficult to get much beyond this because there is a great loss of energy with each step away from those basic plants on which all else depends: a sixth-order consumer simply wouldn't be able to find enough food.

This sort of series is sometimes described as a "food chain," with its links illustrated by some such sequence as grass–grasshoppers–frogs–snakes–hawks. But "chain" is a misleading term. Grasshoppers may eat many kinds of vegetation, and be eaten in turn by many other kinds of animals; frogs, similarly, eat almost any kind of small insect they can catch, and all sorts of things like to eat frogs. We ourselves are first-order consumers when we eat spinach or potatoes; second-order consumers when we eat beef; third- or fourth-order when we eat many kinds of fish. Any attempt to describe a real situation shows a complex network of food relationships, and the whole system is perhaps best called a "food web."

In general, the first-order consumers tend to be small and very numerous, the second-order ones larger and less numerous, and so on, building up a series often referred to as the "pyramid of numbers." Of course small animals sometimes eat bigger ones—mosquitoes or fleas feeding on human beings or dogs—and very big animals sometimes live on very small ones—whales filtering tiny organisms from the seas. And big animals like grazing mammals (or elephants) may be first-order consumers, living directly off vegetation. But the relationship between numbers and size and food level holds in most cases.

Then too we have the *decomposers,* which can intervene at any stage to convert other organisms back to dust again. One can argue that the decomposers are simply a final stage in the consuming system, but there is a certain convenience in treating them as a separate category. Much organic material never goes through the animal consumer system at all: plants grow, die, and are decomposed into their component chemicals. Walking through a woodland, I can imagine this going on even if all of the animals were removed; but I cannot imagine the producer system without the decomposers. If trees never died or, dying, did not rot, the whole forest would become a hopeless mess, without room for any new or continuing growth.

The decomposers are mostly bacteria and fungi. If we wanted to be very precise, I suppose we could class any organism that attacked dead material as part of the decomposing system, so that vultures, hyenas, maggots, and all sorts of animal life would be included. Such animals certainly hasten the breakup process: tree trunks riddled by beetle larvae or termites rot much faster than wood that remains intact. But the final decay, the ultimate dissolution, is largely due to the action of bacteria, molds, and their relatives.

In a general way, then, and allowing for many exceptions, the producers are plants, the consumers are animals, and the decomposers are micro-organisms. The animal part of the system is completely dependent on the plant part, and one cannot imagine either continuing without the microbes—not only because of the importance of decomposition, but also because of the role of microbes in many of the essential chemical cycles of the biological community.

This line of reasoning makes the animals seem relatively unimportant. Insects, to be sure, are useful to plants in pollinating their flowers, birds in spreading their seeds, and earthworms in aerating the soil. But in the grand system of nature all these animals are a sort of frosting on the cake—a complex and fascinating frosting, and one could easily argue that it is the most interesting part of the cake. Yet there would still be a cake without the frosting—though to us, as one variety of animal, it would seem pretty dull.

A food chain.

Animal or Vegetable?

I am using the word "animal" as distinct from "plant." It has two other meanings in common usage: one contrasting with human, the other corresponding with mammal and contrasting with birds, reptiles, and fishes. Neither of these latter

Vultures, feeding on a lion carcass in Africa, do their part in the food web. (Ylla: Rapho-Guillumette)

meanings has any status in biology; but biologists have no patent on the word.

In the matter of "animal" versus "plant," there is room for considerable difference of opinion. We think of animals as moving, active organisms—having "spirit" *(animus)*, to go back to the origin of the word. But a great many animals like corals, sponges, and barnacles are just as fixed as any plant. And then there are the slime molds, which are generally classed as plants but which creep around. Insofar as plants form the producing system, they must have chlorophyll. But the numerous kinds of fungi—mushrooms, molds, and the like—all lack chlorophyll.

Animals and plants are sometimes separated on the basis of how they get their food: animals ingest food, plants absorb it. In other words, animals swallow things and deal with them through a digestive system inside the body, while plants take in the materials they need through the surfaces of roots, stems, or leaves. Yet some parasitic animals absorb food through the body surface. And just to further confound things, there are a few plants, like Venus' flytrap, that catch animals—though these still digest the trapped animals in an outside receptacle and absorb the products.

The sharp-eyed tick bird finds its food on the rhino—and serves in turn as sentinel. (Ylla: Rapho-Guillumette)

There are a number of single-celled organisms that swim actively about and at the same time have chlorophyll. These are claimed as animals by the zoologists, who call them flagellate protozoa, while the botanists classify them as algae. Partly because of this, there is a growing feeling that the time-honored system of two kingdoms, plants and animals, should give way to a system with three kingdoms, plants, animals, and protists or micro-organisms. This seems reasonable to me. Our vocabulary developed for the visible world, the things we can see with unaided eyes. These sort into plants and animals easily enough. With the discovery of the subvisible world revealed by the microscope, there was a natural attempt to fit all of the new creatures into the old system, and many of them do not fit well. Why make them fit? Why not give them a kingdom of their own? For me, animals are still things I can see, or obvious relatives of things big enough to see, and this is the sense in which we shall use the word in this book.

The Diversity of Animals

Our animals are found all through the biosphere, in endless variety, living in their many different worlds. Something like a million kinds have been described, catalogued, and given technical names. The catalogue is practically complete for birds and mammals. There may still remain species undiscovered in the remote mountains of New Guinea or the headwaters of the Amazon, but they are surely few. There are probably more kinds of reptiles and amphibians yet to be described, but not very many. With fishes, we have the tantalizing possibility of unknown creatures lurking in the ocean depths; and there are probably other kinds yet to be found in tropical lakes and streams or around remote reefs.

More kinds of insects have been named and described than is the case with any other class of animals. About 3200 species of mammals are known, 8600 birds, 6000 reptiles and amphibia, and 25,000 fishes. Estimates of insects vary, but 850,000 species is a commonly quoted figure. And in the case of insects, there is a general agreement that the catalogue is still very incomplete. We know a great deal about the conspicuous insects, like the butterflies and some of the beetles, which have

long been favorites with collectors. We have probably at least named most of the species in regions around the older centers of science—western Europe and the eastern United States—though we still have much to learn about their habits even in England, Germany, or New York. But no one can make even a plausible guess about the number of insects that remain to be described in the tropics.

The tiny animals of the seas, the copepods and other shrimplike creatures, are most abundant in terms of number of individuals or sheer bulk of protoplasm— but there are not nearly so many kinds. This undoubtedly is related to the greater uniformity of the marine environment. On land, the varied climates, the inter-rupted pattern of continents and islands, the patchwork of forests, deserts, and mountains, have led to an enormous number of local forms, each adapted to its own little geographical and ecological niche. There are very few cosmopolitan insects or vertebrates on land, except those recently carried around by man; but many marine animals can be found in all of the oceans and seas.

The insects evolved on land and have remained there or in the lakes and streams of inland waters. The sea is a closed world to them, with only a very few trivial exceptions. Yet most of the major invertebrate types are exclusively or predominantly marine. There are nothing like as many species as among the insects, but the types are varied indeed—sponges, jellyfishes, corals, starfishes, and other echinoderms, a long list of classes of worms and mollusks and shrimplike animals. Again it is the larger and more conspicuous forms that we know best, or the kinds, like shells, that are favored by collectors. And if the task of naming and classifying is so great, it is no wonder that we still have much to learn about the habits of our companions on the planet. We have, to be sure, learned a great deal; and our knowledge is neatly stacked away in rows of journals and books. But, diving on a tropical reef or sitting on a log in the rain forest and looking at the life around us, one is overwhelmed by how little we know about what is going on. And it is not necessary to go to the Pacific or to the upper Amazon; there are unexplored worlds in everyone's back yard.

The Diversity of Environments

The classification of animals is one problem; the classification of their environments and of their habits is another. Just as it is convenient to recognize three main groupings of organisms—plants, animals, and protists—so also is it convenient to make three main subdivisions of the biosphere—the seas, the inland waters, and the land. There are transitions between each of these, and there are animals that move from one to another. But these are exceptional, and in many important ways the environments are very different, presenting quite different problems for the development of animal life.

The seas form by far the largest of the subdivisions. They cover something like 70 per cent of the earth's surface. Further, the average depth of the seas is greater than the average elevation of the land, so that if the continents were all smoothed off into the oceans to make a smooth and uniform surface for the planet, this would be totally covered with water to a depth somewhere between a mile and a half and two miles. As remarked earlier, the evidence all indicates that life started in the seas, and it has continued to proliferate there through geological time. There are more species on land, because of those endless insects; but most major animal types are purely or largely marine.

It can thus be reasonably argued that the sea is the largest, the most important, the most fundamental of the major environments of life. We happen to be land animals, and this inevitably influences our outlook on the world—it is not easy to adopt a dolphin's-eye view. But our appreciation of the sea is constantly growing, and we are learning that it may be the greatest resource of the planet even for us.

On land, differences in the availability of water are very important for animals, while in the seas there is water everywhere—which is one of the factors that makes the marine environment more uniform than that of the land. Temperatures also vary less in water than in air; and the seas, unlike the continents, form an interconnected system, so that geographical barriers are less significant. There are many differences in the conditions of life in polar and tropical waters, but the differences are not as striking as on land.

How, then, can the marine environment be subdivided? The most common practice is to distinguish among zones rather than geographical regions. Conditions of life in the open sea, where animals must either float or constantly swim, are quite different from those on the bottom or near shore. At great depths, animals face a distinctive environment because of the absence of light, the continuous cold, and the great pressures. Near shore, conditions vary greatly. In some places, the sea is eroding the land, resulting in a rocky coast line; in others, sand or mud is being deposited; and there are special shore formations like coral reefs or mangrove swamps.

A complicated vocabulary has been developed to describe this zonation. It has a certain shorthand convenience, though we shall not use it much. A basic division

Animal or vegetable?
Below left: Colony of
ostrich-plume hydroids
(*Aglaophenia*), often mis-
taken for seaweed.
(Milo Williams)

Center: This pipefish,
lurking in eelgrass, re-
sembles a plant.
(Milo Williams)

Right: A few plants, like
this sundew or *Drosera*,
turn the tables and eat
insects.
(Hugh Spencer)

is between animals closely associated with the bottom and those that swim or float with no need to come to rest. The first are called *benthic* and the second *pelagic*. A distinction is also often made between animals that live near continental (or island) shores and those of the ocean basins, the first being *neritic* and the second *oceanic*. With either benthic or pelagic animals, the conditions of life are different, depending on the depths at which they live, and attempts have been made to develop a vocabulary to describe this—but since the changes are gradual, any definite separation of zones is bound to be arbitrary.

Another series of changes occurs as we approach shores. When the water becomes shallow enough so that appreciable light reaches the bottom, fixed plants can grow, providing food and shelter for many special animals. Another factor is added where the water is sufficiently shoal for wave action to affect the bottom. And then there are the very special conditions of the intertidal zone, where the animals must be able to withstand alternate drying and submergence and, often, the pounding of surf. Beyond this is the shore itself—dry land, but with its inhabitants depending in many ways on the sea.

If from the sea we enter a bay at the outlet of one of the river systems, we encounter another set of transitions—from salt water to fresh. We move from the world of the seas to the quite different world of inland waters. Because of the salt lakes it is better to say "inland waters" rather than "fresh waters." They are an insignificant part of the biosphere, but they have to be accounted for. Overwhelm-

ingly, however, when we move to inland waters we are dealing with a medium, fresh water, that has a low content of dissolved salts, and this means that the conditions of life are quite different from those in the sea.

Inland waters also differ from the seas in that they are discontinuous, both in space and through time. There is no way an animal can get from the Amazon to the Congo unless it can withstand a long sea trip or fly or float through the air; and there never has been a time when such a passage could be made through fresh water. Some of the great river systems of the world have long histories, but nothing compared with the history of the seas. And most lakes are quite temporary. The Great Lakes of the United States were covered by a solid sheet of ice only a few tens of thousands of years ago; all of their inhabitants arrived, somehow, after that.

The life of inland waters is thus closely tied with the life of the continents for both geographical and historical reasons. Yet conditions in the water are quite different from those out of it; so that, while many animals move back and forth, we are dealing with two very different environments.

Within the world of inland waters, the basic ecological division is between still and running water. The conditions of life in running water vary greatly, from those in rushing mountain torrents to those in the meandering sluggish current in the lower reaches of a large river. There are many differences, too, among the accumulations of still water; in size alone, they run the gamut from puddles to great lakes. Within larger lakes, the marine vocabulary can be applied and a useful distinction made, for instance, between pelagic and benthic animals. A few lakes reach great depths, again presenting special conditions for life.

When we move from water to land, climate becomes of major importance; the conditions of life are governed chiefly by temperature and the availability of moisture. On the moisture scale, we have the range from very dry deserts to regions of high and continuous rainfall. On the temperature scale, we have the range from the continuous warmth of the lowland mid-tropics to the continuous cold of the poles, with varying patterns of seasonal change in between. Both temperature and moisture are affected by elevation, and especially by mountain systems.

As a consequence of these differences, there is on land a wide variety of landscapes—of *biomes,* to use the ecological term. Each biome has a characteristic type of vegetation growing in response to regional climatic conditions, and each is inhabited by characteristic sets of animals. We are again dealing with a series of continuous and gradual changes which have to be broken up rather arbitrarily; one could distinguish dozens of biomes—with corresponding climates—or only a few. In all classifications, certain major types are recognized: tropical forests, grassland (or scrub), desert, temperate deciduous forests, taiga (the coniferous forests of the north), and tundra.

The animals and plants of the deserts of America, Africa, Asia, and Australia are of different species, often belonging to quite different major groups in the system of classification. But the conditions of desert life require similar adaptations in all of these places; and the animals and plants often come to look alike, even though they are quite unrelated. This is equally true of the other biomes. The classification is based on similarity of climate, on similarity of landscape, rather than on the genetic relationships of the organisms. It is an ecological classification.

But let us look in more detail at these many worlds of animal life, starting with the open seas—where life itself began, perhaps two billion years ago.

2

The Open Sea

The economy of the sea depends on plankton—that is, the drifting organisms, mostly microscopic, of surface waters. Looking at the clear water of the open ocean, it is hard to believe that it teems with life. But if a fine silk net is towed through the water, it will accumulate a gelatinous mass of stuff which, if examined under the microscope, will be found to consist of a varied assemblage of curious plants, animals, and micro-organisms.

The producers of the system are all microscopic, and mostly they are classified as single-celled protists with chlorophyll rather than as relatives of the plants we can see; but since their role corresponds with that of true plants in other situations, it is easiest to think of them as "plant cells." They are incredibly numerous. An ordinary plankton haul may show 20,000 or so plant cells per cubic foot of water. But it is now clear that a great many of the protists of the plankton are so small that they easily slip through the pores of the finest nets, which greatly increases the difficulty of estimating their numbers. In the marine laboratory at Plymouth, England, special methods have been developed to determine the numbers of these very small producers. In one carefully worked out case, it was found that there were something like twelve and a half *million* chlorophyll-bearing cells in a cubic foot of water.

The producer system, understandably, is limited to the surface waters which receive the light necessary for the photosynthetic process. The depth to which sufficient light penetrates varies greatly. The more nearly vertical the sun, the greater the penetration, so the productive layer tends to be deeper in tropical waters than in polar regions. Wave action cuts down penetration by breaking up the light; and, most importantly, there are differences in the transparency of the water.

Light of different wave lengths penetrates to different depths: the long red rays are cut out first, and the short blue ones continue deepest. The relatively longer waves, which have less penetration, are most important for photosynthesis. With all of these variables, it is impossible to be precise about the depth of the oceanic productive zone, but six hundred feet is often taken as the average depth for open seas, away from continental shores where suspended materials washed in from the land make for much less transparent water.

The seas vary in productivity, as do the lands, though the differences are nothing like as great. It is often argued that tropical waters are less productive than those of the higher latitudes, chiefly because the commercial development of fisheries has been less successful in the tropics. But there are other possible explanations of this, and the only thing that is clear is that we have a great deal to learn about oceanic productivity, especially in tropical waters. Taking a very general view, it appears that the amount of plant material formed per acre of ocean surface is at least as great as the average for the land; and the abundance of animal life, of course, depends ultimately on the amount of plant material available as primary food.

The plankton includes animals as well as plants but, naturally, not in such spectacular abundance. The series of British plankton hauls that gave 20,000 plant cells per cubic foot averaged 120 animals in the same volume of water. Most of these plankton animals are either microscopic or barely visible, but here one runs into problems of definition. The word "plankton" implies drifting—the Greek is said to mean "that which is made to wander or drift." The actively swimming animals—fishes, squid, and the like—are then separated as a different category of marine life and called "nekton." This word need not trouble us, but it brings up the point that there is a whole series of stages between passive drifting and really effective swimming. The rhythmically pulsating jellyfish is a case in point. Its pulses seem futile in the presence of appreciable current; yet we could hardly call it passive. All of the plankton animals have a considerable ability to move up and down, quite regularly showing a migration from the surface during the day to some depth at night or vice versa. Like so many other terms, then, "plankton" acquires a relative meaning. One practical definition is that the plankton includes all of the animals that are unable to swim vigorously enough to escape being caught in an ordinary plankton net.

Swimming through a school of fish, the sawfish flails its saw from side to side, wounding or spearing its victims. (Fritz Goro: *Life*)

Sea Water and Salt

The behavior of animals in the sea can hardly be discussed without giving some attention to the nature of sea water. It contains, on the average, about 3.5 per cent dissolved salts, which is usually expressed not as a percentage but as a salt content of 35 parts per thousand. This results in a density closely similar to that of the protoplasm that makes up living things: hence animals in the sea do not need support. Most of them can float with little effort. Protoplasm is about 850 times more dense than air—hence floating in air is out of the question for any ordinary animal. On the other hand, high speeds (if you have the right sort of equipment) require less energy in thin air than in dense water. The fastest flight, as far as is known, is that of the duck hawk or peregrine falcon. This bird has been timed cruising at speeds up to 65 miles per hour, and can undoubtedly achieve much greater speeds in dives, though the often quoted figure of 180 miles per hour is probably too high. In swimming, the fastest fishes, mackerels, only manage about 30 miles per hour. Killer whales and dolphins, however, can swim faster than this.

Sea water is remarkably similar in composition everywhere. Surface salinities in the oceans vary between about 34.5 and 36.0 parts per thousand, being lowest toward the poles (because of melting ice) and in the mid-tropics (because of fresh water added by rains), with the highest salinities in mid-latitudes. Greater differences can be found under special conditions. The Red Sea, with a high evaporation rate and no inflow of fresh water, reaches a salinity of 45 parts per thousand. The Baltic Sea, at the other extreme, with a large inflow of fresh water and with low evaporation rates, has a low salt content—as little as 10 parts per thousand in places.

The quantity of dissolved salts thus shows some variation, but the proportion of the different chemical elements present is the same everywhere. Furthermore, it seems likely that the composition of sea water has been about the same over a long stretch of geological time—at least since the beginning of our record in the Cambrian period, several hundred million years ago. Common salt—sodium chloride—accounts for more than three-fourths of the dissolved materials. Next in abundance are salts of magnesium, calcium, and potassium. In all, something like forty-four different elements have been detected in sea water by chemical tests, not counting the dissolved atmospheric gases. The proportions of elements in the sea are quite different from those in the solid crust of the earth's surface, and different again from the proportions in the material that is constantly being washed in by the rivers of the world. The constancy of the composition of sea water is at least partly a consequence of the activities of marine organisms, but we are far from understanding all of the details.

Ocean Currents

The vast mass of ocean water is in constant circulation. This is a result of the rotation of the earth, of the sweep of the winds, and of the zonation of temperature—this last because colder water is heavier and denser, and tends to sink, bringing water movement even to the greatest depths. The details of the drifts and currents

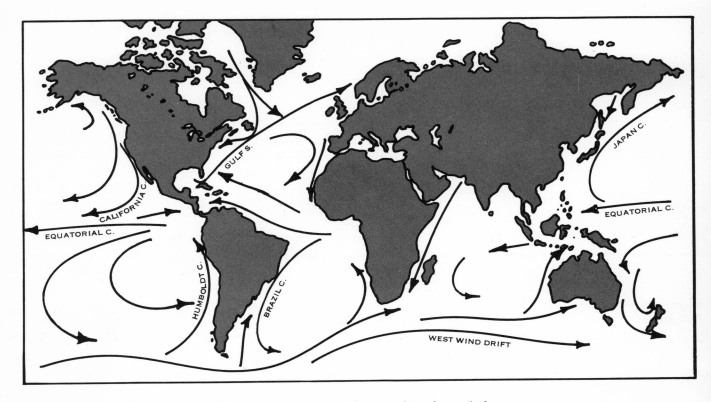

are governed by the patterns of the continents and the wondrously varied topography of the ocean floor. In general, there is a westward drift at the surface everywhere on the equator, with a consequent piling up of water on the east coasts of the continents. This results in warm currents flowing north and south. The Gulf Stream of the Atlantic is one such; another is the Kurochio current that warms Japan. The waters off the west coasts of Africa, America, and Australia tend to be relatively cold because of this pattern—though the western coast of Europe is warmed by the trans-Atlantic passage of the Gulf Stream. The cold polar waters sinking and drifting toward the equator in the ocean depths add another dimension to these movements.

It is the constant circulation and broad interconnections of the oceans that gives a certain uniformity to the life of the open seas. Many animals, to be sure, have adapted to cold waters and others to warm; but many also are tolerant of a wide range of temperatures, and these can be truly cosmopolitan. Quite a few cold-loving plankton animals occur in both the Arctic and Antarctic seas, and it appears that these can pass from one region to the other by way of the eternally cold waters of the depths. As for warm-water species, there are no barriers in the vast area covered by the Pacific and Indian oceans. While the tropical Atlantic is now isolated for such animals by the cold waters north and south, passage was often easy in the geological past when Panama was a strait instead of an isthmus.

Floating World of the Open Sea

The floating world of the open sea, as we pointed out, is possible because of the very similar density of protoplasm and sea water. Nevertheless, animals, partly because of their need for hard supporting skeletons, tend to be slightly heavier than the water and hence need some way to keep from slowly sinking. There are a variety of such flotation mechanisms. Skeletons and other hard parts are apt to be much reduced in plankton animals as compared with related species that live on the bottom. Sometimes light, buoyant materials like fats or oils, or even air or other

The economy of the seas depends on drifting organisms, mostly microscopic, called plankton. Right: Doliolum. Far right: Living zooplankton, including larval worms, and the larvae of mollusks, crustacean decapods, and pilchards. (Douglas P. Wilson)

gases, are accumulated in various parts of the body to reduce the total specific gravity. Commonly, plankton animals have bizarre shapes, with many appendages that serve to increase the body surface in relation to weight—the same principle that enables milkweed seed to float in the air. And then, of course, there are all sorts of ways of swimming and moving just enough to keep from sinking.

The animals of the plankton are a pretty active lot. They may not be able to move fast enough or far enough to escape the plankton net or to combat the eternal drift of the ocean waters, but in a glass jar held up against the light they are seen as specks in a continual dance. The movement often seems random, purposeless, though it obviously enables the animals to catch their food, and helps them to escape becoming food. But the movement also sometimes has a less immediate meaning.

Major surface ocean currents.

It was long ago discovered that animal plankton was scarce in surface water during the day and much more abundant at night. It is now clear that most species have a definite daily vertical migration, sometimes of hundreds of feet. The distinguished British marine biologist Sir Alister Hardy, among others, has devoted a great deal of ingenuity to studying this. He found that some of the tiny shrimplike copepods can climb between 50 and 95 feet in an hour; a larger species, about an inch long, can climb 305 feet in an hour. Downward rates can of course be faster.

This upward and downward movement is characteristic of a whole series of very different kinds of plankton animals. What governs the movement, and why has it been developed? The animals, it would seem, are reacting to light—but some species don't start up until after dark and begin their descent again long before dawn. It would seem that these have some sort of internal clock, a kind of physiological rhythm, that governs their movements, unless it be that they are reacting to a change in the environment other than light. Most animals, on land as well as in the sea, show some sort of daily periodicity in their activity; and while our understanding of this is still limited, the whole phenomenon is being very actively studied.

But why do the plankton animals go to all this effort to avoid the surface water during the day, and come up among the plant cells only at night? Many theories have been proposed, but there are difficulties with all of them. With so many dif-

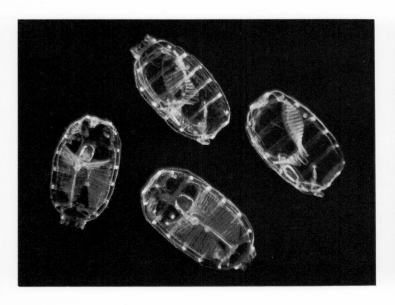

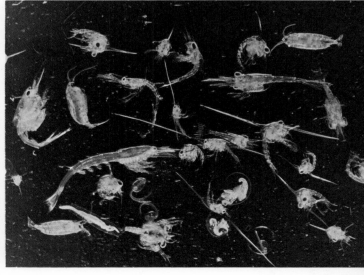

ferent kinds of animals showing the same sort of behavior, it would seem that this pattern must contribute in some way to their survival. The first thought is that by coming to the surface at night and sinking to deeper waters by day, the animals may be escaping predators by staying always in the dark. The trouble with this is that the predators move up and down too, so the interpretation of this as an effort to escape hardly seems convincing.

Sir Alister Hardy has suggested that, by this diurnal migration, the animals move back and forth between two rather different environments, and that this may have advantages. Currents are generally faster at the surface than lower down, and the direction of drift may be different, even at a depth of only a hundred feet. "Vertical migration," Hardy notes, "is thus a means of providing a relatively weak and drifting organism with an extensive power of movement. It can 'hop' from one environment to another by sinking and rising again."

These plankton animals are an extraordinarily varied lot. They include representatives of all the major groups. Two phyla, the Ctenophora or comb jellies and the Chaetognatha or arrow worms, are found only in the marine plankton.

Comparative size of man and the largest animals: blue whale, giant squid, elephant, anaconda, and albatross.

Of course many kinds of animals live in the plankton for only a part of their life history. A large proportion of the swimming or fixed animals of the seas—fishes, mollusks, corals, crabs, and the like—have egg or larval stages that drift with the plankton. Quite commonly among marine organisms, sexual reproduction simply involves liberating eggs and sperm into the water, where the male and female elements meet and fuse to start the new generation. This requires that the sperm and eggs of a given species must be released at about the same time—another "physiological clock" problem—and it also requires that vast numbers be released if any are to survive. Where estimates have been made of the number of eggs produced by single individuals in a season, the figures are of this order: American oyster, 115,000,000; sea hare *(Tethys)*, 478,000,000; Pacific halibut, 3,500,000; ocean sunfish *(Mola)*, 300,000,000.

Copepods—Their Fate Is to be Eaten

The copepods are by far the most important of the permanent animal inhabitants of the plankton, in terms of both number of individuals and bulk of protoplasm. They form an order of the class Crustacea—relatives, in other words, of the shrimps, lobsters, and crabs. They are tiny animals, falling mostly in the size range between a pinhead and a grain of rice. About 6000 species are known, and of these some 750 are found only in the oceanic plankton. They are incredibly numerous, making up about 70 per cent of the animal plankton. They are the key-industry animals of the open seas, playing a role similar to that of the insects on land. There are hundreds of thousands of kinds of insects, compared with the few hundred species of copepods, but in volume of protoplasm, the copepods far exceed the insects.

The reproduction of copepods involves a curious sort of internal fertilization. The adult male collects his sperm into a sort of plastic-wrapped package (called a spermatophore) which by various special devices, depending on the species, is attached to an appropriate female. The sperm package is held in a storage chamber in the female, and from it the eggs are fertilized as they pass down the oviduct. In some species, the fertilized eggs are left free in the water; but in most, the eggs are carried attached in different ways to the mother until the tiny larvae hatch to take up life among the plankton hordes.

The fate of copepods, like the fate of most animals, is to be eaten. We are hardly conscious of the plant cells that the copepods themselves eat—or of the teeming copepods—but we do become aware of the animals at the next level in the pyramid of numbers—the nekton or swimmers. These swimmers that directly or indirectly live off the copepods and other animal plankton are the basis of the fisheries of the world. From the point of view of classification, they are less varied than the drifters. The most important groups are the cephalopods (squids and their relatives), a large assemblage of fishes, and, among mammals, the cetaceans (whales and dolphins).

The Jet-propelled Cephalopods

The cephalopods form a single class of the phylum Mollusca. We ordinarily and rightly think of mollusks as animals with shells—but this is not true of the cephalopods. In the geological past, cephalopods with shells were numerous, but the only conspicuous survivor of this past is the chambered nautilus of tropical seas. The common cephalopods of today fall into two groups: those with eight arms, the octopuses (or octopodes or octopi), and those with ten, the squid and cuttlefishes. All of the octopuses and many of the squid live near shores or on the bottom; but squid, we are coming to realize, are also extremely abundant in the open seas. The cephalopods long ago developed jet propulsion, and their method of swimming is thus completely different from that of fishes and marine mammals, though perhaps even more effective, at least for short bursts of speed.

Squid generally come to the surface only at night, which is why we are so little conscious of them. Ordinarily we live remote from the world of the sea, even when crossing it in a ship, or trying to get samples of its life with nets, or measuring its conditions with instruments lowered into the depths. Thor Heyerdahl, drifting across the Pacific on the *Kon-Tiki*, was closer to this world, and he found that shoals of "flying squid" would sometimes land on the raft. There are at least two species with this flying habit, and this has been known for a long time; but since the squid fly only at night, they are rarely observed.

The squid are so expert at maneuvering, can swim so fast with their jets, that most kinds easily evade capture, and our knowledge of their habits is tantalizingly inadequate. From the examination of stomach contents, it appears that they are the principle article of diet for the toothed whales, for seals, and perhaps for some of the oceanic fish like tunny. Our only knowledge of some of these squid is from specimens found in the stomachs of whales, or individuals stranded on beaches.

The squid fragments found in sperm whale stomachs are generally of moderate size, three feet or so long, with a maximum of about eight feet—a sperm whale *could* swallow a man. The real giants have been found on beaches, mostly in Newfoundland and across the Atlantic in the British Isles. The largest reported so far had a body length of twenty feet and a total length with tentacles of fifty-five feet. Quite a number have been found with body lengths between ten and twenty feet, with correspondingly long tentacles. These, then, are by far the largest of the invertebrate animals, but about their habits we know absolutely nothing. Stories of giant octopuses, by the way, have no foundation. An octopus with a tentacle span of ten feet is a very big one. It is true that a species has been described from the north Pacific with a tentacle span of twenty-eight feet—but with a body about the size of a quart bottle.

About four hundred species of cephalopods have been described, which is nothing in comparison with the thousands of species of fishes. But the importance of cephalopods in the economy of the open seas does not depend on the number of species, since we are now learning that some of the smaller squid are incredibly numerous. The larger ones must be common too, to support the whales, seals, and fishes that feed on them. The oceanic squid could also be significant in human economy. They are important in Japan, where some 600,000 tons are caught annually. They can be very tasty food for man, as any Japanese or Spanish cook will testify; but most Europeans and Americans view them with suspicion. I suppose that when we think of food from the sea, we think of fishes.

The Mysterious Fishes

Fishes have a long geological history, the first fossils dating back five hundred million years or so. These early fishes had heavily armored bodies and, like the lampreys and hagfish of today, they had no jaws. These earliest fossils may well have been inhabitants of fresh or brackish water—there is considerable argument among paleontologists about whether fish evolution started in fresh water or in the seas. Wherever they started, they have continued to be successful in both environments, and in the seas they have adapted to all possible situations, from shore to mid-ocean and from the surface to the greatest depths.

The sailfish is thought to unfold its enormous dorsal fin for use as a sail. (Hal Austin: *Western Ways*)

Right: A halfbeak prowling under a patch of sargassum in the Caribbean. Its long lower jaw is useful for snatching food from below. (Fritz Goro: *Life*)

Our concern here is with the fishes of the open sea, and it is remarkable, though understandable, how little we know about them. The only fauna of which we are more ignorant is that of the great depths below. How does one bring the open sea into the laboratory? Or how can one go out to sea to live with the fish and observe their habits? We can catch them—some of them, at least—and there are many indirect ways of getting information. Only in the great aquaria of the marinelands can we observe directly, and we are learning something from these, though there is always the special problem of confinement.

It is particularly difficult for us to imagine the perceptual world of a fish—the world revealed by its sense organs. Our world is primarily visual; we are surrounded by nearby objects and distant views, by colors and shapes and perspectives. We are also very aware of sounds, and when several people are together there is a fairly constant flow of reciprocal noise. We smell things, but in a rather vague way: think of the trouble we have describing smells. We fuss a bit about the taste of our food. We feel the texture of things—soft, hard, smooth—and we can feel the wind on our faces and the water flowing past us as we bathe in a stream. We have a sense of balance; and only the astronauts are learning to dispense with gravity.

But the environment in which we live is varied, replete with landmarks, and always bounded by the solid earth and distant sky with sun and clouds and stars. How very different this is from the uniform world of the open sea—dark below and light above, and all around, eternally, a uniform mist. How do fishes find their way amid this uniformity? Yet it is known that some, at least, have regular patterns of migration and find tracks, somehow, across the trackless sea. And how do they find their food and their mates, or avoid their enemies?

Fishes have eyes not unlike our own, except that they do not see much detail. Some kinds have been shown experimentally to have color vision. They have nostrils and sometimes, certainly, an extremely acute sense of smell. They have taste buds built like ours, not only in the mouth but often also on other parts of the body. Chemical senses in general are clearly important in the fish world.

But the outstanding sensory system of fishes, the lateral-line organ, is very peculiar and characteristic. It can be clearly seen in most species as a line running along the middle of each side of the body, from head to tail, usually branching into a special pattern of lines around the head. On microscopic examination, this system is found to contain series of special sensory cells arranged in long rows. The cells have little hairlike processes, and apparently by means of this organ fishes can detect slight changes in water pressure or movement. As a friend of mine put it, it is as though with eyes shut and ears plugged we were able through air pressure to detect the exact position of a bee buzzing about our heads. In many fishes it is clear that this sensory system is involved in food finding; it also seems generally to be involved in orientation and balance, and perhaps in the detection of slight changes in water temperature. The universality and complexity of the system indicate that it must be very important in the fish world.

Although tuna (shown here in the Florida Straits) and mackerel are the basis of a great industry, we know little about them. None has ever been raised under laboratory conditions.
(Fritz Goro: *Life*)

Elasmobranchs: Sharks and Rays

By whatever means, fishes—vast numbers of fishes of many kinds—do get around in the open sea. Ichthyologists group them into two main classes: the cartilaginous fishes or elasmobranchs, the sharks and rays; and the bony fishes or "true" fishes. The sharks include the largest of fishes, the whale shark *(Rhineodon)* and the basking shark *(Cetorhinus)*. Both reach a maximum length of about forty-five feet, both are completely harmless—skin divers have even taken rides astride the tail of the basking shark—but not much really is known about the habits of either of them.

The basking shark turns up frequently in European waters and off the California coast. Like the whalebone whales, it feeds on plankton. When feeding, it cruises right at the surface at a speed of about two knots, filtering vast quantities of water to get the minute organisms; someone has estimated that something like two thousand tons of water an hour must be filtered to get sufficient food. These sharks often occur in numbers in Scottish waters in April and May, when plankton copepods are particularly abundant. Sir Alister Hardy reports counting forty-three of the giant creatures one day in Loch Fyne. Although they cruise slowly, they must also be capable of astonishing speed: at least they have several times been seen to leap clear of the water, coming down with a great splash.

Whale sharks are found most often in tropical waters. Apparently they feed on small fishes and squid rather than on plankton, but like the basking sharks they must filter large quantities of water to get enough food. They have sometimes been seen among schools of tuna, both the sharks and the tuna feeding on sardines.

The man-eating sharks like the great white shark are also chiefly inhabitants

of the open seas, only occasionally straying into shore areas where people swim—fortunately for swimmers. Pacific islanders maintain that the dangerous sharks do not enter lagoons, though they often cruise along the seaward side of reefs.

Tuna, Mackerel, and other Bony Fishes

It is interesting that the giants of the open seas are the sharks and whales, and that the biggest members of both classes feed by filtering quite small organisms from the water. This feeding of the huge on the very small also applies to the giant rays or devil rays of the tropical seas, which may measure as much as twenty-two feet across the "wings" and which live by filtering plankton. The true fishes, which we think of as the characteristic inhabitants of the oceans, are certainly infinitely more numerous in individuals and in kinds than either the elasmobranchs or the marine mammals, but none reaches giant size. The biggest are tunas, broadbill swordfish, and marlins, each of which reaches lengths between ten and fourteen feet and weights of as much as 1500 pounds. Big fish, to be sure, but not in comparison with basking sharks and whales.

The tunas and the related mackerels are the basis of a great fishing industry, and the swordfish and marlins are favorites of sportsmen. Yet again we know remarkably little about them: nothing, really, about their breeding habits, for instance. None of these large, oceanic fishes has ever been raised under laboratory observation. But perhaps now with large marineland aquaria more will be learned.

At Home on Land and Sea

Fishes have adapted to every sort of marine and fresh-water environment. Some of them, like the flying fish, can take to the air briefly; others can crawl out on shore or, like eels, slither through wet vegetation; and some can withstand drying for considerable lengths of time. But fish, as fish, have never been successful on land. Among the vertebrates, the move to the land was made by the amphibia—represented in modern times by frogs, salamanders, and the like, which still are chained to water for at least part of their life. But the amphibia developed in fresh water; no modern amphibian lives in the sea and, as far as we know, none did in the past. The reptiles, birds, and mammals, which developed from the amphibia on land, however, all include groups that have evolved adaptations enabling them to exploit the marine environment.

A sandbar shark, found offshore as well as inshore in the Atlantic. (Fritz Goro: *Life*)

Of modern reptiles, only the sea snakes and sea turtles are really inhabitants of the open sea. Yet the turtles go back to land to lay their eggs, and of the sea snakes only one species, the black-and-yellow sea snake of the Pacific, is truly pelagic, the others being found only near shores. But in the geological past, in the "age of reptiles," the Mesozoic, there was a profusion of marine types. The streamlined ichthyosaurs could surely get around as well as any fish or dolphin. The curious plesiosaurs look more awkward, with their long necks and paddle limbs, but from the frequency of their remains, they must have been successful enough. The Oxford geologist Dean Buckland said that a plesiosaur looked like "a snake threaded through the shell of a turtle." There were also marine lizards, the mososaurs, up to fifty feet long; and marine crocodiles. But these monsters have all disappeared.

Among birds we have of course a few kinds that master the skies over all of the oceans; also the fast-swimming penguins of the southern hemisphere. But "marine" is really a courtesy title for such animals, and they are best considered among the inhabitants of the shore, many of which extend their activities far out to sea.

Mammals of the Sea

Among the mammals there is one group that is as truly marine as those ancient reptiles: the Cetacea, including the whales, dolphins, and porpoises. These extraordinary and fascinating animals include the largest and fastest inhabitants of the seas—and the more we learn about them, the more interesting they seem. About a hundred species are known, and while a few small dolphins are inhabitants of tropical rivers or stay mostly near shore, the majority of the Cetacea live in the open sea, and they are masters of this environment.

The blue whale is the largest of all animals—not only the largest living species, but larger than anything we know from the past. These whales reach a length of one hundred feet. One eighty-nine-foot specimen was found to weigh just over 120 tons—the equivalent of forty Indian elephants. The gigantic reptiles of the past, like Brontosaurus and Dipolodocus, might reach almost this length, but since much of this was slender neck and tail, the bulk of the animal would be much less than that of a whale of corresponding length.

We are apt to think that big things take time to grow, but this turns out not to be true of whales. The calves are born one at a time, except for occasional twins;

in the case of the blue whale, the calf is about twenty-three feet long at birth—about a quarter of the length of its mother! The gestation period in this species is eleven months. By the time it is a year old, the whale has reached a length of sixty feet; and in two years it has reached seventy-five feet and sexual maturity. These animals live by filtering out the teeming plankton (krill) of northern and southern waters, and their growth rate is vivid proof of the richness of this diet.

The Cetacea are divided into two groups: the baleen whales, which filter plankton and number a dozen species, all large; and the toothed whales, which live on larger prey. The sperm whale is the largest of the toothed species, males reaching a length of sixty feet, and they apparently live largely on squid, though fish, including an eight-foot basking shark, have also been found in their stomachs. These whales can dive to enormous depths, as shown by specimens that have become entangled and trapped by submarine cables five hundred or six hundred fathoms beneath the surface. The cable, in these cases, is nearly always wrapped around the jaw; possibly the whales are caught through mistaking the cable coils for the arms of an octopus or squid.

Being mammals, whales breathe air; yet they are able to make these very deep dives and to stay under water for considerable lengths of time. Dives of the blue whale have been observed to last for 49 minutes; of the sperm whale, 75 minutes; of the Greenland right whale, 80; with the record held by a bottlenose whale that did not reappear for 120 minutes. Of course there is always the possibility of mistaken observation, but it is nonetheless certain that whales can stay under water for a long time. We are only beginning to understand how they do this. For one thing, they must use oxygen at a reduced rate while diving—the heartbeat, for instance, slows up by about half. But there is also a problem with nitrogen. A man coming up from a deep dive is liable to "caisson sickness," which is caused by nitrogen, dissolved in the blood under pressure, forming tiny bubbles if the pressure is reduced too quickly. The lungs of a whale contract under pressure and the air is forced into rigid sinuses, so that the proportion of nitrogen dissolved in the blood is probably much less than in an animal like man. It also seems likely that the large oil reservoir of deep-diving species like the sperm whale serves to absorb nitrogen as the lungs contract and thus to prevent its getting into the blood stream.

The porpoises and dolphins belong with the toothed whales, and we are beginning to learn quite a bit about dolphin behavior since we have been keeping them in marinelands. The dolphins—all of the whales, for that matter—are highly sociable animals, moving about in herds or packs (a social group of whales may be called a "gam," a "pod," or a "school"). It turns out that dolphins also learn all sorts of complicated tricks easily and quickly. Their proportions of brain to body are about the same as those in man, and their brains, anatomically, are just about as complex. Dr. John Lilly, who has studied them more closely than anyone else, maintains—in his book *Man and Dolphin*—that they are just as bright as we are, which brings up the knotty question of what we mean by "intelligence."

The behavior that seems most intelligent to us, as human beings, is often characteristic of social animals like dogs, monkeys—and dolphins. For one thing, social life requires the development of some sort of communication system and co-operative action among individuals. Dolphins are highly co-operative: they will help a sick or injured companion to stay afloat, and they will work jointly in many kinds of enterprises. They are very playful—and playfulness, too, seems related to intelligence. Dolphins pacing a ship certainly seem to be displaying sheer exuberance; and in the aquaria they develop games spontaneously (like balancing shells on their noses) as well as readily getting the idea of possible games from their trainers. The trainers have found that dolphins respond to rewards like gifts of fish but become negative and unco-operative if punishment is tried. Dolphins also are highly vocal, chattering constantly among themselves, in part using sound frequencies too high to be detectet by human ears. They are also imitative, and Dr. Lilly maintains that they often pick up words they have heard and repeat them in their high, squeaky voices; he thinks that some day we may be able to talk with them.

Dolphins, curiously, seem always to be friendly with people, and even when they get quite irritated with trainers do not attack them. There are many stories, from classical times to the present, of dolphins coming to the rescue of drowning people or joining swimmers to play. But "sociability" does not necessarily mean friendliness to outsiders, and one of the dolphin group, the killer whale, is often rated the fiercest of all animals. A school of killers will attack a large whale and tear it to pieces. They are particularly fond of seals, and will swim up under an ice floe on which seals are resting to tip them into the water. Sharks are frightening enough, but we can be glad that killer whales live in water too cold for human swimmers; they have never tried raiding a bathing resort for a meal of people.

Some of the Cetacea, as we have seen, can dive to great depths. But these are brief expeditions because, as mammals, they must always soon return to the surface for air. They are then essentially a part of the surface world of the seas, a very different place from the abyss with its eternal cold and darkness. Not long ago it was believed that no life could exist in the depths of the oceans, but we know now that it is the habitat of a whole special fauna which deserves a chapter to itself.

The Open Sea

1 A twenty-foot narwhal in the Arctic Sea. His tusk, here visible as a fine white line in front of him, may reach a length of ten feet. (John R. T. Molholm)

2 Below: A pilot whale in Marineland of the Pacific. (John Tashjian)

Margins of the Seas

3–5 The stresses of life in the alternately wet and dry intertidal zone are great, yet many forms of life meet them. From the California coast we have the sea anemones, mussels, and sea cabbage shown below; an ochre star to the right; and an eel grass community, bottom right. (Donovan Roberts)

6–7 The edible crab, above, rarely leaves the water; but sand crabs, like the one at the left, emerge from their holes to scurry over the beaches. (Above, Donovan Roberts; left, Jack Dermid)

8 Right, above: The colorful nudibranchs, or shell-less mollusks, are often found in tide pools. (Donovan Roberts)

9 Right: Sea anemones close up when exposed to air at low tide, while starfishes, not concerned about drying out, wait for the water's return. (Milo Williams)

10 Left, above, A species of *Acmaea,* one of over a hundred kinds of limpets found along the California coast. (Donovan Roberts)

11 Left, below: A brown sea anemone and a starfish next to a colony of tunicates in shallow Mexican waters. (Ron Church)

12 Right: A sluggish horn shark lurks under an overhanging coral ledge. (Ron Church)

13 Below: A keyhole limpet on a bit of stone that it has cleaned of algae during its feeding. (Ron Church)

14 In many parts of the tropics and subtropics mangroves form a special habitat along swampy coasts. (Eliot Porter)

3

The Ocean Depths

On January 23, 1960, Jacques Piccard and Lieutenant Don Walsh of the United States Navy reached the bottom of the Challenger Deep in the bathyscaph *Trieste,* 35,800 feet below the surface of the Pacific. This is thought to be the deepest part of the oceans; man had reached the last frontier on the surface of his planet. The achievement seems to me much more significant than the first ascent of Mount Everest, or even the first arrival at the North or South Pole, because it represented more than a great feat of endurance and fortitude: it demonstrated the possibilities of a new way of dealing with one of the major environments of the earth.

Man, after all, is a land animal, and he has only slowly learned ways of dealing with the sea. Coastal fishing cultures have a long history, as do rafts and various types of boats. The Polynesians, two thousand years ago, may have been the first to deal confidently with the open sea, followed later by the very different Vikings—though the Arabs have been crossing the Indian Ocean in their dhows over some unrecorded span of time. Western European exploration of the oceans has a rather short history. It can well be argued that it began with Prince Henry the Navigator, who founded his astronomical observatory in 1420 and started the Portuguese expeditions south into the Atlantic, leading to the exploits of Columbus, Vasco da Gama, and Magellan, and starting the development of precise methods of navigation.

Life in the Depths

The surface was opened, but the depths remained a mystery. Skilled pearl divers can reach eighty feet or slightly more and stay down briefly, but that was about as far as men could get until the present century. Attempts have been made to devise diving apparatus at least since the days of the Greeks—usually with war operations in mind. This has remained true of the development of submarine ships. The first of the modern naval submarines was launched in 1888 by the French, and these ships have been improved constantly up to the long-range nuclear-powered vessels of the present—but they seem always to have been designed for war instead of for the collection of knowledge.

Diving suits became practical at about the same time as submarines, but the diver was tethered by his air hose and depended on the crew manning the pump above. Diving suits were often used for biological exploration, but they were awkward and expensive. Then Captain J. Y. Cousteau and Emile Gagnan developed the aqualung in the early 1940's, and now, with masks, flippers, and scubas ("Self-contained Underwater Breathing Apparatus"), man can, for brief periods, join the world of the fishes—near the surface. But even with scuba or diving suit we are still confined, principally because of pressure problems, to the top three hundred feet of water.

The pressure from the weight of the air of the atmosphere is about 14.7 pounds per square inch at sea level. As one goes down into the sea, this pressure increases rapidly and greatly because of the density of water. Atmospheric pressure is doubled at a depth of ten meters (thirty-nine feet), and in the great depths pressures are a thousand times that of the atmosphere. It was long argued that because of these immense pressures, life would be impossible at any considerable depth. In fact, it was calculated that the zero of life, the maximum depth that organisms could withstand, would be about three hundred fathoms (eighteen hundred feet). Then, in 1858, one of the submarine cables that had recently been laid in the Mediterranean to carry telegraph messages broke, and was hauled up for repair. The cable had been lying at a depth of about a thousand fathoms—yet it was found to be encrusted with a variety of bottom-living animals!

The fallacy of the pressure theory then became obvious. Animal protoplasm is liquid or at least semifluid, and liquids in general are only slightly compressible. This fact was demonstrated when Robert Dietz, on one of the dives in the bathyscaph with Piccard, packed half a dozen eggs in a plastic bag which was tied outside the float of the *Trieste*. Since eggshells were semiporous, it was believed that sea water would seep in to equalize the pressures inside and outside, so the eggs would not break. Sure enough, the eggs survived their voyage down into the pressures of the great depths without developing a single crack. Similarly, in marine organisms, the fluids inside the body and outside are at exactly the same pressure, so that the weight of the water above means no more to an animal in the sea than the weight of the air above does to us. Of course, if the animal had air or other gases inside its body, it would be a different story—the gases would be compressed by the pressure of water and the animal would be destroyed. As we saw in the case of the whales, special adaptations can neutralize this, at least to some extent. But with a physiology like that of the human species, there is a clear limit to the pressures that can be withstood.

The proof of life in the depths given by the submarine cable started a long series of studies. The problem became that of devising means of collecting materials and making instrument measurements at great depths, and oceanographers developed many ingenious kinds of apparatus. In 1872, the British government sent H. M. S. *Challenger* on a voyage over the oceans of the world that lasted for three and a half years. Animals were collected and measurements made at all possible depths, and the fifty large volumes of the *Challenger Report* form the basis of modern oceanography. Other governments sent out other deep-sea expeditions, and knowledge began to grow steadily. During the Second World War, the development and perfection of echo location provided a means for mapping the topography of the ocean bottoms—depths had been known previously only from the slow process of sounding with lines. We have developed methods of taking photographs at great depths, and of lowering television cameras and other complex apparatus. But with all of these advances, man is still sitting on the surface, without direct experience of the world he is sampling.

Bathysphere and Bathyscaph

The first men to have direct experience with the depths (and return to tell about it) were William Beebe and Otis Barton. In 1935, they built their bathysphere, a heavy steel sphere with thick quartz windows designed to withstand great pressures. Inside there was a supply of compressed oxygen, as well as chemicals to absorb excess carbon dioxide and moisture. The bathysphere was lowered from a mother ship by a cable with a telephone line, so that observations could be reported back directly.

With the bathysphere, Beebe and Barton descended to a maximum depth of three thousand feet in waters off Bermuda. They were unable to go deeper because of the great danger that the cable might foul, leaving the observers helplessly trapped. But at this depth they were far into the region of eternal darkness, the first men to see the bizarre creatures of this zone in action. The idea of the bathysphere was not followed up, perhaps because of the definite limitations and dangers of an apparatus that had to be lowered overside from a ship and handled with a winch.

The principle of the bathyscaph is essentially similar to that of the balloon: the one depending on a balance between materials lighter and heavier than air, the other on materials lighter and heavier than water. The "blimp" of the bathyscaph consists of a large, thin-walled tank of gasoline, with openings to allow free flow of water in and out, so that pressures will always be the same inside and outside of the float. For ballast, iron pellets are used, held in place with electromagnets; the ballast can be released by breaking the current, and the relatively light gasoline will then inevitably lift the apparatus back to the surface. The gondola swung under this blimp is an improved version of Beebe's bathysphere, with thick windows of plastic instead of quartz—more safely resistant to great pressure—and no longer dependent on cable and winch.

The Zones of Life in the Depths

It has long been held as a general principle that the greater the depth, the fewer the number of kinds of animals and the fewer the number of individuals. This is because all life below the lighted upper layers—say the top two hundred to six hundred feet—must depend on living or dead materials that drift downward from the producing system at the surface. Available food would thus become increasingly scarce with increasing depth. In general, catches with nets towed at different depths have tended to support this proposition. Yet both Beebe and the later divers in the bathyscaphs have reported seeing many more animals than would be expected in the middle depths, particularly between one thousand and three thousand feet. Cousteau has described this as like "a great bowl of living soup extending on down and growing thicker the deeper into the 'tureen' we go."

In this connection, a curious phenomenon was discovered with the development of echo-location devices during the Second World War. A continuous tracing of ocean depths can be made from a ship by sending sound waves which bounce back from the bottom, giving a measure of depth by the length of time the sound waves take to reach bottom and come back. Any large underwater object—submarine, whale, or school of fish—will also show up on the tracing. It soon became evident that almost everywhere, except in the Arctic and Antarctic seas, there was a curious something between the surface and the bottom that reflected a certain proportion of the sound waves, appearing as a sort of smudgy intermediate line on the charts. Throughout, this was discovered at a depth of about twenty-five hundred feet during the day, rising toward the surface at night.

This diurnal movement would suggest animal plankton, which, as we have seen, tends to move upward at night. But this plankton is most abundant in the Arctic seas, where the sound effect does not occur. In the ocean, anything containing air gives off a particularly strong sound reflection. It has been discovered that many of the small deep-sea fishes have air bladders, and one suggestion is that perhaps these fishes are much more abundant than had been supposed—abundant enough to cause the sound effect. The explanation is still not clear; but, taken along with the observations from bathysphere and bathyscaph, it is another indication that life may be more abundant at intermediate depths than once thought.

Cousteau suspects that there may be "somewhere an unsuspected link in the cycle of marine life yet to be discovered." Perhaps there is some kind of a producer system completely unknown to us. Certainly everyone would agree that we are far from having a satisfactory knowledge of the ways of life in the ocean depths, and almost anything is possible. But it may also be that the food materials drifting down from the surface support larger populations of animals than has been thought likely. Or perhaps, too, these animals are concentrated in layers, thus giving the sound effect.

Aside from the pressure gradient, there is a zonation of light and of temperature in the seas. The water of the depths, everywhere, is cold. Below about six thousand feet the temperature quite uniformly is 3 degrees C. (37.5 degrees F.) because water is densest at about this temperature, so that cold polar waters sink and fill the ocean basins. If water were heaviest in the solid state, like other substances, the ocean basins would be solid ice, which would make for very different climates around the earth from those we know. As it is, the waters of the depths, even though uniformly cold, slowly circulate. Temperatures near the surface, of course, vary with latitude, with seasons, and with current conditions—though seasonal effects are hardly felt much below six hundred feet. The animals of the depths are apparently as much influenced by temperature as by pressure or light, and they may be found quite near the surface in regions of upwelling cold waters.

But light is the most obvious gradient in the sea. Depth of penetration depends, among other things, on the wave length of the light. The long, infrared "heat" rays are cut off in the first few inches of water; the visible red in the first few feet. Blue rays have the deepest penetration. Divers in the bathysphere and bathyscaph have reported being able to detect some light to depths of seventeen hundred, nineteen hundred, or even two thousand feet.

The human eye is incredibly sensitive; we can detect light when it has an intensity of a billionth or less that of full daylight. But many animals—owls, for instance—have eyes that are more sensitive in dim light than ours, and it is probable that this is the case with some of the deep-sea animals. Robert Dietz has suggested that the absolute limit of light as an environmental influence in the sea may be something like twenty-four hundred feet.

Light? No, the correct word is sunlight, because light is a factor all through the abyss in the form of bioluminescence—living light.

Top to bottom: A pelican fish or eel *(Eurypharynx pelicanoides)*; an angler fish *(Linophryne arborifer)*; and hermit crabs, one with a colony of sea anemones on its shell.

Living Light

Everyone who has had much to do with the sea is familiar with phosphorescence. Sometimes, leaning over the bow of a ship at night, one sees scattered points of light from individual animals that have been disturbed. But sometimes the whole sea turns into liquid fire as it is churned. This massive phosphorescence is apt to be periodic or seasonal, but there are a few bays in the tropics—one is on the southern coast of Puerto Rico—where the water turns to fire night after night, all through the year. This massive bioluminescence is produced chiefly by micro-organisms, species of a few genera of flagellate Protozoa, which at certain times and places become unbelievably abundant.

But the extraordinary thing, when you start to look into the matter, is the number of very different kinds of marine organisms that show bioluminescence. However the different phyla, or major groups, are classified—and there is little agreement on many of the details—it turns out that about half of them include some species that are capable of luminescence. This means that the ability to produce living light must have developed quite independently many times in quite different animal groups in the course of evolutionary history. From this, one would further judge that light production must have some deep biological significance—though no one has any idea what it might be.

Curiously, no animals that live in fresh water are known to show biolumines-cence. On land there are various luminous species of earthworms and centipedes, as well as the more common and widespread glowworms and fireflies. In some New Zealand caves vast numbers of larvae of a species of crane fly, *Bolitophila luminosa,* make a spectacular sight, but otherwise luminescence seems to be absent in cave animals. Among plants, only some bacteria and fungi are light-producers. The luminescent bacteria can sometimes be seen glowing on decaying matter; and it seems likely that contamination with such bacteria accounts for the glow some-times found in normally nonluminous animals.

Bioluminescence, then, occurs among a few land animals, including one cave species; but it is overwhelmingly a phenomenon of the sea. There it is shown by a very wide variety of animals, living from the surface to the greatest depths. Its greatest development, however, especially among fishes, is at middle depths—from something like fifteen hundred to fifteen thousand feet. William Beebe made a special effort to determine the abundance of luminous fishes at these depths in the waters near Bermuda. He examined more than a hundred thousand specimens, and found that 66 per cent of the species had luminous organs. These light-produc-ing species, however, were the commonest kinds, making up 96.5 per cent of the specimens captured.

The light organs are very elaborate affairs in most of these fishes. In some cases the light itself is produced by luminescent bacteria living in certain patches on the skin; but in other cases the light is produced directly by special tissues of the fishes themselves.

The lights are arranged in many different sorts of patterns, depending on the species of fish; but in a large proportion of the cases they are on the lower surface, pointing downward. This seems curious, and no good explanation has yet been proposed. In general, one can guess that the light arrangements serve for species and sex recognition, and species with well-developed light systems tend also to have well-developed eyes—an understandable relationship in the eternal night of the depths. But why so frequently on the underside of the fish?

Sometimes the light appears to serve specific functions. In a few cases, for in-stance, it is projected forward, like the beam of a searchlight, and one might guess that it serves in finding food. Sir Alister Hardy quotes from a biological log kept by the late E. R. Gunther, who observed some deep-sea fishes at the surface at night in Antarctic waters. One of these, an eel-like species, had a headlight system:

"From a pair of luminous organs in the orbital region, the fish (which was 9–12 inches in length) emitted a beam, of varying intensity, of strong blue light which shone directly forward for a distance of about two feet. The fish had the habit of lurking at a depth of 2–6 feet below the surface, poised at an angle of about 35–40 degrees from the horizontal—this gave the beam an upward tilt: occasionally the fish swam round and with a quick action snapped at the cloud of krill above it."

In other cases the light seems to serve as a lure for possible prey. This at least is presumed to be the explanation for the peculiar structure of the angler fishes. One of the dorsal fin rays has moved forward and become greatly elongated, supporting a luminous spot directly above the gaping mouth. It certainly looks like a device for attracting possible food within easy reach; and many marine animals, like insects on land, will come to a light. This positive reaction to light must be very hazardous, though, with many angler fish about, and one would think that species with this habit would have been eliminated by natural selection long ago. But perhaps there is some value in being attracted to lights that counterbalances the danger. It is curious that so many small animals show this attraction—and that no one has been able to think up a reasonable explanation for it.

In still other cases an opposite function has been suggested—that the lights help their possessor to avoid being eaten. The theory is that the sudden turning on of the lights would confuse a pursuer and increase chances of escape. In support of this, there are deep-sea shrimp and at least one species of squid that, when alarmed,

Top to bottom: A snipe eel *(Nemichthys scolopaceus)*; an angler fish *(Gigantactis macronema)*; and a sea spider *(Nymphon)*.

emit clouds of luminescent secretion. I have been writing mostly about fishes, but it should always be remembered that a wide variety of inhabitants of the deep show luminescent phenomena, including shrimp, squid, and pelagic worms.

The fishes of great depths are predominantly black, the shrimp predominantly dark red, which in the absence of red light would appear black. This is curious, because in caves, another environment of constant darkness, animals tend to lose all pigment and become white. The difference may be due to the presence of bioluminescence in marine animals and its absence from those of caves (except for that New Zealand glowworm). Even though no daylight penetrates to the depths, luminescence would still make the concealment of color important in the blackness, while in caves, color loses all biological meaning. In relation to this animal light, eyes are often highly developed in creatures of the deep seas, whereas the eyes of cave animals tend to become atrophied.

Shape in the Depths

Top to bottom (not in scale): Benthosaurus; a stomiated fish (*Flagellostomias boureei*); and amphipods.

The fishes of the depths are a bizarre-looking lot, with unusual shapes and often with odd and greatly attenuated appendages of various sorts. The streamlined form that we think of as notably fishlike is little in evidence. Most of the species that we know are quite small, often only two or three inches long; but this may be because these kinds are most easily caught in the awkward process of towing nets at great depths. While the fishes tend to be small, they tend also to have relatively enormous mouths, and specimens have been caught that had succeeded in swallowing other fish larger than themselves.

The small size and big mouths are generally explained as a consequence of the scarcity of food. If everything must depend on the surface plankton, it is understandable that food would become increasingly scarce with depth, so that a mouth big enough to catch anything coming along would be an asset. The ocean depths, then, may be a world of miniatures—but at the same time, apparently, it is an extremely fierce and highly competitive world.

We now know that life does continue to the very bottom of the greatest depths. As the bathyscaph *Trieste* was settling down on the floor of the Challenger Deep, Piccard saw lying on the bottom, just beneath the craft, "a type of flatfish, resembling a sole, about one foot long and six inches across." The only other life they saw during the twenty minutes they were on the bottom was "a beautiful red shrimp." Life was not overwhelmingly abundant seven miles down—but it was there.

The ocean bottom almost everywhere away from the continents is covered with thick layers of very fine ooze—about the consistency, someone has said, of warm butter. Piccard and his companions in the *Trieste* always made every effort to settle on the bottom as gently as possible, because of the ease with which this ooze could be stirred up into great muddy clouds, making it impossible to see. And there was always the very real danger that if the bathyscaph plunked too heavily into this ooze, it might get stuck.

The animals that live on this ooze need special means of support, and we find crabs and the like with very long legs, often with hairs on the terminal joints to increase support. Fixed animals like sponges and polyps sometimes grow on the ooze, but they too must have special structures to keep from sinking into the mud. In

some places observers in the bathyscaph have found mounds and holes in the mud—evidence of burrowing animals. They have also observed patterns of ripples and waves, apparently caused by currents flowing over the bottom, even at very great depths.

The Landscape of the Depths

It is becoming apparent, as we accumulate more and more data on depths by echo soundings across the oceans, that their basins are wondrously varied. The greatest mountain ranges lie buried in the seas, with cliffs and canyons and mountain peaks that dwarf the landscapes we know. This topography is presumably the consequence of the restless movements of the earth's crust, causing bucklings and rifts. As we learn more about these formations, we shall be better able to reconstruct the forces that have molded the surface of our planet. But about the possible relations of these submarine mountains to animal life we know nothing. This last frontier has been touched, but it has scarcely yet been explored. Only as we come close to the continents does our knowledge become more certain.

4

The Margins of
the Seas

In the open sea, geography does not matter much. The animals of warm tropical waters are, to be sure, apt to be different from those of colder regions; but the animals of the mid-Atlantic are hardly different from those of the mid-Pacific. With increasing depth geography becomes even less important, because in the abyss the conditions of life are similar everywhere.

As we approach the continents, however, geographical patterns become clearer. The North Sea, the Mediterranean, the Caribbean, the China Sea are different places, inhabited for the most part by different kinds of animals. When we do find the same species, they are apt to be intruders from the open sea. The faunas of the Pacific and Atlantic coasts of the United States are different, partly because of different shore and water conditions, but also because the regions are separated.

Near the continents the seas are relatively shallow almost everywhere; it is as though the continents were partially flooded, extending out for a way into the surrounding oceans. This submerged region is called the "continental shelf" and it is generally considered to extend to the line where the average depth becomes greater than six hundred feet. This shelf tends to be widest off regions with broad lowlands and near the mouths of great rivers; along mountainous coasts it may be virtually absent. For the earth as a whole, it has an average width of about thirty miles.

Animals of the Continental Shelf

The shallow seas are the rich seas in terms of animal life. Perhaps this is partly an effect of compression. The animals, after all, depend on the producing system, and the producers can live only in light-penetrated surface water. A square mile of surface in mid-ocean may support a consumer complex extending down six miles, while over the continental shelf the consumers could be spread out through a depth of at most six hundred feet. Thus if a given area of surface supported the same number of animals in each of the two situations, they would be at least fifty times as crowded over the shelf, which would give the effect of richness.

Beyond this, where sufficient light can reach the bottom, fixed plants will be able to make their contribution to the energy stores built up by the plankton floating above. And food materials near land are added to the oceanic system by the waters of streams and rivers.

It would, of course, be very difficult to measure exactly how much animal life is supported by a given surface area in deep seas as compared with shallow seas. Perhaps the space available in great depth allows the development of more complex systems, so that animals live nearer to the possible limit allowed by the volume of plant production. Certainly, as we have noticed, the amount of animal life in the depths is surprisingly large, so that the effect of compression may be to some degree counterbalanced; fifty to a hundred times as much animal life per unit surface for continental seas seems rather large. But unquestionably animals near shore are more noticeable; and it is in this area, too, that the great fisheries of the world are located.

Fishes of the herring family, which includes sardines and shad, have become an important element in human economy in many parts of the world—and they also are important in the economy of the coastal seas. Herring travel in vast schools which may cover several square miles. Thomas Henry Huxley, of evolutionist fame, calculated that there must be more than five hundred million individuals in each square mile of a school; I don't suppose anyone has ever ventured to guess what the total herring population of the seas may be. Since each herring lays at least ten thousand eggs, it is obvious that herring, in growing up, are providing food for a large number of other creatures—as well as taking in a considerable quantity of food themselves.

Most marine fishes lay eggs which float free with the plankton, but the herring deposits its spawn in great masses on the bottom, thickly plastering stones, shells, and even the backs of crabs. The tiny, newly hatched fish feed on the microscopic plant cells of the plankton, turning to the somewhat larger animals like copepods as they grow; and the baby herring themselves, of course, fall prey to animals that are bigger than they are. When the herring are about an inch and three-quarters long, they undergo a sort of metamorphosis, shifting from a slender, eel-like form to a proper herring shape and acquiring for the first time a coat of tiny scales.

At this stage the herring start to gather in schools, and a great many of them come into large river estuaries. In England, herring at this stage are called whitebait. After six months or so, according to Sir Alister Hardy, they disappear and do not turn up in the big herring schools until they are about four years old. One can tell the age of a herring (and of many other sorts of fishes) by examining the scales, which are marked with "growth rings" comparable with those found in tree trunks. The herring grow rapidly during the summer months, and survive the winter on their food reserves, hardly growing at all; each scale carries the mark of these spurts of growth.

The Schooling Habit

Why do the herring come together in vast schools? These are perhaps the most spectacular of fish aggregations, but the schooling habit is widespread among many different sorts of fishes in many kinds of habitats, from ponds and streams to the open sea. Such a widespread pattern of behavior must have some special significance, but there is no agreement about what it may be. Herding in many animals gives protection, since an alarm by any individual can alert the whole group. This sometimes happens with fishes; often, watching a school of minnows from a wharf, one sees them suddenly disperse in the face of danger, to reform when the danger has passed. But this would hardly apply to the vast and dense schools of fishes like herring. Of course, the schooling is a great convenience for human fishermen and for other predators, since the food animals are neatly and conveniently packed together.

Some fishes school only when young, others only as adults; there are many different behavior patterns and perhaps an equal number of different meanings. In many fishes that school as adults, the sexes look exactly alike, and egg and sperm are simply released into the water, so the schooling may well have reproductive advantages.

Herring, the animals they eat, and the animals that in turn eat them, are mostly pelagic, swimming in the waters over the continental shelf. The similarly important cod and their relatives are more closely associated with the benthos—the bottom fauna—as are a host of other kinds of creatures.

Attached to a horseshoe crab, these barnacles live on food brought to them in the currents created by their waving feet. (Fritz Goro: *Life*)

Many kinds of fishes have the schooling habit. (Fritz Goro: *Life*)

Life on the Bottom

The bottoms of great oceanic depths, as we noted in the last chapter, are everywhere covered with a very fine ooze—the final resting place of the skeletons of microscopic plankton drifting down from above. The continental shelf, on the other hand, is generally covered with detritus from the land, eroded by waves and streams, which may vary all the way from fine mud to a rather coarse sand. The bottom is rocky only off mountainous shores or in places where strong currents keep sediments washed away. Thus the shelf bottom offers firmer support for animals than the ooze of the great depths; and in the shallower water more food is available. As a result, the continental benthos includes a numerous and wide variety of animals.

One can group these animals according to their way of getting food. Many are *suspension feeders*, filtering plankton or fine organic matter out of the water. Others are *detritus feeders*, living on organic material that has settled to the bottom. Still others are *predators*, preying on the animals of the first two groups. There are no true herbivores, of course, until the water is shallow enough so that the light reaching the bottom allows the growth of fixed plants.

Sponges: Fixed Animals

Sponges are prominent among the suspension feeders. Something like forty-five hundred species have been described. There is one small group of fresh-water species, but the vast majority are marine. They occur from the greatest depths to the intertidal zone of the shore, but they are most abundant in the region of the continental shelf, especially in warmer seas.

All sponges show a fixed plantlike growth, but they unquestionably belong with the animals—though they are very odd animals in many ways. They have no special organ systems like nerves or digestive tract; a sponge seems to be a sort of colony or aggregation of large numbers of single cells. Yet each species has a characteristic way of growth, and each individual acts as a coordinated organism. The association among the cells, however, is not as close as it is in more highly organized animals. It has been found in the laboratory that some types of sponges can be pressed through a fine sieve so that most of the cells become separated into a confused mass, and that these cells then reorganize, coming together again to form a unified and functioning individual.

Sponges do not have a definite "mouth," but water circulates continuously through the porous body and food is extracted by the cells lining the passages; this food is somehow shared with the cells lying in deeper layers. The form of the sponge is maintained by a "skeleton" composed of thousands of minute spicules secreted by the cells. In one class these spicules are made of lime, in others they are silica; and the skeletons of the sponges of commerce are made of a flexible material called 'spongin.' The microscopic spicules come in a fascinating variety of shapes. Sponges apparently are not often eaten by other animals, perhaps in part because these multitudinous glasslike spikes are hard to deal with.

The porous sponge body, however, does provide homes for a considerable variety of creatures. Nearly 13,500 other animals were found living in one tub-sized sponge growing on the reefs of the Tortugas Islands off Florida. Of these, 12,000 were small shrimps, but the remainder included eighteen different species of worms and copepods and one species of fish. Sponges obviously provide excellent hiding places for other small animals, but we are far from understanding all of the relationships involved. Some of the sponge-dwelling animals are too large to get in and out of the pores, which open to the outside, so they must have been imprisoned. These animals are ordinarily classed with the sponges as "commensals," but it is hard to see what benefit the sponge gets from the association; and one wonders, too, how there can be food enough for both the sponge and the host of hangers-on.

Sponges, understandably, grow most abundantly on firm or rocky bottoms. This is true of most of the fixed, suspension-feeding animals—they have to be attached to something. Along with the sponges grow many kinds of coelenterates—sea anemones, corals, and coral-like animals. Many other groups of invertebrates have taken up the suspension-feeding habit, including those curious animals the barnacles.

Mangrove roots provide a perch for a zoological garden of fixed animals and a muddy habitat for these hatpin urchins. (Fritz Goro: *Life*)

Barnacles

The hard-shelled barnacles, growing over rocks or piling or fouling the bottom of a ship, look like some kind of a mollusk; but it was long ago discovered that they were really crustaceans, relatives of the shrimps and copepods. A barnacle, as Thomas Henry Huxley remarked, is a "crustacean fixed by its head and kicking the food into its mouth with its legs." How proper crustaceans got started on this peculiar barnacle way of life is a mystery—fossil barnacles appear far back in the geological record, but nothing has been recognized that could be called a half-way stage between the ordinary crustacean form and the fixed barnacle. That they are crustaceans, however, is shown clearly enough by their life history.

The barnacle eggs develop inside of the parent shell and are released into the

water as clouds of microscopic larvae of the nauplius form, hardly distinguishable from the first life stage of other crustaceans. These larvae live in the plankton for several months, finally changing into a form called the cypris larva, which presently sinks to the bottom to find a suitable place for attachment. The cypris larva is apparently rather fussy, touching down and rising repeatedly before finally settling on some firm object to metamorphose and start secreting a proper barnacle shell.

The barnacles we commonly see are on pilings or rocks near shore, where they survive the exposure of low tide firmly closed up in their shells. The ones that get the most serious attention, however, are those that foul the hulls of ships, and a great deal of research has gone into the problem of finding types of paint that would discourage their growth. But barnacles live in many sorts of situations. One species lives on the skin of whales; and some, instead of simply finding support on other animals, have turned to a parasitic way of life, living off other crustaceans, including crabs and shrimp.

Barnacles live on food brought to them in the currents created by their waving feet. They in turn are eaten by many other things, particularly starfish and snails. Certain marine snails have a special tooth on the outer lip of the shell which serves nicely to pry open the plates of barnacles so that the proboscis can be inserted and the soft animal inside eaten.

Barnacles, corals, sea anemones, sponges—the fixed suspension feeders—all are most abundant on rocky or gravel bottoms, though some of them have special root-like organs that enable them to live on softer ground. Some of the mollusks and worms that live in mud are really suspension feeders, living on materials brought to them by currents they create. But most of the animals on a mud bottom are detritus feeders, living on the organic materials that settle down from above.

Bottom Dwellers

Photographs of a muddy bottom will often show it to be covered with a tangled mass of brittle stars, their long arms nicely adapted for support on a soft surface. The brittle stars form one of the classes of the phylum Echinodermata, which includes starfish, sea urchins, sea cucumbers, sand dollars, and sea lilies as well. All are bottom dwellers (though they have larval stages in the plankton and some of the sea cucumbers can swim), and for the most part they live on detritus (though starfish are mostly predatory).

It is curious to think of an animal as sluggish and as apparently inept as a starfish in terms of predation, but in the sedentary world of the sea bottom almost anything can happen. Starfish move by means of numerous "tube feet" on the undersides of the arms—a sort of hydraulic suction system that doesn't allow for any appreciable speed but that enables the animal to cling to a hard surface with great force.

Most species feed on mollusks, and they are sometimes great pests in oyster beds. It was long thought that starfish opened oysters by the sheer force of their tube feet, that they embraced the prey and exerted a strong and steady pull on the shells until the tired oyster opened enough so that the starfish could get its eversible stomach inside the shell and digest its prey at leisure. Recently it has been suggested that this is not true, that the starfish, rather than having more power than the oyster, has more patience. According to this, an alarmed oyster, given enough time, presently opens its shell slightly to try a resumption of normal life; the embracing starfish injects a paralyzing poison and then starts the external digestion. But whatever the method, the starfish gets the oyster.

Except for the starfish, most echinoderms feed on whatever they can get—which means a scavenging way of life. But enough food of one sort or another reaches bottom, especially near shore, to support a surprisingly numerous fauna. In sand or mud, a large proportion of these animals, including some of the echinoderms, burrow both for protection and to sift out food materials.

The Burrowers

A lemon shark off the Bahama sand flats. (Chuck Meyer)

Biologists—like children—tend to be fascinated by holes in the ground. But finding out what makes the holes is not always easy. Donald Abbott, a marine biologist of Stanford University, points out that there are really only two possible approaches to the hole problem, both of them worked out long before scientists had turned up in biological communities. One, the cat approach, is to wait patiently beside the hole to see what comes out; the other, doglike, is to dig the place up.

The cat technique takes a lot of patience and can be very exasperating, especially when it turns out that there was really nothing in the hole. The dog approach is more actively satisfying, but it often results only in confusion under an obscuring cloud of mud. Scurrying animals can be sifted out of the muddle of debris, but one is never sure which animal made the hole. And of course many of the animals of the mud simply force their way along without making definite passageways with openings to the surface.

The marine underground is a relatively secure world—there are few predators. Animals at the surface are easily picked up by the passer-by, but they are harder to find if buried in the mud. One phylum of predaceous marine worms, the nemerteans, has a number of mud-burrowing species. These have a curious eversible proboscis which can be greatly extended to explore the mud ahead for possible prey: when this proboscis finds the trail of an annelid worm, it shoots forward and wraps itself around the victim. The nemertean then retracts its proboscis and digests the prey at leisure. Some of the nemerteans are incredibly long when fully extended, one species sometimes attaining a total length of seventy-five feet, the longest of any invertebrate.

Besides worms of all kinds, the burrowers include some sea anemones and many echinoderms, mollusks, and crustaceans. Sometimes, especially with crustacea such as crabs and shrimp, the hole is only a hiding place; but with most burrowers it is a total way of life. Many of the clams and oysters are burrowers, some just beneath the surface, others to a depth of a foot or so. Some of these mollusks make permanent tunnels in which they move about; others, though buried and immobile, are able to extend their siphons to the surface for respiration and food.

Bottom-Living Fishes

The predators that roam over the bottom include mollusks like conchs and octopuses, many sorts of shrimp, lobster, and crabs, and many kinds of fishes. Life under the mud seems fairly safe and that on the surface extremely hazardous—yet somehow life multiplies enough to support this voracious horde of higher-order consumers. The bottom dwellers include some of the most important commercial fishes such as the members of the cod family and such flatfishes as halibut, flounder, plaice, turbot, and sole.

The flatfishes form a special order, with five families and some six hundred species, found mostly in coastal waters—though the one fish that Piccard saw at the bottom of the Challenger Deep belonged to this order. Flatfishes start life in an ordinary way, the eggs floating in the plankton and hatching into tiny, normal-looking fish. In a few days or weeks, however, the two sides of the fish begin to grow at different rates; the skull becomes twisted and deformed so that both eyes are on the same side of the head, and the whole body becomes flattened. In the plaice this process starts when the fish is a month old and is completed in another two and a half weeks, after which the fish drops down to start life on the bottom.

Some flatfish species have both eyes on the right side, others both on the left—and sometimes both right- and left-eyed specimens are found in the same population.

Most are small or medium-sized, but the Atlantic halibut may reach a length of ten feet and a weight of seven hundred pounds. Generally flatfishes are protectively colored, to match the kind of bottom on which they live; and some are able to change their pattern as they move from mud to sand or gravel surface—an ability shared with octopuses in the sea and chameleons on land. Many species, when they settle down, make a shivering movement that throws mud or sand over their bodies, adding to concealment and leaving only eyes and mouth uncovered. These fishes look awkward, but when potential food swims overhead, they can dash to the capture quickly enough.

The rays—elasmobranch relatives of the sharks—share the flatfish habit of often lying flat and partially buried on the bottom. These bottom-living rays have powerful grinding teeth with which they crush the clams and other mollusks that form their food. One group, the sting rays, has a sharp, poisoned spine at the base of the tail, which can inflict an extremely painful and sometimes dangerous wound on anyone who happens to step on it. In ray-infested waters it is therefore a good idea to shuffle over a sandy or muddy bottom. One would think this sting would be an effective defense for its owner, but apparently some of the sharks specialize in eating rays, and many embedded stings are found inside their mouths without, it seems, any special inconvenience to the sharks.

The rocky shore of Bear Island, between Cape North and Spitzbergen, provides protected nesting grounds for these fulmars. (Svante Lundgren)

But I have been writing as though nothing but animals lived in these coastal waters, depending ultimately on microscopic plankton for their food supply. To be sure, the plankton are probably always the most important primary source for animal energy; but as soon as the water becomes shallow enough for adequate light to reach the bottom, fixed plants begin to occur.

Life among the Seaweeds

The fixed plants of the sea are mostly algae—very different in structure and physiology from the seed plants and ferns (or "higher plants") that are so familiar on land. The algae, of course, play the same role in the economy as the seed plants—building up chemical energy through photosynthesis. Chlorophyll, then, is always present in these algae, but its green color is frequently masked by other pigments, so that the plants do not necessarily look green. Botanists, in fact, classify algae into major groups with common names that depend on the predominant colors in the group— green algae, brown algae, red algae, yellow-green algae.

The common rockweeds of cool coastal waters are brown algae, and so are the giant kelps of deeper waters. One Pacific species that grows off the coast of Chile is said to reach the surface from depths as great as 250 feet, though more commonly the kelp forests are 50 feet or so in depth. The sargassum weed that forms great drifting masses of vegetation in the tropical Atlantic is also a brown alga.

Two families of seed plants have marine forms, amounting to a total of about thirty species—an insignificant showing indeed compared with the variety on land. But these few species, especially the eel grasses of the north and the turtle grasses of the tropics, sometimes form vast meadows in shallow coastal waters.

These marine forests and meadows provide shelter and support for a wide variety of animals but, curiously, they are of little importance as a direct source of food. It is said that the sea turtles really eat turtle grass, and that the manatees—

sea cows—graze on seaweeds. The marine iguana lizards of the shores of the Gala-pagos Islands eat algae, and so do some other shore animals in other places. But these are intruders from the land. No group of animals has taken up the caterpillar niche in these forests of the seas.

But the fixed plants, even though not much eaten, furnish support for all sorts of other things from microscopic algae and minute animal polyps to barnacles. Snails, slugs, and various worms crawl over the surfaces, eating this encrusting growth—and each other. And fishes nibble delicately at the seaweeds, not to eat the plants but to pick off the small animals that infest them.

Here among the seaweeds protective coloration becomes common, and all sorts of animals have taken on the shapes and patterns of the plants among which they live. Among the most bizarre of these are the pipefishes and sea horses. One species of long and slender Oriental pipefish has the habit of standing on its nose amid beds of turtle grass, looking for all the world like another blade of grass gently waving in the current. One of the Australian species, called the "sea dragon," which lives among red seaweeds, trails a weird collection of long filaments from head, tail, back, and belly, to blend perfectly with the background vegetation.

Roseate spoonbills sift the mud around Florida mangroves. (Florida State News Bureau)

The sea horses and their relatives have habits as odd as their appearance. They are one of the scattered groups of animals in which the female has succeeded in passing responsibility for the young to the male. Courtship behavior may be both complex and prolonged; in some species the males court each other for several days before taking up with the females. But in any case the female eventually slips her eggs into a brood pouch on the abdomen of the male. Here, presently, the eggs hatch, the young thus being born of their father.

Life between the Tides

Life near the shore everywhere is affected by the tides, which come and go twice each day on a cycle of about twelve and a half hours—just different enough from the daily cycle of the sun so that there can be no regular relationship between being alternately wet and dry and alternately light and dark. The extent of the tides varies greatly, from as little as a foot in inland seas like the Mediterranean to fifty feet or so in the Bay of Fundy in Nova Scotia. In some parts of the world one of the two daily tides rises higher and falls lower than the other; and tides at the time of new moon and full moon are generally greater than at other times. The extent of the intertidal zone thus varies from day to day as well as from place to place.

The kinds of organisms living in the region between the tidal limits depend very much on whether the shore is rocky, sandy, or muddy. Rocky shores have the most obviously rich faunas, because of the firm anchorage for both animals and plants and because of the many small pools left by the retreating seas. Sandy shores, especially when exposed to surf (as they usually are), have the fewest kinds of animals—it takes special structures and habits to withstand the shifting sands, the pounding breakers, and the alternate wetting and drying. In general, the animals of the intertidal zone are distributed according to the amount of exposure they can withstand, from the region that is dry only briefly at very low tides, to the upper limit that is reached by the sea only about every two weeks at the time of the highest tides.

This zone, caught between the sea and the land, would seem to be among the most difficult of animal habitats: yet it has a rich and varied fauna. It really includes three quite different ways of life. First there are the permanent residents that stay where they are as the water comes and goes; then there are the sea visitors, the active fishes, crustaceans, and cephalopods that come in with the tide and then retreat; and finally there are the land visitors—the shore birds that patrol exposed areas by day, and the raccoons, skunks, rats, and other mammals that prowl the water's edge by night. When we think of the hazards of the physical environment, and the double jeopardy of predators both from land and sea, the persistence of the teeming shore population seems even more surprising.

The permanent residents of the intertidal zone are almost all marine forms or relatives of marine groups. Their adaptations, then, help them endure the period out of water. Many of the simpler invertebrates resist drying without trouble; sea anemones have been kept out of water for as long as eighteen days, coming to look like dried raisins, but promptly reviving when placed in sea water. Forms with shells, like barnacles and mollusks, simply close up tight when the tide leaves them above water and wait for the water to come back. Snails, starfish, sea cucumbers, and the like may move into protected spots or linger in tide pools. The burrowers often simply dig deeper and thus stay moist.

Crabs, skittering over the mud or retreating shyly behind rocks, seem to be the masters of the intertidal environment. Of course crabs of many different sorts are found everywhere, from the greatest ocean depths to dry land (though land crabs tend to dig holes down to water level). There is even a crab that lives in water collected by bromeliad plants high in tropical forests. It is not remarkable that such versatility has enabled so many species to live in the changing environment of the region between the tides.

Many of the shore species, like the swift-running ghost crabs, are most active at night. But the brazen fiddler crabs run busily about all day. Perhaps "brazen" is not a just adjective, despite the great single claw that makes the males look so ferocious. The fiddlers on mud flats race to their holes quickly enough when alarmed, and on rocks or piling they are expert dodgers. To watch them going about their business, you must sit very quietly and at a little distance.

This is not true of the comic hermit crabs that scrabble about above the tide line so awkwardly. The hermits are not "true" crabs, but are relatives of crayfish and lobsters that have lost the hard armor of their abdomens and taken to living in abandoned snail shells. As the hermits grow, of course, they must find larger and larger shells, and house-hunting becomes an important activity. The beach species are hardy creatures; even small boys manage to keep them in captivity without much trouble, and watching their fights over scraps of food or a new shell is amusing to both young and old.

Male sea lions congregate in a bachelors' colony on Point Reyes, California, between breeding seasons. (Milo Williams)

Mangrove Swamps

On tropical shores along lagoons and inlets or other places protected from the sweep of surf, there is a special intertidal community built around mangrove trees. There are many species of mangroves, but most of them belong to a plant family called the Rhizophoraceae. On both the African and American shores of the Atlantic there is a single predominant species, the red mangrove, *Rhizophora mangle,* and this has somehow crossed the land to grow also along the Pacific coast of America. Most of the similar swamps of the far Pacific, however, are made up of other species.

The mangrove trees rise out of the water on high-arched stilt roots. These roots provide a perch for oysters and other mollusks, barnacles, sponges—a whole motley zoological garden of sessile or fixed animals. The roots also block currents so that mud settles, providing a habitat for a collection of mud-loving species. The sluggish channels through the swamps make rich hunting grounds for many fishes, which with the rising tide can forage also among the mangrove roots. One of these fishes, the mudskipper of the Orient, lives more out of water than in it, searching the mud and roots for insects as well as small crustaceans. Among the mangroves, life from the land becomes completely mingled with life from the sea.

The Shore

The influence of the sea extends well above the high-tide line across the beach to the pioneer plants that must be able to withstand the salt spray of daily surf or occasional storms. And this shore area forms a special habitat for a whole group of animals. Some of them are permanent residents, but others come down from the

land periodically to prey on the richness of the sea, and still others come in from the sea to stay awhile on its land margins.

The shore birds are particularly conspicuous in numbers and in variety—plovers, sandpipers, and the like—gaining their living by scrounging through the debris of the sea. The great American ornithologist, Roger Tory Peterson, has remarked that "no habitat can boast more birds per square yard than a good mud flat at low tide." But sandy beaches and rocky shores have more than their share of inhabitants, too, especially because the sea birds come to breed there. Inaccessible cliffs and rocky shores provide protected nesting grounds for these masters of the air, and the birds are often incredibly numerous in favored areas, to which they return year after year.

Niko Tinbergen, an outstanding contemporary student of animal behavior, has written a beautiful book, *The Herring Gull's World*, on what is essentially the world of the seashore. The gulls are highly social, and while their behavior is very different

Sea turtles lay their eggs in the sand of tropical coasts and then return to the water.
(Fritz Goro: *Life*)

from that of man, their posturings and squabblings often seem a caricature of human actions. As Tinbergen remarks, "it is as if the animals are continuously holding a mirror in front of the observer, and it must be said that the reflection, if properly understood, is often rather embarrassing." He adds that "much of what little understanding I have of human nature has been derived not only from man-watching, but from bird-watching and fish-watching as well."

Tinbergen studied gull colonies nesting in the sand dunes along the Dutch coast. During the winter, the nesting sites are abandoned, and the gulls wander widely; but in the spring they return to ancestral nesting sites. There is evidence from several parts of the world that these gulls tend to return for nesting to the place where they were born, despite their ability to roam almost anywhere over the face of the earth. It appears that as a rule the gulls pair for life, though they separate for winter foraging. This means that individuals must recognize each other on arrival at the nesting grounds, and there is much evidence of such recognition. It is hard to understand how they tell one another apart—but perhaps gulls would have trouble in understanding how human beings recognize other human individuals.

One can argue endlessly about the "intelligence" of gulls or other birds. They have a complex set of cries and posturings which serve for communication, but these, like most of their behavior, are stereotyped—what we call "instinctive." They sometimes seem extremely stupid. Gulls often pick up shellfish, for instance, and fly steeply into the air to drop the shell, which breaks nicely if it lands on a rock. But gulls will drop shells endlessly on sand or shallow water, though they never break: Tinbergen once watched a gull drop a shell into shallow water thirty-nine times in succession before it became discouraged. One would think they would learn. Yet gulls are among the most successful of birds, adapting even to the conditions of man's harbors, so their behavior is obviously well adapted to the shore conditions under which they live.

The fin-footed mammals—the seals, sea lions, and walruses—are conspicuous inhabitants of the shores in many parts of the world. Some kinds spend all of their lives near shore, living as much out of the water as in it. Others come ashore only for the breeding season. All, however, are more adept at swimming and diving than at crawling on land, where they seem awkward and out of place. Some species are expert enough in the water to have no trouble catching their diet of fish; but other species live chiefly on mollusks, starfish, sea urchins, and similar less active animals, and seaweeds may also prove to be an important element in their diet.

Many species, such as the Alaskan fur seals, form vast social breeding colonies. These colonies have the appearance of a confused and noisy crowd. But under the confusion there is a certain order, with each old bull trying to keep his particular harem within a certain territory and always alert to fight off the eager adolescent males that try to intrude.

Most of the seals and their relatives live in the colder waters of the southern and northern hemispheres. One species of the fur seal and one of the sea lion are, however, found only around the Galapagos Islands, located on the equator in the Pacific; and one species, the monk seal, is found in the Mediterranean and neighboring waters. A species of seal was once common in the Caribbean, but it is now found only in a few isolated spots.

Many species of seals, flopping about awkwardly on land, have been easy victims for greedy and rapacious man, and they have disappeared from many places where they were once common. International protection, however, has been particularly successful in protecting the great fur seal herds of the Pribiloff Islands, whence come most of the sealskin coats of the world. By 1911, when the international agreement was achieved, they were on the verge of extinction, but now they again number in the millions.

There are, of course, many other shore animals. On tropical coasts there are marine crocodiles; and the sea turtles come out to lay their eggs in the sand. A whole series of insect species finds a home on the beach: speeding tiger beetles, biting midges, a variety of flies that breed in the debris, grasshoppers that blend with the sand, and so on—without mentioning the rich fauna of the salt marshes, where land and sea animals mingle.

There are many bridges, then, from the sea to the land. But before we follow any of these, we should look at the most complex of all marine communities, the coral reefs of tropical shores.

5

Coral Reefs

The coral formations of tropical seas have aroused the wonder and curiosity of Europeans since the days of the first modern explorers. They have also aroused respect—mariners rapidly learned to deal with them cautiously. Captain Cook piled his ship, the *Endeavour,* on the Great Barrier Reef of Australia in 1770, but he was able to repair the damage and continue. Other explorers, missionaries, and traders were less fortunate, and the list of ships wrecked on coral reefs is a very long one. Reef-strewn waters had a protective function, too—pirates could safely hide in waters where only they knew the passageways. And some of the world's finest harbors have been built by coral polyps.

Coral reefs are essentially tropical, because the reef-building organisms will not grow in cold waters. Or it would be more precise to say that for some reason not well understood, the massive deposition of lime by animals occurs only at temperatures of about 18 degrees C. (55 degrees F.) or more. We can therefore assume from reef deposits laid down in the geological past in regions no longer tropical that the seas in which the organisms were growing must have been warm. This also provides us with a clue to past climates on the earth.

At the present time, growing reefs occur throughout the tropical mid-Pacific and Indian Oceans, in the Caribbean Sea, and along the Atlantic coast of Brazil. They are generally absent along the Pacific coast of America and the Atlantic coast of Africa because of cold currents. Where currents carry warm waters outside of the tropics, reef growths occur; this is the case with Bermuda, which lies in the latitude of the Carolinas but is bathed by the waters of the Gulf Stream, still warm enough there for the coral organisms. The most extensive reef of all is the Great Barrier Reef of Australia, which extends for some twelve hundred miles from the tip of Cape York along the coast of the Coral Sea and ends almost precisely at the line of the Tropic of Capricorn.

Reefs, Atolls, and Darwin

The most striking of the coral formations are the atolls: roughly circular reefs, in part barely submerged, in part rising just above the water to form low islands covered with coconuts or scrub, or sometimes, in wet climates, with luxuriant vegetation. Each circular reef encloses a lagoon, an area of quiet water cut off from the restless seas around. The lagoons may be a mile or less in diameter or may be

Reef construction is due as much to plants such as the coralline algae, which secrete limy skeletons, as to the coral animals. (Fritz Goro: *Life*)

many miles across; probably the largest is the lagoon of Kwajalein Atoll in the Marshall Islands, fifteen nautical miles wide and sixty-six long. The rim of the atoll, whether underwater reef or exposed land, is typically three or four hundred feet across. Because of the generally circular form, these atolls look like nothing so much as volcanoes submerged just to the rim of the crater; and many years ago this was one theory of their origin. There are, however, no signs of volcanic activity in connection with any of the atolls, and no rock except limestone, which clearly originates from the coral growth.

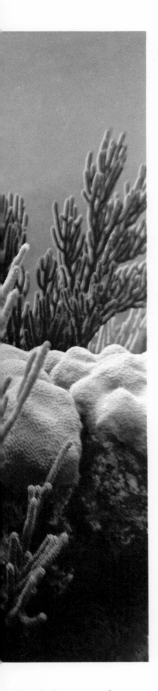

Coral shapes are bewilderingly diverse. Above: Gorgonian or horny coral in the Bahamas. Left: Indo-Pacific brain coral, Great Barrier Reef, Australia. (Fritz Goro: *Life*)

When Charles Darwin crossed the Pacific in the course of the voyage of H.M.S. *Beagle,* he became fascinated with the reefs, and especially with the atolls, as had all naturalists who visited the area before him. But Darwin, looking at the variety of reef and island formations, went beyond wonder and developed a theory—the first manifestation of his lifelong tendency to form general theories about the phenomena of nature. Some of his theories (notably that of evolution through natural selection) have withstood the test of time; others, such as his theory of heredity, have not. His atoll theory is still good; with rather minor modifications, it remains the best explanation of these curious island forms.

Darwin noticed that in many parts of the Pacific there were numerous mountains rising out of the sea. Often, around the coasts of these mountain islands, there was a rich fringing growth of corals. Now the reef-forming corals grow in regions of strong water currents like those caused by pounding surf. They depend on the food supply of microscopic plankton brought to them by the water. Also, although they are animals, they grow only in well-lighted surface water, hardly extending to a depth below 150 feet. We know now that this is because the coral animals live in a symbiotic relationship with single-celled algae, which require light.

Darwin imagined that if a mountain island, with its fringing coral reef, were to start subsiding—sinking into the sea—the corals would continue their growth on the surf-washed outer edge of the reef, their slow rate of growth keeping pace with the slow subsidence of the island. The result, presently, would be a barrier reef, with a zone of open water between the reef and the island. Darwin found numerous examples of such barrier reefs, and he knew well enough that the mountain systems of the unstable earth were often in a process of subsiding, or of rising. He reasoned that if this process continued until the mountain island had disappeared completely under the sea, only the continually growing, encircling reef would be left—an atoll.

This remains the most reasonable explanation of the origin of atolls, though there is another element, that of change in sea level. It is now clear that during the last of the geological periods, the Pleistocene, going back about a million years, there were four great periods of glaciation when immense amounts of water were locked up in huge ice sheets extending over the continents. It has been estimated that at the height of a glacial period the amount of water removed from the seas would result in a sea level about three hundred feet below that in interglacial periods, when the continents were free of ice. The last glacial maximum occurred something like thirty thousand to fifty thousand years ago, and we still have large glaciers with us over Antarctica, Greenland, and the like. If all of these glaciers melted, the seas would rise perhaps sixty feet above their present level; and the evidence indicates that the sea level is rising something like a quarter of an inch per century.

Any understanding of present coast lines, of island and reef relations, has to take this fluctuation of sea level into account. Thus the present form of atolls need not depend on continuing mountain subsidence: it can be explained instead by a rise in sea level itself of two or three hundred feet as the great glaciers over Europe and North America melted, with the coral organisms keeping pace with the rising seas.

In the long run, we need Darwin's subsidence theory. The outer slopes of the atoll reefs drop rapidly into great ocean depths, and we have to have some way of explaining how the coral growth got started in these particular places. The crucial test would be to bore down through the lime of the atoll to find the underlying rock. And this was tried, at first with uncertain results. At depths of a thousand feet, the reef structure was still coral limestone. Finally, in the course of the studies carried out by the United States Navy at Eniwetok Atoll, the borings were continued to the underlying basalt rock, which was encountered at a depth of four thousand feet. This reef, it appeared, had started its growth in the geological period known as late Eocene—about fifty million years ago. From an examination of the changing structure of the lime, it seemed that at times the reef had been uncovered by the retreating seas and appeared as an island. But generally over this vast stretch of time, the earth's crust in this atoll region has been subsiding, with the tiny coral organisms building busily on the skeletons of their ancestors to keep near the ocean surface.

Atolls show a curiously limited distribution. E. H. Bryan, Jr., of the Bishop Museum in Honolulu, has made a list of 409 islands in the world that can reasonably be called "atolls." Of these, 136 are in Polynesia, 92 in Micronesia, 66 in Melanesia, 15 in Indonesia, 5 northwest of Australia, 68 in the rest of the Indian Ocean, 26 in the Caribbean Sea, and only one in the Atlantic (Rocas Reef, 135 miles off the coast of Brazil).

Fringing and barrier reefs are far more numerous, occurring everywhere in warm, shallow tropical seas. To the skin diver, watching animal activities, it makes little difference what kind of reef he is on. There are, to be sure, great differences between the lagoon and the seaward side of a reef; and most of the animals in the Caribbean Sea belong to different species from those in the Coral Sea. But the basic organization of life, the activities of the animals and their forms and colors, are similar everywhere. Of course the general principles of ecological organization apply to all biological communities, whether coral reef, mangrove swamp, or tropical rain forest. But the various roles are played by quite different sorts of organisms in a reef and in a forest. From the point of view of intruding man, used to the arrangement of things on land, the reef world is a topsy-turvy place.

The Reef Community

It is conventional to speak of "coral" reefs. Corals are animals, members of the phylum Coelenterata, along with sea anemones, jellyfish, and the like. It has long been known that the construction of the reef is as much due to plants as to animals, and especially to a group of red algae known as the coralline algae that secrete limy skeletons. Botanists, always jealous of the amount of attention people give to animals instead of to their very important plants, have long resented the name "coral reef"— but it seems likely to stick. In a way this is only fair: most biological communities are named for conspicuous plants, e.g. mangrove swamps, spruce forests, and the like. The reef is one place where the animals have a chance, and, regardless of whether the algae or the corals are more important, the latter are undeniably conspicuous.

The "true corals" or "stony corals" belong to the class Anthozoa ("flower-animals") of the Coelenterata, and they make up a group of animals of about 2500 species, known to zoologists as the Madreporaria. These come in all sorts of shapes and sizes and live in a wide variety of marine environments. Relatively few species are actually involved in the building of the massive reefs. In general, there are many more reef-building species in the Pacific and Indian Oceans than in the Atlantic; and also, the warmer the water, the more species there will be. Thus 180 species of madreporarians were found associated with reefs in one Philippine locality, but 128 species have been listed from the Red Sea, while but 30 species are known from the Tortugas and only 10 in the Bermuda reefs.

Coral shapes are bewilderingly diverse, depending in part on the species of coral and in part on the conditions under which it is growing. Some form rounded masses, with the surface sculptured in grooves like those of the human brain; hence they are called brain corals. The staghorn corals branch in a fashion reminiscent of the antlers of deer; others grow with finger-like branches of various sizes and lengths. Some kinds of true corals live as single animals, but the ones we notice most are vast colonies of individual polyps which have jointly secreted the limestone skeleton. The coral animal itself ranges from the size of a pinhead to that of a pea. By day it is generally retracted into the skeleton, extending out only at night to catch the drifting plankton with its tiny arms.

Many other fixed animals grow along with the corals. The sea fans, with their fronds gently waving in the currents, are also colonial animals and belong to the same general class as the corals, but their skeletons are formed of a hornlike substance rather than rigid limestone. Other coelenterates, like the fire corals and organ-pipe corals, which are not related to the true corals, also secrete lime skeletons. There are also sponges, sea anemones, tunicates, barnacles, mollusks—all sorts of animals that have lost the power of movement, at least for part of their life cycle.

The living scenery, the fixed structure, of the reef is thus made up most con-

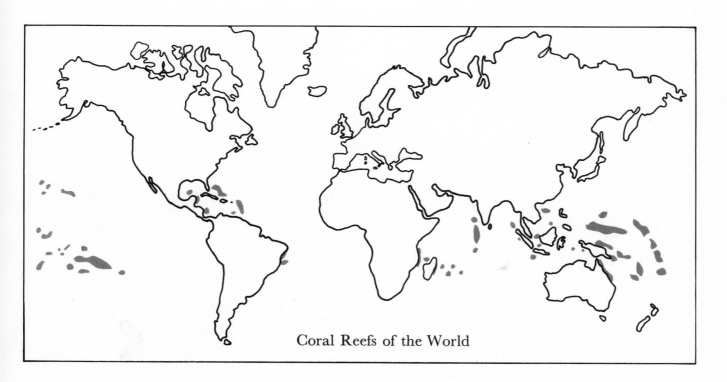

Coral Reefs of the World

spicuously of animals. And instead of the general green of land vegetation contrasting only with the browns of trunks and stems and leaf litter, the scenery is splashed with the whole color spectrum—blues, greens, browns, reds, and purples, for the most part in pastel shades. There are, to be sure, true plants growing among these colorful animals—and some of them, like the turtle grass and the algae growing in sandy patches, look properly green. But the most abundant plants are the coralline algae, which look something like gigantic lichens in their delicately branching form; their colors, however, are red, purple, brown, or yellowish brown.

The action in front of this colorful backdrop is chiefly that of gaudy fishes. There are many other animals there—every major phylum has representatives somewhere in the reef complex—but they are mostly hiding, or quiet, or inconspicuous. Fishes dominate the scene, playing all of the visual roles that on land are divided among the butterflies, birds, lizards, squirrels, and the like. But it takes an act of will to realize this, for there is no feeling of monotony. In fact, any land community seems tame compared with the variety of activities going on around a reef. Perhaps this is partly because fishes have not yet learned to be afraid of skin divers or swimmers with mask and snorkel: they go right on about their business, treating the human observer as an odd sort of log that has happened to drift in.

There may be hundreds of kinds of fishes around a single reef area. Not all of them, to be sure, are conspicuous, but their variety is shown by some of the names that have been given them: butterfly fish, angel fish, damsel fish, squirrel fish, parrot fish; and wrasse, groupers, grunts, pipefish, and snake eels. Some of them appear as bright, metallic clouds hovering insect-like in mid-water; others patrol the corals singly or in pairs with slow dignity; many skip aimlessly around the coral caverns or peer out curiously from the safety of their caves.

To anyone watching daytime activity around a coral reef, the overwhelming impression is of color. Nowhere else in the living world does color show such richness and variety, such exuberance.

Color and Pattern

Human beings live in a world that is primarily visual: most of the events of our daily lives turn on reactions to things we can see—to colors and shapes. We tend quite naturally to think that the world we perceive is the real world, important not only to us but to all of the other animals living in it. Yet, when we start to explore the matter, we find that the perceptual world of every animal is somewhat different— that the senses take on different roles. We hear fairly well, but we cannot detect the supersonic squeaks that guide a bat unerringly through the twistings of a dark cavern. Our nose, obviously, is not very good. We have no idea at all of the things that excite a dog on a walk through the woods—how he can tell that a rabbit passed by a few hours ago and know, by the smell, in which direction the rabbit was going. And when we try to imagine the world revealed by the lateral-line organ of a fish, we get into even greater difficulties.

But we do see well, and we can discriminate colors, which means that different wave lengths of light affect the retina of our eyes differently. It turns out that this is not very common in the animal kingdom. Among mammals, it appears that only some of the other primates share our ability, although there is increasing evidence

Coral Reefs

15 Striped angelfish and a parrot fish on the Johnston Island reef in the Pacific. (Ron Church)

16 Left: Heron Island, on the Great Barrier Reef of Australia. (Fritz Goro: *Life*)

17 Below: The lagoon of an atol (Ifaluk, in the Caroline Islands) the dark areas are patch reefs of coral growth. (Marston Bates)

18 Right: A spiny lobster off La Jolla, California. (Ron Church)

19 Right, below: Blue-banded gobi lurk among the spines of a sea urchin. (Ron Church)

20 Above: The lionfish, with poisonous spines, is common around all tropical Indo-Pacific reefs. (Ron Church)

21 Left: *Tridacna,* or giant clams, with their colorful mantles, are prominent members of all Pacific reef communities. (Ron Church)

of some sense of color among the hoofed mammals. It seems that birds in general discriminate color as well as we do; and at least certain fishes have good color vision. The experiments to test particular species are so tedious and difficult that we don't really have anything like a thorough survey of the animal kingdom, though we at least know enough to be sure other animals do not necessarily see things the way we do. Such insects as butterflies and bees discriminate colors; but their vision differs from ours in that they can see farther into the ultraviolet than we can and not so far into the red. Thus the color pattern of a particular flower may appear quite different to a bee and to a human being.

What we see around a coral reef, then, may be quite different from what the inhabitants see, and any interpretations must be speculative. But the reef community was not arranged for man to admire—the arrangement turns on the interactions of the members of the community. After making all due reservations, we must still assume that the color has significance. And there is direct experimental evidence that some of the fishes react to colors as such.

Much of the color of the world clearly is a consequence of what might be called chemical accident. That sulphur is yellow and coal black is a result of the structure of the material, so that certain wave lengths of light are absorbed and others reflected. On the other hand, it is no chemical accident that a lady puts on a red dress or that a soldier in guerrilla warfare daubs his face and clothes with green and brown to blend with the foliage. The color itself is always the consequence of chemical structure of the materials, but sometimes the distribution of the materials is random, and sometimes it is consciously selected by man, or by the grand process of evolution in nature.

We could distinguish, then, between chemical and biological coloration. The gaudy Painted Desert of the southwestern United States and similar stretches in the Eastern Desert of Egypt clearly have no more biological meaning than the colors of the rings of Saturn. But bright flowers are developed only by plants that need insects for pollination. Is the reef like the Painted Desert, or is it a natural flower garden?

The answer probably is that aspects of both are involved. Perhaps, in dealing with living organisms, it would be better to shift our vocabulary and, instead of distinguishing between chemical and biological coloration, try to decide whether meanings are physiological or ecological. The red of hemoglobin in the blood is physiological, a consequence of its structure. The green of chlorophyll is also structural, though here it can be argued that the particular light absorption of chlorophyll is the most efficient for the photosynthetic process, which makes the distinction more fuzzy. But then there is the curious question of why, in shallow seas, the green of chlorophyll is so often masked with other pigments, so that the coralline algae, for instance, are red or purple or brown and yet grow at the same depth of water as other algae that are green.

On land, the insects, lizards, and snakes that live among foliage tend also to be green; in this case the coloration is clearly ecological, serving for concealment. Concealing coloration is also common enough in the reef community. Crustaceans like crabs and shrimp often have colors and shapes that blend perfectly with their background. The octopuses carry this to an extreme, since they can change their colors rapidly to fit with the particular surroundings in which they happen to come to rest.

Ecological coloration can serve for concealment, but it can also serve for advertisement. This is the usual explanation of the bright colors of insect-pollinated flowers. Poisonous animals also often advertise: bright wasps, butterflies that have acquired a nasty taste, gaudy and deadly coral snakes. Yet most vipers blend with their surroundings, and in the sea the well-protected sting rays conceal themselves on bottom sand. Whether to advertise or to hide is a nicely balanced question.

It seems that colors and patterns often serve for species recognition, and this is especially likely to be the case with many of the vividly marked fishes of the reef. Why, then, don't all fishes have striking recognition colors? The fishes of the open sea or of northern waters are relatively drab and uniform compared with those of the reef. Perhaps in the vast distances of the open sea, recognition by pattern would have less usefulness; and in northern waters, where light is less reliable, other senses like smell and hearing may take over from vision. Visual stimuli, it seems to me, assume a particular importance in clear, sunny tropical waters, especially where many different kinds of animals are associated in a restricted habitat. In this regard, the functions of the bright patterns of the reef fishes would be comparable with the functions of the luminescent patterns of the deep-sea forms. This does not explain the colors of the fixed backdrop—the corals, sea fans, and algae. Perhaps the colors here are accidents of physiology; or perhaps they have biological meanings still unknown.

In discussing concealing coloration and warning coloration, we are concerned with the competitive aspects of the community—with animals chasing and escaping, with the struggle for existence. But by a switch of the mind, we can just as easily consider the community as a cooperative enterprise, in which many diverse organisms work together in maintaining life processes. Recognition colors are cooperative signals between males and females or between individuals schooling together; but they also may serve for interspecies cooperation, as flowers are signals for the pollinating insects. We must at least glance at some of the cooperative aspects of the reef community.

Reef fishes have fantastic shapes as well as colors; this species, the surgeonfish, carries a sharp scalpe near the base of its tail. (Bernard Villaret)

Left: The Moorish idol is found throughout the tropical Pacific. (Bernard Villaret)

These catfish (*Plotosus anguillaris*), equipped with poisonous spines, are among the most dangerous of reef animals. (A. Van Den Nieuwenhuizen)

Cooperation among Reef Organisms

While skin diving in tropical waters in different parts of the world, the late Conrad Limbaugh of the Scripps Institution of Oceanography was greatly impressed by the number of times he observed one kind of fish cleaning or grooming some other fish, and he started to collect systematic observations on this kind of behavior. Of course it has long been known that some animals specialize in cleaning others: egrets taking ticks from cattle and tick birds removing the pests from rhinoceroses are always mentioned in the textbooks. William Beebe observed crabs taking ticks from the marine lizards of the Galapagos Islands, and later, while diving near Haiti, noticed small fishes of the wrasse family cleaning parrot fish. But Limbaugh found this behavior to be widespread, and he felt that it was really significant in the life of the reef community, and not just an oddity of natural history.

Limbaugh found twenty-six species of fishes and six species of shrimp that specialize in cleaning parasites and dead or diseased tissue off other fishes. The cleaning species, particularly in coral-reef waters, are brightly and conspicuously

marked. They take up stations at particular points on the reef, and the client fishes then come to these stations for cleaning. Limbaugh once counted approximately three hundred fishes coming to a station on a reef in the Bahamas for this purpose during a six-hour daylight period.

Not the least interesting aspect of this is the way a predatory fish will patiently allow a shrimp or small cleaning fish not only to go over his body but even to enter his gills and mouth. Mistakes are sometimes made, and Limbaugh reports finding cleaning shrimp in the stomachs of moray eels, but the mistakes, he notes, hardly ever occur with the highly specialized reef species of cleaners.

The cleaning relation of fish and fish, or shrimp and fish, is one example of a considerable number of cooperative relations that have been observed among reef organisms. The beautiful little damsel fishes of the genus *Amphiprion* live among the poisonous tentacles of the large sea anemones with complete immunity, apparently because a mucus secreted by the damsel fish inhibits the action of the anemone stings. The damsel fish clearly benefits from this arrangement by having a safe lair, and it is thought that the anemone benefits also from the extra food morsels brought back by the fish from their brief forays abroad.

One animal providing lodgings for another is common on the reef; for example, the sponge mentioned in the last chapter had 13,500 other animals living in its cavities. The corals and other fixed animals provide a wide variety of homesites, and there are other specific relations, exemplified by the small fishes that live only in the digestive tracts of large starfish or sea cucumbers. It is often hard to decide whether both species benefit from such associations or whether one has all of the advantages. This rapidly leads into vocabulary problems with words like "mutualism," "commensalism," and "symbiosis." Attempts to give words like these precise and distinct meanings have not been notably successful, and there is no way in which one scientist can make another adopt his particular vocabulary. It would seem best to leave mutualism and commensalism for the looser relationships among species, like those of the cleaners with their "clients" or of the damsel fish with its sea anemone, and to use symbiosis for intimate, permanent relation like that between coral polyps and the algae that live in their bodies. The trouble is that there is no place in such a series where you can draw a sharp line—and often we simply don't know enough about what is going on to label the relationship.

All of the reef corals contain within their bodies large numbers of tiny photosynthetic algal cells. It seems logical that these should provide vegetable food for the corals, in return for the benefit of support in the coral structure. But it appears that the corals never digest these plant cells: if the corals are starved or kept in the dark, the plant cells are ejected instead of being eaten. The best guess currently is that the algae serve to remove carbon dioxide rapidly from the coral polyp body and to use up other waste materials.

A Bahaman file shell, a tube worm, and two kinds of wrasse. (Fritz Goro: *Life*)

Parrot Fishes

Among the conspicuous inhabitants of coral reefs everywhere are the parrot fishes, so called because of their parrot-like beaks—though they are also about as gaudy as the birds. They come in a variety of colors, but greens and blues are most common; some are red, and still others have black-and-white patterns. Those most commonly

seen are a foot or two in length, traveling over the reef in small schools; some species grow much larger, however, and there are records of gigantic old bulls twelve feet long.

No one is sure how many kinds of parrot fishes there are. There were supposed to be about eighty species in the world, but studies made on Bermuda reefs by John Bardach of the University of Michigan and Howard Winn of the University of Maryland show that, in some cases at least, the two sexes have been described as separate species. Bardach and Winn, watching schools of these fishes, noticed that one individual was often more brightly colored than the others. As the "herd" grazed slowly across a reef, the gaudier individual would sometimes show curious behavior, dashing out as though to pick a fight when a solitary fish of the same kind appeared. It looked like the action of a stag or bull protecting his harem—but how does one determine the sex of a fish?

With most fishes, there is no way of determining sex except by operating to examine the reproductive organs. Bardach did this, and found that the brightly colored herders were always males. To check this, he tried some experiments in aquaria, injecting the plainer individuals with male sex hormones. And with this treatment, they took on the bright male coloration. This turned out to be true of several species, so it may be that there are only about half as many kinds of parrot fishes in the world as had been previously supposed.

With their constant browsing, parrot fishes play an important role in the breakdown of the reefs. They are constantly nibbling at the corals, scraping off not only algae but considerable quantities of the lime skeletons. The lime may serve to break up the algal food, acting like the grit in the gizzard of a bird; or it may have some chemical function in the process of digestion. Whatever the purpose of this behavior, the limestone itself is indigestible, and the parrot fishes regularly defecate clouds of fine white sand.

Bardach began to wonder how important this might be in producing the coral sands of the tropics, and he decided to try some calculations. He repeatedly counted the number of parrot fishes in different reef areas, finding that on the average there were about a hundred individuals per acre. The fishes browse constantly through the day. To find out how much time elapsed between eating and excretion, Bardach tried feeding charcoal to a few individuals and timed its reappearance; he found that it took from two to eighteen hours for the material to pass through the fish, depending on the size of the individual. From all of this, he calculated that the parrot fishes deposit at least a ton of sand per acre every year on the Bermuda reefs. If one considers that the Bermuda reefs cover several hundred square miles and have existed in their present form for several thousands of years, it is obvious that the parrot fishes account for quite a lot of sand.

Hazards of the Reef

It is curious how afraid we are of sharks. There are something like thirty deaths reported each year around the world from shark attack, mostly in Australian waters, but this is trivial when one thinks of the millions of people who go swimming in ocean waters each year. Automobiles are obviously far more dangerous—though not nearly as frightening.

Skin divers in the tropics consider moray eels more dangerous than sharks: and certainly they are among the most vicious-looking and -acting creatures that nature has devised. If a patch of reef is watched closely, a snakelike head may sometimes be seen sticking out of a hole, slowly weaving back and forth like a cobra under the spell of a charmer. The moray is scanning the water for a possible victim; generally his mouth is wide open, showing the multiple rows of fanglike teeth. During the day, though, the eels usually stay well withdrawn in their holes, coming out to search for their prey at night, when they depend on their incredibly keen sense of smell. A basic rule for a skin diver in the tropics is never to stick his hand into any part of a reef when he cannot see what is there, because a moray may be lurking within and resent the intrusion. Morays come in various sizes and colors; most species reach a maximum length of four or five feet, but giants up to ten feet long have been reported.

Sharks, moray eels, and the like are really psychological hazards more than anything else. The true hazards of the reef—like the nettles and poison ivy of land—are more trivial. It is easy to get cut on the coral growths themselves, and such cuts are notorious for healing slowly and often becoming infected. One special group of reef growths, called fire corals or hydrocorals and distinct from the true corals, causes a painful burn if touched, and one soon learns to recognize and avoid them. Then, of course, there are stinging jellyfish and Portuguese men-of-war, and some kinds of sea urchins have poisonous spines that can cause very painful stings. There are a few other creatures that are much more dangerous, such as a species of Pacific cone shell that, if handled carelessly, can inflict a sting with its radula that may be fatal. But the pleasures of skin diving around a reef outweigh all of these hazards.

The reef community is one of the most distinctive of marine environments. But the corals and other organisms, with their lime skeletons, are also busily involved in building land. Barrier reefs and atolls have large areas that are always submerged, other areas that are exposed at low tide, and often small islets where currents and winds have piled up the coral accumulation to form dry land. The boundaries between sea and land in such a situation become blurred, as they do along every coast.

I once spent a summer with Donald Abbott of Stanford University, trying to work out community relationships on a tiny Pacific atoll—Ifaluk, in the western Caroline Islands. No matter how we tried, we could find no logical way of sub-dividing this environment into a series of discrete biological communities. We came to the conclusion that the meaningful community included the whole atoll situation: land, reef, lagoon, and immediately surrounding seas. The individuals depended equally on the land and the sea for their food. The hermit crabs that crawled every-where over the land went to sea to lay their eggs, as did the coconut crabs and the land crabs. The sea turtles crawled out of the lagoon to lay their eggs in the sand. The influence of the sea was everywhere. It even determined what plants and animals were living on the land because all of these, to get there, had to have some means of crossing the sea unless they had been purposely or accidentally brought by man.

From the coral reef, then, one could move easily enough to a tropical landscape. But the same kind of move could be made from a mangrove swamp or across any beach. Before making this move from sea to land, we should look at the environments that in so many ways are intermediate—the various worlds of life in water that runs or stands on land.

6

Water on the Land

Water is extraordinary stuff. In large measure, the nature of life turns on the properties of water as a chemical. All other liquids become more and more dense as they cool, until finally at some characteristic temperature they solidify. The solid form is denser than the liquid form, and consequently sinks. But fresh water reaches its greatest density at 4 degrees C. (39 degrees F.) above the freezing point, then expands slightly. The result is that solid water floats on liquid water. If water did not have this odd behavior, the earth would be a very different place. Ice would accumulate in the bottom of the seas, and only the surface layers would ever thaw. Coldness would be stored, changing the whole aspect of our planetary surface.

Brewster's egret, a species once endangered by plume-hunters. (W. Grant McFarland: U. S. Fish and Wildlife Service)

Water has other peculiar properties. For one thing, it is one of the best of all solvents. Gasoline is notably effective, but water will dissolve many more different kinds of chemicals than gasoline will. Think of the forty-four elements in solution in sea water, including metals like silver, nickel, and gold. Water dissolves other materials so readily that it is extremely difficult to prepare it—or to keep it—as a "pure" chemical. Water coming down as rain is already loaded with many other substances when it hits the earth, not only with dissolved gases from the atmosphere but with materials picked up from the dust of the air. And water in contact with soil or rock is slowly but constantly adding to its load of chemicals.

We all learn about the interconnecting systems of atmosphere and hydrosphere early in school, but even the dullest textbook cannot kill the marvel of it. The seas are the vast reservoir from which the water comes and to which, in one way or another, it eventually returns. Warm air holds more water vapor than cold air. Water from the ocean surfaces is constantly evaporating into the air; when, in the course of atmospheric circulation, the air rises and cools, the water precipitates out as a fine mist—clouds—and under certain circumstances it coalesces to form the drops of rain that are pulled back to the earth by gravity. Thus the simplest cycle, from sea to air to sea again.

If the rain falls on land, a number of different things can happen, and scientists have busied themselves for years with precise calculations of water relations in different sorts of cycles. As civilized man has come to depend more and more on having vast quantities of water available, knowledge of these cycles has become of direct practical importance, and it has always been important to any understanding of the workings of the biosphere.

Most of the rain sinks into the soil, to form part of the ground water underlying land everywhere. This ground water may be picked up by plants and returned to

the atmosphere through the process called "transpiration"; or it may seep slowly through the earth, to emerge in marshes or springs or to return directly to the ocean without ever reaching the surface again. But in considering water in relation to the conditions of animal life, we are interested chiefly in the surface systems—in the streams and rivers formed by the water in its seaward progress, and in the ponds and lakes that occur when this progress is temporarily slowed or blocked.

The amount of free water available in rivers or lakes to form a habitat for animals is rather trivial from any world-wide point of view. It has been calculated that there is sixty thousand times as much water in the seas as there is at any one time in streams and lakes on land. But however trivial the quantity of inland water, it forms a major kind of environment for life.

Life in Fresh Water

The conditions for life in inland waters are different from those in the seas. For one thing, the chemistry of sea water is quite uniform everywhere, whereas the chemistry of water on land is very variable. The kinds of salts and the amount of organic matter in solution depend on the soil with which the water has been in contact, and of course this differs from place to place. As every housewife knows, some water is "hard" (with a relatively high calcium content), some is "soft." The water may be acid or alkaline. In open systems (that is, except in lakes that have no outlet) the total salt content is far less than in sea water. Animal protoplasm, similar in density to sea water, thus has a higher salt content than the surrounding water. For this reason, all fresh-water animals have to have some way of maintaining a barrier between the water inside them and the water outside, which is not necessarily true of marine animals.

The fresh-water environment is discontinuous, both in time and in space. The discontinuity in space is obvious enough. Each river system is a thing-in-itself, isolated from other systems by the divides that separate the headwaters. Man has now often connected rivers by digging canals, but such connections are rare in nature. An exception is the Casiquiare Canal of northern South America whose sluggish waters open both into the Orinoco and into the Rio Negro of the Amazon system. These two great river systems thus form a sort of vast and infinitely subdivided inland sea threaded through a large part of the continent. Generally, passage from one river system to another is only through the sea or overland.

Most lakes can be regarded as parts of river systems, way stations in the flow of water from the highlands to the sea. The lakes in any one area, then, are connected by the pattern of streams, and movement from one lake to another requires only the ability to make the change from still to running water—which is not always easy. Some lakes are completely isolated, like the crater lakes of extinct volcanoes. In others, especially in limestone country, the flow in and out is underground.

It is now known that mountains are thrust upward and, with the passage of geological time, eroded away. Glaciers form, advance over the continents, and presently melt again. Seas have sometimes covered great areas that are now land, and regions now covered by seas were once parts of the continents. On this restless surface of our planet, it is easy enough to visualize how transitory are the patterns of the streams and lakes. This great lake or that broad river was not here yesterday and may be gone tomorrow. The conditions for the evolution of life are thus quite

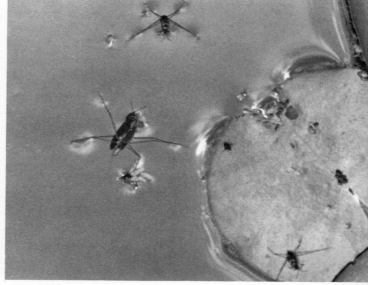

different from those in the continuing seas or on the persisting land masses of the continents. That is why the discontinuities in time, as well as those in space, are significant.

In the Estuaries

There are always transition zones between one zone and another. Every river that reaches the sea has an estuary, a region where fresh waters mingle with salt, presenting intermediate conditions for life. The influence of the tides may be felt far up the river, resulting in daily shifts of currents and water level. Each estuary presents special conditions. In some cases almost all of the fresh-water animals drop out as soon as the water becomes appreciably salty; and since many marine forms cannot tolerate appreciable dilution of sea water, the estuary becomes almost an "aquatic desert." But in other estuaries life may be especially abundant, apparently because the food-laden waters of the rivers are dammed up by the sea, allowing for a heavy growth of plankton on which other animals can feed.

Many essentially marine fishes, like tarpon and mullet, pass easily from salt to fresh water. Many crabs and shrimp also have this wide tolerance. In both Europe and North America, oysters are often "farmed" in estuaries. They will not breed in brackish water, but "sprat," or small fish, moved into this rich environment fatten readily. Estuary animals mostly move in from the sea rather than down from the upper reaches of the rivers; but there are a few animals that are found in brackish water and nowhere else.

Just as the scattered estuaries are transition zones between fresh water and the seas, every riverbank and lake shore presents a transition between fresh water and land. The change, however, is generally abrupt, and marshes and swamps present a more truly intermediate sequence. There is every sort of intergrade, from land that is only soggy underfoot through vegetation-choked water to open surfaces. Here we find a host of mammals, snakes, turtles, amphibians, and insects that move freely back and forth from water to land, so that often the decision whether to call them "aquatic" or "terrestrial" is arbitrary.

Far left: Water fleas (*Daphnia*) are one of the key-industry animals in fresh water. (Otto Croy)

Left: This water strider is truly aquatic, but it lives on water rather than in it, relying on surface tension for support. (Otto Croy)

Fresh-Water Animals

There are, however, plenty of animals that are purely and truly inhabitants of the fresh-water environment. This fauna is made up in part of animals belonging to groups that are largely marine, and in part of animals whose ancestors clearly have adapted to the water from the land. According to one theory, the bony fishes got their start in brackish or fresh water, and the amphibia presumably began as swamp animals. But in general, fresh waters themselves have not been the scene of major evolutionary advances.

Of the great marine animal phyla, the sponges are represented in fresh water by only a few species of a single family. The coelenterates—corals, jellyfish, and sea anemones—include a few tiny hydra in fresh water, fascinating enough but hardly spectacular; and a very few kinds of small jellyfish, about which little is known. The echinoderms—starfish, sea cucumbers, and the like—have not developed any species capable of living outside of the sea. This is true also of a number of the smaller marine phyla.

Yet, as every fisherman and aquarium owner knows, there is no lack of variety in fresh water. The key-industry animals of the plankton, like those of the sea, are mostly tiny shrimplike crustacea of varied forms. The crustacea are also represented by numerous crayfish, some of which reach quite respectable size, but in most parts of the world one misses the crabs that are so conspicuous among the inhabitants of the margins of the sea. Mollusks—snails and clams—are numerous, but none of the cephalopods, such as the squids, has ventured out of the sea.

There are many kinds of worms in fresh water: round worms, flat worms, and segmented worms. Most of these live inconspicuously in the mud of the bottom where they are hardly noticed, but they nevertheless play an important role in the economy of the aquatic community by feeding on animal and vegetable detritus. The segmented worms (annelids) of fresh water are mostly relatives of the common earthworm—quite different from the annelid groups in the seas. The leeches (Hirudinea) are annelids that live mainly in fresh water, though there are species in the seas; and there is a notorious land leech in the rain forests of southeast Asia.

Most leeches are small and inconspicuous and they show a variety of food habits, though all are carnivorous. Only a few are primarily bloodsuckers, including the European medicinal leech, which in many parts of the world is still much used for treating bruises and is a great pest in many marshes and lakes of Europe. Leeches swim with a graceful undulating movement. At the hind end of the body all of them have a suction disk which they use in clinging to plants or rocks; and many of them also have a suction disk at the front end, so that they can move by looping along somewhat in the fashion of an inchworm. Leeches are hermaphroditic—every individual is both male and female—but they cannot fertilize themselves; they must copulate in order to reproduce. Some species carry the eggs in a gelatinous capsule on the underside of the body until they hatch; others deposit their eggs in a sort of cocoon attached to a solid object.

As transition between fresh water and the sea, estuaries are good for diamond-backed terrapins. (Leonard Lee Rue III: Annan Photo Features)

Insect Life

Many animal groups are lacking in fresh water, but the insects compensate for this. Insects, to be sure, are primarily land animals, and it is clear that, breathing air, they evolved as such. They are everywhere; incredibly numerous, endlessly varied, and many very different kinds have found ways of taking up life in inland waters. Any discussion of fresh-water fauna is inevitably much concerned with them.

It is curious that insects, which have found ways of adapting to deserts, to rivers, to caves, and even to snow fields, have failed to gain a foothold in the sea. It is not that animal groups that evolved on land are unable to adapt to the sea; the marine reptiles of the past and marine mammals of the present show well enough that this can happen. It also is not true that insects cannot adapt to salt water; many species live in salt marshes and other shore environments. To be sure, there are two or three little-known kinds of water striders that are found around coral reefs or sometimes skipping over the surface far out at sea. But the trivial exceptions make the general failure of insects to invade the oceans even more puzzling.

In fresh water, however, insects have been very successful. There are few species

in the open water of larger lakes, but they teem in every pond and stream, occupying a whole series of special niches in the network of food relations.

Most aquatic insects spend only part of their lives in the water. Their success, like that of the amphibia, is a consequence of metamorphosis, of change in form in the course of growth and development. Since the adult animals are able to live out of the water, the great handicap of the discontinuity of ponds and streams is overcome. Insects and amphibia are truly capable of "environment hopping" in a much more vivid sense than the vertically migrating plankton of the open sea described in an earlier chapter. They can exploit the rich food possibilities of fresh water, yet avoid extinction if and when the habitat dries. Insects like dragonflies that are powerful fliers in the adult stage can spread through scattered bits of water over a wide area.

Many different groups of insects have taken to this double way of life. The list includes stoneflies, mayflies, dragonflies, gnats of various sorts including mosquitoes, and a variety of bugs and beetles. Occasional species among many other insect groups have aquatic stages; there are, for instance, a number of kinds of moths of several families with larvae that live in water. And aside from the true insects, many mites and spiders are aquatic.

These insects have developed several different ways of getting oxygen from the water. Many of the larvae or nymphs have developed gill systems; some are able to absorb oxygen directly through the skin; some, like mosquito larvae, have developed tubes to get air from the surface while staying submerged. Spiders and some of the insects keep air trapped by thick body hair, or have some other means of carrying a bubble of air under water with them. And then there are insects that stay on the water surface, like water striders, whirligig beetles, and water boatmen. They are truly aquatic, but they live *on* the water rather than *in* it, relying on surface tension for support—the principle of the floating needle that every child learns.

Mosquitoes are good examples of the insect way of life in fresh water. Something like 1500 different kinds have been described and named. Most of them are tropical: there are 121 species in North America north of Mexico, and 125 species in Europe and northern Asia, while more than 500 kinds have been found in South America and almost 400 in Africa. The larvae in all instances live in water, and almost every kind of water accumulation has some kind of mosquito adapted to its conditions. Some kinds live in mountain brooks, breeding in the quiet pools under waterfalls; others live in the water in old tin cans or in puddles that last for only a few days after a heavy rain. Since mosquito larvae make fine food for many other aquatic animals, they are found mostly in protected places where there is some chance of survival; none is found in the open water of lakes where there would be no protection from passing fish.

Mosquito larvae breathe air, and they will drown in a few hours if prevented from reaching the surface. One group of species, however, has solved the oxygen problem by living with the breathing tube inserted into aquatic vegetation, getting air from the tissues of the plants. When the larvae are full grown, they change into a pupal stage during which the whole body is transformed into the flying insect that is so familiar to all of us. Not all mosquitoes are bloodsuckers: some live on the tissues of plants, and in any case, it is only the female that bites. After her blood meal, she develops a batch of eggs to be laid in the water, so continuing the double way of life.

Otter on spring ice in Sweden. With its webbed feet it is more at home in water than on land. (Sven Gillsater)

Fresh-Water Vertebrates

All of the classes of vertebrates are involved, in one way or another, with communities in inland waters. The elasmobranchs—the sharks and rays—almost form an exception. They often venture into brackish waters and have sometimes been found quite far upstream in rivers, but they remain essentially marine. Yet there is one genus of sting rays *(Potamotrygon)* which has several species living in the Amazon and Orinoco River systems. These occur both in the lower reaches of the rivers and far up in the foothill streams of the Andes, thousands of miles from the sea. But there are no other truly fresh-water rays. Of the sharks, only one species is found exclusively in fresh water—*Carcharhinus nicaraguensis* of Lake Nicaragua. It is closely related to the common cub shark of the Atlantic, and its ancestors presumably were isolated in the lake at some time in the geological past when its draining river became impassable. It is curious, though, that this has not also happened with other sharks in other places.

Of the "true" or bony fishes, a large number of species, families, and orders are found in inland waters, playing roles similar to those of the fishes of the marine environment. They have adapted to almost every sort of fresh-water habitat that has any permanence at all—rushing mountain torrents and underground pools and

streams, as well as the more usual ponds, lakes, and rivers. Sometimes it is difficult to imagine how they reached the places where they are found. The German naturalist Irenaus Eibl-Eibesfeldt, by arduous climbing over barren volcanic rocks, reached a small crater lake in the remote Galapagos Islands—and found fish in the lake! His guess was that they were carried by ducks. "Quite recently we obtained evidence that ducks do occasionally carry young fishes in their plumage," he remarks. "These fishes, in fright, swim between the duck's feathers when the feeding bird disturbs them." It sounds farfetched, but the fish must have got there somehow.

Pandaka pygmaea of the Philippines is usually cited as the smallest of all fishes—full-grown adults are less than one-half inch long. It lives in fresh-water streams and lakes. At the other extreme, some of the fresh-water bony fishes reach as large a size as the largest marine fishes. The record seems to be held by a sturgeon from the Volga River; it weighed 2250 pounds and was 14 feet 2 inches long—as long as the tunas, swordfish, and marlin of the seas, and even heavier. There are very large fishes in the Amazon and Orinoco too, and it is probable that the biggest ones have so far escaped measurement. As for being the most dangerous, I think the piranha of South American waters deserves that distinction. These average only a foot or so long, but they travel in schools, have magnificent teeth, and are unmatched in ferocity.

The amphibia—frogs and salamanders—are characteristically fresh-water animals, at least in the larval or tadpole stage. Some tropical species pass through the aquatic tadpole stage very rapidly, so that they are land animals most of their lives; a few have even become completely independent of open water, going through metamorphosis within the egg placed in some protected and moist spot. But overwhelmingly the amphibia are aquatic. And while a few can live in salt marshes or other coastal habitats, none is in any real sense marine.

Reptiles presumably evolved from the amphibia as land animals, but numerous species, especially of turtles and snakes, have taken to the water again. Some reptiles, like the sea turtles and sea snakes as well as the ichthyosaurs of the geological past, have adapted very well to the marine environment, but the fresh-water species are far more numerous than the marine ones. For the most part they are able to live either in the water or out of it, and thus move over land from one stream or pond to another.

As for birds, hosts of waterfowl—ducks, geese, herons, and the like—are very much parts of various fresh-water communities. They live by eating the fish, insects, worms, mollusks, or water vegetation. They may not be able to survive for any length of time under water, but they are expert at swimming, diving, or wading. Since they are mostly associated with lakes and marshes, they will be considered in that connection in the next chapter.

Mammals in Fresh Water: from Bats to Beavers

Mammals are associated with water on land in all sorts of ways, but none of them is as completely adapted to the water as the whales, dolphins, seals, manatees, and the like are to the oceans. There is a certain fresh-water dolphin that lives in the Amazon and Orinoco; manatees may venture inland for hundreds of miles in rivers; and there is a particular seal *(Phoco sibirica)* found in that most ancient of lakes, Baikal in Siberia. But these exceptions only help to explain the rule. The Amazon River and Lake Baikal both have long geological histories, giving time for the development of special adaptations. Ordinarily there would be little advantage for a mammal in fresh water to develop extreme specialization, like that of whales and dolphins, so that it could not live outside the water. Here again is an example of the fact that fresh water is limited in extent and discontinuous in space and time; it is advantageous to be able to get in and out of the water easily and thus make the best of both worlds.

There are even four species of bats that are known to live on fish: two in Asia and two in tropical America. How they manage to catch fish has been a matter of some controversy since it is not easy to make careful observations of bats skimming swiftly over water in the dark of night. The fishing bats have the hind claws of the feet enlarged to form sharp, gafflike hooks, and zoologist Donald Griffin, of Harvard, who is intimately acquainted with bat behavior, believes that these really are used as gaffs, "making it possible to secure a three- or four-inch fish, if it is within about an inch of the surface." Whatever their fishing method, these bats, by reason of their habits, would be members of the aquatic community.

In his book *Aquatic Mammals,* A. Brazier Howell, an anatomist at Johns Hopkins University, lists seventeen mammal families with species that are primarily aquatic in their habits. These range from the duck-billed platypus of Australia and a water

Water on Land

22 Above: The European perch, like its American cousin, prefers slow-moving streams and is a favorite of anglers. (Ernst Zollinger)

23 Right: The burbot or eelpout, the only fresh-water member of the cod family, lives in lakes and rivers in Eurasia and North Amercia. (Ernst Zollinger)

24 Left, above: Raccoons, natives of North America, come down to the river to wash their paws or their food rather than to fish. (Ed Park)

25 Left: Crocodiles, such as this one on a river bank in Uganda, shuttle between land and water. (George Holton)

26 Above: Alaskan brown bears
come to a river to take
advantage of the salmon run.
(Steve McCutcheon)

27 Left: A coyote uses a frozen
river as a highway. (Ed Park)

opossum in South America to the hippos of Africa and the tapirs of tropical America and Asia. Otters, muskrats, and beavers are examples of familiar animals that have ponds or streams as their basic habitat.

Most mammals, including rabbits, mice, and moles, can swim if necessary. The aquatic mammals, however, are especially good swimmers. Many of them have developed webbing between the toes as a swimming aid: this is true of the platypus, of the water opossum, of beavers, and of some of the water rats. Others, like various species of otters, have partial webbing between the toes; but this is also true of some mammals that are not particularly aquatic. Some mammals, like the water shrews, have fringes of stiffened hairs, which serve as swimming aids, on the sides of the feet and toes. Many animals use only the hind legs in swimming: for example, the beaver, which swims with the front legs folded back under its chest. Beavers are able to "scull" at a slow rate of speed with the flattened tail, a type of swimming behavior that is even more characteristic of muskrats.

Beavers are especially interesting because they so obviously modify—or in a sense create—the environment in which they live. This has got them into difficulties with man, who does not tolerate having other animals change the landscape by damming streams, cutting trees, and digging canals. Beavers are regarded as pests by farmers; this, plus the facts that their flesh is tasty and their fur valuable, has threatened their survival in regions where the human species has come to dominate the landscape. Beavers were once common along streams all through the Temperate Zone woodlands in North America, Europe, and Asia, but they disappeared from the British Isles in about the twelfth century and from most of continental Europe a few centuries later. Though they survive now along a stretch of the Rhone in France and the Elbe in Germany under strict protection, they have lost the habit of building dams and lodges, and taken to living in burrows in stream banks. Protective measures have saved them from extinction in North America.

Beavers do not form part of the aquatic food network: they live on the bark and wood of the trees and branches that they cut and store in their ponds. The water serves them chiefly for protection. By building a dam across a stream, beavers achieve a fairly stable water level, so that their lodges are not in danger either of flooding or of being stranded with the entrances exposed to animals less adept at swimming. The lodges also serve as places to store winter food supplies under water.

Beavers are proverbially industrious, and much has also been made of their "cleverness" in building and repairing dams and lodges, and in digging canals which they use to float logs to their dam sites. Certainly beavers are busy enough, but very little is known about the psychological basis of their construction work—it is not easy to get a beaver colony into an experimental laboratory. They have been known to build dams up to a hundred yards long and as much as twelve feet high. Most of the dams are much smaller, of course, but their cumulative effect in changing the landscape by creating ponds, which then slowly silt up, may be considerable.

Streams

Beavers are occupied with turning streams into ponds, running water into still water. The division in the study of limnology, as the study of inland waters is called, is

28 Hippos, here shown in Uganda, are more at home in water than on land. (George Holton)

between running and still water. The distinction is useful enough but it is far from absolute. A mountain brook and a lake are obviously different, but both brook and lake may have similar marshy banks; also, there are many gradations among perceptible current, imperceptible current, and no current at all. It is like trying on land to decide where "desert" ends and "semidesert" begins; it becomes a matter of arbitrary definition. Yet both deserts and streams are "real" enough, and completely different from forests and lakes.

Let us first consider running water in the form of river systems, since this is the basis of water on land. Water is essentially always running downhill, making its way back to the reservoir of the sea. Its course may be slowed or blocked for varying lengths of time in accumulations of standing water, but even the largest lakes can be looked at as hardly more than minor incidents in the vast circulating system of the hydrosphere.

What a variety of stream types there is! One thinks of the arroyos of the American southwest, dry except for flash floods after a rain; of streams that run for part of the year and then are dry for the rest, sometimes with persisting pools, sometimes not. There are streams tumbling down steep mountainsides; others that barely move, the water seeping through forested swamp or lowland meadow. In size moving water runs the gamut from tiny trickles on a rock face to the Amazon, a hundred miles across. There are streams with bottoms of rock, gravel, sand, and mud; with high banks and marshy banks; streams that are always clear and others that are always muddy; some always cold, some never; and between each extreme there is every possible intergrade.

Geographers commonly divide a river system into three parts—upper, middle, and lower. In general, the conditions for animal life are most difficult in the torrential streams of the headwaters and most favorable in the sluggish rivers of the lowlands. The number of kinds of animals found in a particular river system correspondingly increases from the headwaters toward the mouth.

Living in a Current

Far left: Damming streams and digging canals, beavers help shape the landscape.
(William Vandivert)

Left: Making their way back from the sea, salmon buck currents and waterfalls to spawn in the same stream where they were born.
(George B. Kelez: U.S. Fish and Wildlife Service)

The chief problem of animals in running water is to keep from being swept away—to remain stationary, or to overcome the power of the current by swimming. The greater the force of the current, the greater the problem. Since drifting organisms are helpless, swept always onward toward the sea, plankton as we know it in the sea and lakes cannot exist. Plankton organisms often exist in streams, but they are an overflow from swamps and lakes, not a self-perpetuating community. The producer forms of rushing streams are filamentous algae, diatoms, and water mosses that encrust boulders or form mats over the stream bed. This fixed vegetation provides shelter as well as food for many small animals—insect larvae, crustaceans, and so on—which in turn become food for the active fishes.

There are many kinds of special adaptations to life in rapid currents. Many mayfly and stonefly nymphs have thin, flattened bodies and cling closely to the bottom; other insects have developed suction disks to hold them to boulders. Some fishes of the high streams in the Andes and Himalayas have also developed methods of clinging to rock surfaces. Caddisfly larvae build cases of sand grains held tightly together with silk and firmly attached to the bottom. Blackfly larvae live on rocks washed by waterfalls or rapids, holding on by means of suction disks and silk anchorings. Such fixed animals have to depend on the water to bring them their food, as do the fixed animals of the sea.

There are quiet spots in even the most torrential of streams: pools behind waterfalls and little back eddies among the boulders. Many animals live in such locations, surviving through behavior that keeps them away from the current rather than through adaptations to resisting its force. But the physical hazards of life in mountain streams are immense, and not very many kinds of animals have found means of overcoming them. Even though the types are few, the individuals may be numerous enough: the swarms of blackflies along some rushing brooks are proof that species which adapt to these conditions can be very successful.

As the stream widens and the current slows, gravel beds and sand bars provide protection for more numerous animals, and vegetation along the banks and in the river bed itself becomes more and more important. The stream becomes less an incident in the landscape and more a unit in itself, a special biological community.

River and Sea

Finally, in the bottom lands, where the rivers meander across the plains in great sweeps, new situations with new possibilities for animal life appear. The meanders get cut off, leaving the formation known as oxbow lakes. A network of separate channels may develop, like the bayous of the lower Mississippi and the jungled maze along the Amazon. These conditions, of course, are not necessarily found only near the river mouth: the great papyrus swamps of the upper Nile, two thousand miles from the sea, have the same character.

Along the major rivers, life in the water tends to merge with that on land. Hippos, crocodiles, anacondas, tapirs—depending on the part of the world—slide in and out of the water. Hosts of waterfowl live off the river animals. Fishes become abundant, both as individuals and as species, fitting into the variety of niches offered by the wide and varied stream bed.

The rivers are the paths whereby life from the sea first reached fresh water, and whereby some kinds of fresh-water life again entered the sea. In several cases this stamp of the past is still on the animals of the present. Fresh-water fishes that have taken to the sea come back to the streams to spawn, and marine fishes that have come to live in inland waters reverse the process.

Some species of sturgeon, salmon, and shad are among the fishes that come back to fresh water to spawn. The most spectacular, the most puzzling, of these are the salmon, who come in from the sea to make their way against the strongest currents, even leaping waterfalls, to reach the same mountain brook in which they themselves were spawned. How, wandering the seas, do they find their home river again; and how, in the river, do they distinguish each branch to come again to the brook from which they started? Yet the recovery of tagged fish has shown that they do this with some regularity. It is likely that these fish find their way by a highly developed sense of smell or taste, a fine sensitivity to chemical differences in the water, but this is difficult to prove, much less to understand.

Fresh-water eels of Europe and eastern North America show the reverse habit: they come down the streams and rivers to the ocean and eventually reach the Sargasso Sea in the mid-Atlantic, where they spawn. A Danish biologist, Johannes Schmidt, was responsible for much of the careful detective work that eventually unraveled this story. The tiny, transparent eel larvae, called *leptocephali,* form part of the ocean plankton. They become bigger and bigger as they are collected nearer Europe or North America, until eventually, near the estuaries of the rivers, they are recognizable as eels, though still transparent—a stage in which they are called glass eels. Finally, making their way up the rivers, they become a darker color and are called elvers.

European and American eels differ in the number of vertebrae in their backbones, so they are distinguished as separate species. Although both apparently spawn together in the Sargasso Sea area, the leptocephali of each, drifting with the ocean currents, find the right continent. This theory is not easy to believe, but there is no other explanation for the evidence accumulated by the patient work of the oceanographers. As to how the eels navigate across the vast oceans, we have no idea.

7

Lakes, Ponds, and Marshes

Any pattern in the contours of the land that holds up the flow of water toward the sea results in a lake, pond, or marsh. Like man, nature makes lakes or ponds either by building dams or by digging holes. A variety of geological processes may be involved in both the digging and the damming.

The numerous lakes of northern America and Europe were generally produced by the action of the great glaciers that covered those continents so recently. The ponderous movements of the ice sheets scoured out depressions, and the great weight of the ice itself warped the earth's crust to form basins like those of the Great Lakes. As the glaciers melted, accumulated rubble would often be dumped across valleys, forming glacial moraines that blocked stream flow. Lakes formed in these various ways are all classed as "glacial lakes."

Many lakes, both large and small, are the consequence of the restless movements of the earth's crust, movements that are constantly changing the topography of the continents and ocean basins. The oldest and deepest of lakes—Tanganyika in Africa and Baikal in Siberia—were formed in this way. Tanganyika lies in a great and ancient crustal slip or rift that runs from Rhodesia to Israel. The basin of the Great Salt Lake in Utah is the result of mountain uplift that left no drainage outlet. On a smaller scale, there is Reelfoot Lake in Tennessee, which was formed in the course of the New Madrid earthquakes in 1811–1813.

Lakes may also result from volcanic action. There are many crater lakes in the world, usually clear and deep and isolated, sometimes mysteriously appearing and disappearing, as forces within the volcano open and close passageways. Or a lava flow, crossing a stream, may form a lake by damming action.

In limestone country lakes are formed by the solution of lime by underground streams. The process can be seen clearly in Florida and Yucatan; "sink holes" form where the surface collapses into a cavern that has been dissolved away by water action. These sink holes sometimes gradually enlarge to form lakes of respectable size, or they may remain as a series of round, disconnected, deep ponds, whose inlets and outlets are below the surface.

There are other ways in which the earth may be dug out or streams blocked: oxbow lakes are left by meandering rivers; shore ponds result from dams built by the action of ocean waves; ponds are formed in depressions scooped out by the wind. Beavers started making dams before men did, but today men everywhere are digging and damming to make lakes for water supplies, for power, for fish culture, for sport, or as an incidental result of such an activity as quarrying.

The kinds of animals found in lakes depend on many different factors: size and depth; geological age; connections with other lakes and river systems; geographical location; chemical and physical conditions of the water. Temperature conditions in lakes take on a special importance because of the peculiar properties of water and their effect on the circulation of materials. On this basis, lakes are grouped into three main types—polar, temperate, and tropical.

Water Circulation

Water, as we have already mentioned, is densest (heaviest) at 4 degrees C. above the freezing point. It is this property that makes for quite different patterns of water circulation in the three classes of lakes. In the temperate zones, in regions where air temperatures are below freezing for extended periods, the water in lakes circulates completely twice a year. As the surface water reaches 4 degrees C. with the onset of winter, it sinks to the bottom, and eventually the whole water mass reaches this temperature. With continuing cold, the surface water starts to freeze, but the ice rarely extends to any great depth and, as every ice fisherman knows, animal life continues actively in the subsurface water.

When spring thaws reach the point where the surface water is again at 4 degrees C., the whole water mass reaches an unstable equilibrium, and wave action tends to result in a complete mixing—the spring overturn. In this way oxygen is carried from the surface to the depths twice a year, and nutrient materials like phosphates are returned from the bottom mud to the open water.

Lakes in climates where it is never cold enough to bring the surface water down to a temperature of 4 degrees C. do not have this water turnover. As a result, water is mixed only to the extent made possible by wave and current action, and oxygen is absent except near the surface. As a consequence, animal life becomes impossible at any great depth.

In polar lakes the surface waters never get appreciably warmer than the critical 4 degrees C., so that the waters are mixed only once a year, in the midsummer period. Shallow ponds and lakes may freeze completely in the winter, and at least one type of fish, the Blackfish *(Dallia)* of Alaska and Siberia, can live for weeks frozen in solid ice. It is recorded that one of these fish, frozen, was swallowed by a dog, thawed out in its stomach, and was vomited up alive.

In some arctic lakes the surface waters warm above the critical temperature during the summer; such lakes show a "temperate" rather than a "polar" type of water circulation. On the other hand, the surface waters of many lakes located geographically in the temperate zones never get cold enough to sink. Such lakes—for instance, those at the southern base of the Alps, like Lake Geneva—belong to the "tropical" type.

Death of a Lake

Once a lake is formed, the outlet stream starts the slow process of erosion of the blocking land; the inlet streams begin depositing the mud and gravel they have washed from their courses; and as the plants and animals of the lake itself die, they

European eels, like their American relatives, reverse the salmon's journey, returning to spawn in the Sargasso Sea. (Ernst Zollinger)

accumulate as bottom detritus. Thus the lake starts toward extinction as soon as it is formed.

In many parts of the world we can see lakes and ponds in different stages of extinction, right down to the final stage of rich farm land that not long ago, as geological time is counted, was clearly the bottom of a lake. The process is in some ways self-accelerating. Plankton forms the first producer system. As the bodies of plankton organisms begin to form a bottom mud, rooted vegetation grows; it slows wave and current action, allowing increased deposition and providing more materials for deposit. Vegetation, starting near the shore, creeps outward year by year. Shrubs and trees become established around the swampy margins and start their slow progression outward. In this way the body of water evolves from lake to pond to swamp to dry land, if no new geological event intervenes to set the process back.

Ancient Lakes

Only a very few lakes show evidence of great geological antiquity: Baikal in Siberia, Tanganyika in Africa, Posso in Celebes, Lanao in the Philippines, and Ochrida in the Balkans. Baikal and Tanganyika are also the deepest lakes, the first having a maximum depth of 5595 feet and the second of 4707 feet. Baikal is far enough north for temperature effects to produce considerable water turnover, and there is life in the lake at least to a depth of 2000 feet. Tanganyika, however, is a tropical lake, with no water movement except that due to wave action. The water below about 200 feet is consequently entirely devoid of oxygen—and of living animals.

The great age of these lakes is indicated by the large number of peculiar animals that inhabit them—species that are found nowhere else in the world. These endemic species, genera, and families must have evolved in the lake, a process which would take a long time.

Baikal has the most distinctive fauna of any lake. There is a seal there, *Phoca sibirica,* found nowhere else except in small nearby Lake Orion. There are also several hundred species of crustaceans in the lake, almost all of them found only there, and the numerous species of mollusks and worms are mostly endemic.

Like Baikal, Tanganyika has a high proportion of endemic crustaceans and mollusks. Of the 188 species of fishes collected in the lake and tributary streams, 140 have been found only there. Of these fish species, 93 belong to the single family Cichlidae, a family found commonly in fresh waters in both South America and Africa. Some of the cichlids are popular with aquarists; for instance, the fresh-water angelfish belongs to the family. But 91 of the 93 Tanganyika cichlids are found nowhere else in the world; and these are so distinctive that they have been classified into 34 endemic genera. Evolution has been taking an independent course in this lake for a very long time.

Life in Lakes

The economy of life in lakes is similar in many ways to that in seas. Its basis, in both cases, is plankton, including both plants and animals. The "key-industry animals" are chiefly members of the plankton, and these, as in the sea, often show a daily vertical migration. And then there are the swimming animals, the nekton; and the bottom inhabitants, the benthos. In fact, much of the marine vocabulary can be applied to lakes, though there is no intertidal zone, and except in the case of Lake Baikal, there is no special fauna at great depths.

Lake water tends to be less clear than sea water, so that light does not penetrate to as great depths, and the producer zone is correspondingly narrower. The plankton within this producing zone, however, is often luxuriant, supporting large populations of fishes and other consumers. Rooted vegetation is possible where light reaches to the bottom, and this plays an important part in the economy of most lakes. But there is an interesting difference here between lakes and seas. In the marine environment the rooted vegetation is very largely made up of different kinds of algae, and "higher plants"—seed plants—are rare, including only a few species. In fresh waters, however, higher plants that have moved from the land into the water in the course of their evolution predominate. Some of these are entirely submerged; others, like the water lilies, have leaves that float on the surface; and still others, like the reeds, grow up through the surface.

The aquatic vegetation around the shore of a lake provides both food and shelter for a teeming animal life. There are snails, crustaceans, and many kinds of insects, providing food for fishes, frogs, and turtles, and for the wading and swimming birds. There is another fauna in the mud and sand of the bottom, including clams, various sorts of worms, some kinds of insects, and a host of microscopic things.

Lakes, Ponds, and Marshes

29 Above: African wood ibises in the lake region of the Congo. (Twentieth Century Fox)

30 Right: The black-necked stilt, like many long-legged birds, can swim and dive but prefers to wade for its food. (Allan D. Cruickshank: National Audubon Society)

31 Right: The cypress swamps of the southern United States are a special fresh-water habitat that is rapidly being destroyed. (Max Hunn: National Audubon Society)

32 Below, left: Canada geese. (Ed Park)

33 Below, right: The Amazonian guará. (Harald Schultz)

34 Above: Wilson's phalarope. (Ed Park)

35 The Brazilian horned frogs, below, like most amphibians, are strictly aquatic but sometimes come out of the water to rest. (James R. Simon)

Fishes

One theory has it that the bony fishes first evolved in fresh water or in the brackish water of river estuaries, far back toward the beginning of the geological record. Certainly fresh-water fishes have a very long history, and the living species include a rich variety of forms. For the most part the fishes of the lakes and of the large, slow-moving rivers are hardly different in any particular region. Again this probably reflects the temporary history of most fresh-water lakes—they do not last long enough to permit the evolution of special lake forms. The Great Lakes of North America look as permanent and unchanging as the sea, yet only thirty thousand or so years ago they were nonexistent, the region lying under a great sheet of ice. As the lakes were formed by the retreating ice, the only possible fish inhabitants were those that could enter from the south through the river systems.

Many fishes can move between fresh and salt water, as was pointed out in the last chapter. Such species form an important part of lake faunas in many parts of the world, but in the Great Lakes such a source of fauna was cut off by the break in the St. Lawrence at Niagara Falls. With the building of the Welland Canal, enabling ocean shipping to reach the lakes, the way was opened for ocean fishes.

One species, the sea lamprey, managed to reach the lakes, with disastrous results. This very primitive, jawless fish is an inhabitant normally of both shores of the Atlantic, entering streams to spawn in the early spring months. The lampreys of the Great Lakes continue the habit of moving into streams to spawn.

The lampreys are "parasitic" on other fishes. They attach themselves to their victims with their disklike mouths and suck their blood, moving on to another victim when one has been exhausted. Whether this is called "parasitic" or "predatory" behavior depends on what definition you use, but the effect on the victims is unfortunate by any definition. Ordinarily, lampreys are not notoriously damaging to other fish populations; but in the new environment of the Great Lakes they multiplied enormously and completely ruined a once thriving fishing industry. This is one of the numerous cases of explosively disastrous consequences from the movement of animals into new environments as a result of human action: in this case as an indirect and unexpected result of the construction of the ship canals.

Australia and New Zealand have very limited faunas of native fresh-water fishes, since they have probably never been connected with the main continental land masses where inland fishes evolved. Such fishes as trout, introduced from North America and Europe, have thrived in this new environment. But here the results, from the human point of view, are entirely fortunate. Trout in Australia and New Zealand grow much more rapidly than in their native waters, presumably because of less competition from other fishes, though no one is really sure why the growth rate is so different.

The fresh-water fishes of the different regions of the world thus differ greatly. Except for forms that can live in fresh and salt water, they have necessarily had long separate evolutionary histories in the different water systems. The "tropical fish" in any aquarium give some idea of how diverse—and how gaudy—these fishes can be. But while the fishes in a living-room aquarium may look as bright and varied as the fishes around a fragment of a coral reef, the inhabitants of even a small aquarium probably come from many different parts of the world, and no single fresh-water habitat in nature would be able to rival any coral reef. The

36 A pair of swans nesting in a Swiss lake. (Oscar Schmid: Annan Photo Features)

fishes in the Caribbean or the South Pacific bear far closer resemblance to each other than do those of a lake or pool on each of the continents. Geography, relatively unimportant in the sea, becomes very meaningful in lakes and rivers.

But productivity—if measured in such terms as pounds of fish growing each year per acre of surface—may be just as great in a tropical pond or shallow lake as in a coral reef. Fresh-water fisheries in general are at present relatively unimportant, but fish farming, anciently practiced in the Orient, holds great promise as a source of protein for growing tropical populations.

Fishes are most abundant in the marginal or shallow areas of lakes where rooted vegetation can become established. A large proportion are bottom feeders, and a number of special adaptations for this habit have developed. Several unrelated groups have developed beardlike "feelers" thickly set with nerve buds which aid in the search for food through muddy water; one thinks first of catfishes, but sturgeon, carp, and species of other families have similar "feelers." The mouths of sturgeon, carp, and American suckers can be protruded to collect food from the bottom; and there is also a curious African family, the Mormyridae or elephant-nosed fishes, with long snouts that appear to serve for mud-probing.

Many of the African mormyrids also produce continuous electrical discharges, which serve to guide the fish in muddy water, just as sonar guides a ship. Any object—food, enemy, or obstacle—falling within the electrical field can be located precisely. Many species of South American knifefishes produce a similar low-voltage electric field, which aids them in finding their way about and in locating food. This electric navigating system is quite different from the powerful high-voltage discharges of the African electric catfish and the South American electric eel.

The "electric eel" is not an eel at all but a relative of the knifefishes and a member of the large order Ostariophysi, which embraces a high proportion of the true fresh-water fishes, including minnows, suckers, carp, catfishes, and the like. It is a large fish—the record length is nine and a half feet, and six-foot specimens are not uncommon. Most of the animal is a huge electric organ, the usual body functions being concentrated in about the first fifth of the total length. These eels can deliver a shock of as much as 600 volts, though 350 volts is the average. The amperage is low enough so that the shock is not usually fatal to man, though swimmers may be knocked unconscious and die through drowning.

The powerful discharge serves as a protective device, though the electric eel is not known to have any natural enemies except man. In addition to the battery producing the high-voltage shock, the eel has a low-voltage system which serves for guidance through the water. The adults are blind, and they depend entirely on this electrical system for finding food and avoiding obstacles.

The African electric catfish is smaller than the electric eel, reaching a maximum length of about four feet, and is capable of delivering a shock of about one hundred volts. The function is apparently both defensive and aggressive. It is not known to have any electric navigation system.

Water Birds

Many different kinds of birds are involved in the food network of inland waters. Some, like herons, have developed long, stiltlike legs for wading in shallow water.

With long legs for wading and long necks and bills to reach down into the mud, these flamingoes feed in western Kenya's Lake Nakuru.
(Arthur Christiansen)

The Jacana, or lily-trotter, walks easily on floating flora and makes its nest in aquatic vegetation. (Loke Wan-Tho)

Left: With its extra-ordinarily long neck, the anhinga is a natural spear-fisher. (Loke Wan-Tho)

Others, like the ducks, are expert swimmers and divers. Still others, like the king-fishers, patrol the water from the air or watch from some strategic perch, to dive or skim the surface when they spot likely prey. Where to draw the line in such a series between "aquatic" and "terrestrial" again becomes a rather arbitrary matter of definition. Since food relations form the cement that holds the biological community together, perhaps any bird can be called "aquatic" if most of its food supply is derived from the water, regardless of where it spends the rest of its time.

In the case of the penguins, the extinct great auk, and a few other birds like the steamer duck of the Falkland Islands and the flightless cormorant of the Galapagos, swimming has replaced flying as the chief means of locomotion. This loss of flight and complete dependence on swimming or walking has not developed among the birds of inland waters, and one is tempted to explain this again in terms of the discontinuity of fresh-water habitats. The two exceptions illuminate—if they do not prove—the rule. There is a flightless grebe *(Centropelma micropterum)* in Lake Titicaca in the Andes, and another *(Podilymbus gigas)* in volcano-girded Lake Atitlan in Guatemala. The Atitlan grebe looks as though it should be able to fly, but since the species is found only in this lake we can safely assume it doesn't fly much.

If loss of flight can develop so readily, one wonders why it has not occurred more often. Perhaps there is no great advantage in flight in these particular tropical lakes but, in general, the ability to get easily from one patch of water to another is important for the animals of inland waters. The water birds of the north, particularly, must be able to migrate when winter freezing seals off their food supply.

The wings of water birds, then, remain organs of flight and are not often modified

for swimming; the ability to swim turns, rather, on foot structures. Webbing between the toes has evolved independently in several groups of aquatic birds. Ducks and loons have webs between the second, third, and fourth toes. The snakebirds *(Anhinga)* have all four toes webbed, as do their marine relatives, the cormorants, pelicans, gannets, and boobies. Lobes on the toes as an aid in swimming appear in the grebes, rails, phalaropes, and sun grebes or "finfoots."

The long legs of waders make requisite long necks and often long bills to reach down for the food. Neck length seems to reach its most absurd development in the snakebirds or anhingas, though these are really swimmers rather than waders. The necks of these birds are used for lightning-like fish-spearing. Only the anhingas and one of the grebes are known to use their bills commonly for spearing; most fish-eating birds use them as forceps. Spoonbills use their flattened bills for stirring up the mud; and flamingos filter plankton and larger prey from the water.

Wading over soft mud presents special problems. The flamingos overcome this by webbing between the toes; the herons by having the toes greatly elongated. The extreme of toe development is reached by the jacanas or "lily-trotters," which spend most of their lives walking about over the water on lily pads or other surface vegetation, and even build their nests on floating flora. The jacanas are inhabitants of marshes and swamps rather than lakes; this involves another category.

Drying Up

Lake, pond, swamp, marsh: these are all common English words that we use without hesitation but they are impossible to define precisely. In ordinary usage the difference between a lake and a pond is a matter of size, but it is doubtful that anyone has ever attempted to decide at exactly what size a "pond" becomes a "lake." In both cases one thinks of open water, while marsh and swamp imply water choked with vegetation. Marsh implies herbaceous growth; swamp, woody growth—trees. We thus speak of cypress swamps and salt marshes.

A lake is permanent, in the sense of having open water all through the year. Ponds, swamps, and marshes may be permanent, or they may dry up for part of the year, and this makes a great difference to the animals living there. The inhabitants of a small but permanent pond are hardly different from those of a neighboring lake, but animals living in a temporary pond must have some way either of getting out of the pond when it dries or of surviving the period of drought.

The problem of living in water that is liable to dry up has been met in a number of ways. Animals like water bugs and water beetles that can live readily in the water or out, move easily enough, and are liable to turn up in any water puddle that lasts for more than a few days. Many insects and amphibia that are aquatic at one stage in their life and terrestrial at another must have a seasonal pattern that insures that the aquatic stage will occur at a time when water is available.

Many insects and crustaceans have eggs that are resistant to desiccation: they may survive for years, ready to hatch as soon as they are submerged. Species that are adapted to living in water that lasts for only a few days have very rapid growth rates, so that the adult form, capable of reproduction, may be reached before the water dries up. This is true, for instance, of many kinds of mosquitoes; some of them can grow from egg to adult within a week.

A surprisingly large number of different kinds of fishes, especially in the tropics, are able to survive for considerable periods dried in the mud of ponds. The most spectacular performance of this sort is that of the African and South American lungfishes. An African lungfish has been known to survive out of water for as long as four years. This animal makes itself a mud ball, or cocoon, with a small opening directly in front of the mouth for breathing. The South American lungfish makes itself a mud tunnel rather than a cocoon. The Australian species, unlike the others, cannot estivate.

Marshes in the Treetops

Puddles, pools, and ponds are fascinating enough, but there is another whole category of fresh-water habitats that is perhaps even more interesting, though most ecologists hardly notice them. These habitats are the water that is accumulated and held by various sorts of plants.

The commonest plant containers of water are rot holes in trees. These are the only kind in northern forests, and there are a number of insects and other things that live only in this peculiar habitat. In bogs in North America there is a plant, the pitcher plant *(Sarracenia)*, that accumulates water in its leaves. Though the plant is carnivorous, getting food from the decaying bodies of insects that have been trapped in its little hoard of stinking water, one species of mosquito successfully breeds in this water and nowhere else.

In tropical forests there are many kinds of plants and plant parts that hold water, and these have come to be the home of a quite special fauna. With almost daily rains, and with a high humidity that cuts down evaporation, water is caught and held in many different sorts of places besides rot holes: in leaves, flowers, and fruit husks on the ground; at the bases of the leaves of several kinds of plants; and in certain types of flowers. The big spathes that shield the flowers of palms make fine water containers when they fall to the ground, and things like mosquito larvae and water beetles teem in this water. Coconut husks, the pods of cacao beans, and the hard shells of other large fruits also collect water.

The most abundant plant containers of water in tropical America are the bromeliads, the plants of the pineapple family. These are mostly epiphytic—that is, they grow on trees, not as parasites but using the tree as a perch. There are many hundreds of species of bromeliads, and in most of them the bases of the leaves are broad and closely spaced, making a "tank" which holds water. A big bromeliad may have several quarts of water in its tank, with many sorts of aquatic animals living there. One species of frog, for instance, breeds only in bromeliads, as does a species of dragonfly; and many species of mosquitoes and other flies, as well as beetles, worms, and various microscopic organisms, are found only in this habitat.

One of the most curious of the container habitats is the water that accumulates in the internodes of growing bamboo. Boring insects frequently make tiny holes in the bamboo stalks, and water trickles into the hollow stem through these. In this water one finds a very special fauna of aquatic insect larvae, including mosquito "wrigglers"—but very queer wrigglers, so unexpected that they inevitably make one think of the odd forms of deep-sea fish. One kind of larva has a breathing tube much longer than its body, looking like a tiny dog attached to an immensely attenu-

A good home for many animals: a cypress swamp in Florida. (Rutherford Platt)

To stay under water,
aquatic spiders draw on
air bubbles trapped in
their thick body hair.
(Wilhelm Hoppe)

ated tail. Why they have this very long breathing tube is not known; other kinds
of larvae in the same water have very short tubes and seem to get along all right.
One of these short-tubed larvae is very hairy, looking like a tiny wooly-bear caterpillar, which again seems out of place in a mosquito larva.

The habits of these mosquitoes are also odd. Often the entrance holes in the
bamboo are so tiny that one cannot imagine how a mosquito can get in or out, yet
the larvae are there, and the adults, often brightly colored, are flying in the forest
outside. Pedro Galindo, working at the Gorgas Laboratory in Panama, discovered

that one of these mosquitoes has the habit of hovering outside of these worm holes, shooting its eggs into the holes with great force and accuracy. A species in Ceylon that breeds in bamboo lays its eggs on one of its legs, and then sticks the leg into the hole, so that the larvae are deposited inside. But when the mosquitoes hatch, how do they get out of their prison?

It turns out that these bamboo-breeding mosquitoes are expert jail-breakers: common wire netting, for instance, will not hold them at all. An ordinary mosquito flies up to a screen, bumps against it, and gives up. A bamboo-breeder, encountering a wire screen, sticks its head into the meshes, gives a few twists to its body, and wriggles through. When these mosquitoes hatch out in laboratory vials plugged with absorbent cotton, they work their way up into the cotton until they become hopelessly entangled. Obviously they are good at wriggling through small holes in order to get out of their breeding places.

The more one studies a tropical forest, the more one becomes impressed with the endless variety of ways that animals have found for living there. The water held by rot holes, leaves, and flowers in the trees is only one of the special habitats. It is odd enough, forming, as someone has remarked, a sort of vast marsh scattered through the treetops. The water containers in the forest canopy, and the puddles, pools, swamps, and streams over the forest floor, represent an intrusion by the world of fresh water. But the forest itself is terrestrial—one of the environments of life on land. It provides us with a good place to start our look at these continental worlds of animal life.

8

Tropical Forests

On land, water becomes an important problem for animals. In a way, all organisms are packages of sea water, packages that always leak a little, so that water somehow must be found or made and kept. Temperature is important both in water and on land, but the effects are different because air temperatures change much more easily and quickly than do water temperatures, with the result that daily and seasonal changes are greater and more abrupt. On land as everywhere else, light is necessary for the photosynthesis of the green plants of the producing system.

Temperature, moisture, and light: these are the basic ingredients of weather and climate. Weather is the day-to-day change in these factors; climate is the general regional or geographical pattern. The kind of climate governs the kind of vegetation, and both climate and vegetation affect the lives of animals.

The most favorable climate for life on land involves continuous warmth, easy availability of water, and abundant light throughout the year. These are the conditions that prevail over a good part of the mid-tropical region, and that result in the kind of vegetation known as *rain forest:* a type of vegetation that supports a bewilderingly large number of diversified kinds of animals.

The majority of monkey species inhabit the rain-forest canopy. Old World monkeys, such as this guenon in Africa, do not have prehensile tails. (Emil Schulthess)

Rain Forest

If a map of land vegetation is compared with one of climatic zones for the earth, it is apparent that forests cover the land except where conditions are too dry, in which case we find scrub, grassland, or desert, or too cold, which results in tundra or persisting ice. Forests, of course, are made up of trees, a special plant form involving a columnar, woody trunk, which lifts the photosynthesizing leaves high into the air, requiring a firmly embedded root system to support the heavy superstructure.

The tree form allows plants to take maximum advantage of sunlight by filtering it down through many layers of foliage. Light can be used in depth by trees, as it can by plankton in the upper layers of the sea. Because of the difference in the nature of water and of air as supporting media, the most efficient producers in the water are very small organisms; in the air the most efficient are very large ones.

Thousands of species of trees grow in many kinds of combinations to make different types of forests. Probably no two experts would agree on how many forest types there are, or on the exact definition of any one type. But all would agree that

the rain forest is the most complex; it is composed of the largest number of different kinds of trees, and supports the largest number of species of animals. By definition, rain forest is a consequence of heavy rainfall all through the year, so that water is always easily available. Where to draw the line limiting rain forest, however, is a matter of opinion. With increasing altitude in tropical mountains, rain forest gives way to cloud forest, characterized by fog and coolness. With lower rainfall, and especially with large seasonal differences in rain, there appears monsoon forest, characterized by one or two seasons of drought in each annual cycle.

According to some definitions, rain forest in the tropics occurs wherever there is more than 80 inches of rain a year, with at least 5 inches in the driest month. I would put the limit higher but do not really want to argue about it. For the most part, the great tropical rain forests are in areas that receive 150 inches of rain or more each year—often much more. However you look at it, this is a great deal of water.

There are three major areas of tropical rain forest: the American, the African, and the Indo-Malayan. They include all of the land masses crossed by the equator except the east coast of Africa, which has a pronounced dry season.

The American forest is the largest, the most continuous, and so far the least disturbed by man. It covers much of the Amazon drainage, extending south along the inner side of the Andes into Bolivia and the drainage of the Plata, and north into Colombia and the drainage of the Orinoco. Across the northern Andes there is a Pacific strip along the coast from Ecuador to Panama, which continues through Central America along the Caribbean coast almost to the line of the tropics in Mexico.

The African forest is the smallest of the three, and there is considerable debate about both its present limits and its former extension. Essentially, it covers the drainage of the Congo River system, with extensions north and west along the Gulf of Guinea to Liberia.

The Indo-Malayan forest is the most fragmented, divided among most of the large islands of the East Indies—Sumatra, Borneo, Celebes, the Philippines. On the mainland it covers much of the Malay Peninsula, with outlying areas on the west coast of India, in Burma, and on the coast of Vietnam.

The northern part of Queensland in Australia is covered with rain forest, as is much of New Guinea. The animals of Queensland and New Guinea are similar, but they are markedly different from those of the Indo-Malayan region, so that this might well be treated as a small but distinctive fourth area.

The forests of these different geographical areas are composed of different kinds of trees and inhabited by different species of animals; yet they give a very similar impression to the visitor. The taller trees reach a height averaging about 150 feet, with occasional giants towering above the canopy to a height of 200 feet or so. No trees more than 300 feet tall have been reported in rain-forest regions.

"Rain forest" and "jungle" are often used as synonymous words. But according to the dictionary, jungle means wasteland or wilderness. It can apply to anything from a desert to a forest that is uncultivated—and it is probably better left with this vague meaning. Jungle carries all of the wrong connotations for rain forest: thick vegetation, poisonous snakes, hordes of biting insects, and all of the other ingredients of green hell. Certainly there are poisonous snakes in most rain-forest areas, as well as a great many insects, but both are apt to be inconspicuous,

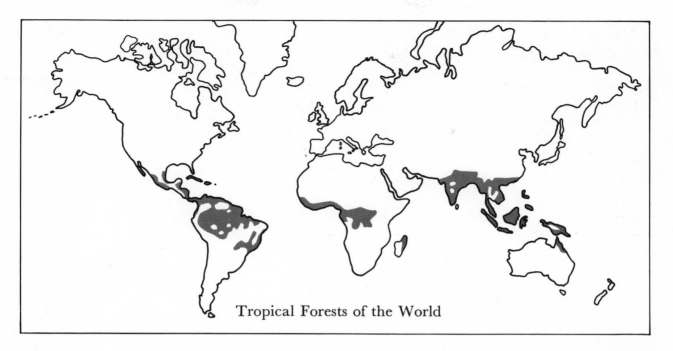

Tropical Forests of the World

and the vegetation at ground level is more apt to be open than dense. The general idea of "jungle" fits the second growth of abandoned cultivation better than it does the undisturbed forest.

The total effect of the rain forest on intruding man is gloomy rather than hellish. There is little shrubby vegetation because not enough light reaches the ground for most kinds of plants. There are scattered tree seedlings, which have no chance to grow unless some accident opens up space. There are a few ferns, and sometimes dwarf palms, and occasional thickets of broad-leaved ariods and similar plants—the sorts of things that grow well in the dim light of apartment living rooms or hotel lobbies.

The Forest and the Sea

There are many interesting analogies between the biological structure of the forest and that of the sea—especially between tropical forests and tropical seas. Both environments have depth, and the conditions for life differ greatly from the surface to the bottom. The treetop canopy of the forest corresponds with the pelagic zone of the sea, the region of active photosynthesis where sunlight provides the energy to keep the whole complex biological community going. The forest floor corresponds with the benthos, where animals live on second-hand materials that drift down from above: on fallen leaves, fallen fruits, or roots and logs. In between, life tends to be distributed in horizontal layers related to the intensity of light.

To continue the analogy, green leaves form the plankton producer system of the forest, and the multitudinous insects that eat them are the key-industry animals, filling the role of the animal plankton in the sea. On these is based the network of higher-order consumers—the conspicuous larger animals that attract so much of our interest.

In the sea, the vertical gradation of the environment depends on the properties of water, especially its density; in the forest it depends on the arrangement of vegetation. In both cases, conditions near the bottom are most constant: there is least change in temperature; light, even at midday, is dim; and there is little movement of air or water. Temperatures near the ground in tropical forests change little from day to night or from season to season. At midday the air becomes warmer as one climbs, until the open sunlight above the canopy is reached, where light intensity increases five hundredfold or more. There is a gradient in humidity in the forest that has no counterpart in the sea: at the forest floor the air is nearly always saturated with moisture, becoming drier as one moves toward the top on a sunny day. The mass of vegetation, or the mass of open water, tends to have an insulating

The long arms and light body of the gibbon make him the outstanding trapeze artist of the Oriental forest.
(Ylla: Rapho-Guillumette)

Left: Although heavy-bodied, the African gorilla is a good climber.
(Weldon King)

effect, reducing all change. Of course the scale is different; to compare the gloomy depths of the forest with the gloomy depths of the sea is really farfetched, since in one case the scale is 150 feet or so, and in the other thousands of feet.

The point of view of man is quite different in the two environments; in the forest he walks on the bottom, whereas in the sea he floats on the surface. To explore a forest environment, he must climb; to explore the sea, he must dive. With the invention of scuba gear, diving—at least in relatively shallow water—has become much easier than climbing. It is too bad that we do not have some sort of a small balloon attachment so that it would be possible to float around among the treetops or just skim over the forest surface. As it is, we must always depend on the support of the trees; we can enter the world of fishes more easily than we can that of birds.

The problem of movement for animals is very different in the forest and the sea. In the sea, adaptations are for swimming and floating; in the forest, for climbing and flying. Flight is only partially comparable with swimming because it takes much more energy for an animal to support itself in air than in water. Seed, spores, and a few animals like spiders that cling to long threads of silk truly float in the air, but only for short periods. No animal can spend its entire life drifting in the air in the way that the plankton animals drift in water.

The problem of getting to the top in the forest involves the network of trees—of trunks, branches, twigs, and leaves. Animals have worked out a variety of ways of scrambling through this network. There are claws that can cling to the irregularities of bark or leaves; feet that can grasp branches or twigs, like the hands of monkeys and men; suction disks on the toes, as in some tree frogs; adhesive slime like that of snails; special organs like the prehensile tails of some reptiles and mammals. And then, of course, there are all sorts of adaptations for jumping, gliding, and flying.

Life in the Treetops

There are many more animals in the canopy than on the forest floor, though exact statistics are hard to come by. An ornithologist, Paul Slud, studying the habits of birds in a rain-forest region in Costa Rica, found that there were fourteen species that foraged mostly or entirely on the ground and six more that dropped to the ground regularly. But there were eighteen species living in the "understory" of shrubby growth, fifty-nine in the lower canopy, sixty-seven in the middle canopy, and sixty-nine in the upper canopy.

Perhaps it is not fair to use birds for such a comparison, since birds are so characteristically aerial or arboreal, but Slud's statistics do show strikingly that there is far more bird food high in the forest than near the ground. Even the mammals in a tropical forest are primarily arboreal. In British Guiana, for instance, thirty-one of the species of forest mammals live primarily in the trees while only twenty-three are mainly ground dwellers.

It would probably be safe to say that the most completely arboreal of mammals are the tree sloths of tropical America. There are two main types of these: one with two heavy, long, curved claws on the forelimbs, and the other with three. Both spend their lives hanging upside down from branches high in the forest canopy, moving slowly but securely through the treetops. They were given their English name of "sloth" because of the deliberateness of their movements, but the two-clawed type, at least, can lash out rapidly and powerfully with the forelimb if attacked. The sloths have a kind of alga that grows on their fur, giving them a greenish cast that helps concealment. (It is curious, incidentally, that mammals in general and tropical mammals in particular have failed to develop green colors, though there are many green birds, reptiles, amphibians, and insects in the forest canopy.) The larva of a species of moth lives on the sloth alga, resulting in a curious association of mammal, plant, and insect.

Tree sloths have no tails, but a number of the other arboreal mammals of tropical America, quite unrelated to each other, have developed prehensile tails which serve as a sort of extra limb for life in the treetops. The common opossum, which ranges far outside of the tropics to both the north and the south, has such a tail, as do its handsome tropical relatives, the four-eyed opossums and the wooly opossums. Two of the anteaters, the tamandua and the pygmy anteater, also have prehensile tails, which give them firm support while they pull apart tough ant and termite nests high in the forest. And there is a series of species of arboreal porcupines in the American rain forest with such tails. The kinkajous—distant relatives of the raccoons, but with a monkeylike appearance because of their flat faces and short, soft fur— have prehensile tails as well.

Then there are the monkeys themselves; it is not generally known that any monkey that can hang by its tail comes from tropical America, though not all of the American monkeys are so equipped. It is curious that mammals with prehensile tails should be characteristic only of the American rain forest and that such an organ should have failed to develop in forest mammals of the Old World (except for a very few species in Australia and New Guinea). There are lizards and snakes with prehensile tails in both hemispheres, but not mammals. I suspect that the great Amazonian forest has a very long and continuous geological history in comparison with the forests of the Old World tropics, and that during this time animals were able to evolve more highly specialized adaptations for forest life than in other parts of the world. But this would be difficult to prove.

Elephants are at home in the forest as well as in more open country. (Ylla: Rapho-Guillumette)

There are more kinds of forest birds in tropical America than anywhere else in the world, but this may reflect the history of the South American continent in general rather than that of the forest in particular. South America is aptly called the "bird continent" by students of animal geography, and approximately fifteen hundred of the species found there belong to bird groups that are found only in America—hummingbirds, toucans, antbirds, ovenbirds, manakins, and the like. We are apt to think that Australia has the most peculiar fauna of any of the continents because of the marsupials, but in most groups of animals, South and Central America turn out to have as many odd types as Australia. This is because South America, through most of geological history, has been just as isolated as Australia is now; as geological time is reckoned, the land connection at Panama is recent.

Toucans are among the most curious of the treetop birds of the American forests because of their huge, gaudy bills; a toucan, glimpsed flying high in the canopy, seems to be absurdly trailing through the air after its own bill. Toucans are highly sociable, and this is true of many of the canopy birds, along with birds from lower in the forest. They sometimes move in bands composed of a number of different species: woodhewers, ant shrikes, ovenbirds, and flycatchers, for instance, may all travel together. Toucans are brightly colored, and this is also true of many of the canopy birds—and of canopy animals in general, for that matter. The butterflies

as well as the birds that live high in the trees tend to be much brighter than the species that live near the ground; even the mosquitoes of the canopy tend to have brilliant metallic colors.

The parrots and their relatives are forest-canopy birds in all parts of the world, though more species are found in New Guinea and Australia than elsewhere. Here again, bright colors and sociability seem to go with life in the treetops.

When we think of animals living high in the trees of tropical forests, however, our first image is likely to be not of birds, insects, or reptiles, but of monkeys.

Monkeys

Quite properly monkeys are associated with tropical forests. The primate order is overwhelmingly tropical, and it seems likely that this has been true also in the past. Man, to be sure, now lives all over the earth, but it is probable that he was tropical or subtropical in origin, and today his ability to withstand cold climates depends more on clothing, housing, and fire than on physiology. One monkey species gets as far north as Tokyo in Japan, and there are the "Barbary apes" around Gibraltar in Europe, but such exceptions only underline the rule.

It is puzzling that the primates should be so overwhelmingly tropical in distribution. The Japanese monkeys seem to thrive even in light snow; and some kinds of monkeys in captivity survive the winter easily enough in open cages—as do many tropical birds, for that matter. Perhaps the problem is food rather than temperature. Primates live mostly on insects, fruits, seeds, tubers, or in some cases leaves, and all of these things are hard to come by in winter. Monkeys cannot migrate, as birds do; they have not developed a means of hibernation; and except for man, no primate has developed the squirrel habit of storing food. Yet if animals like raccoons manage in the north, why not some primates?

Primates are classified into four groups, the prosimians, the New World monkeys, the Old World monkeys, and the great apes. The prosimians are a rather miscellaneous group of animals including the tree shrews of the Orient, the lemurs of Madagascar, the bush babies or galagos and the pottos of Africa, and the lorises or "slow lemurs" of tropical Asia. They are almost all forest animals, but they are generally nocturnal (except for many of the Madagascar lemurs), so that not much is known about their habits.

The monkeys of the New World and the Old World are quite different, even though they often have similar habits. None of the Old World species has a prehensile tail; on the other hand, none of the American species has the naked, bright-colored buttocks that are so conspicuous on some of the African and Indo-Malayan species. For the mammalogist, the important differences are in details of anatomy, especially of nostrils and teeth, which indicate that the two groups have had separate evolutionary histories for a long time.

The marmosets (Callithricidae) are grouped as a separate family from the other American monkeys (Cebidae). Marmosets are tiny animals of the deep forest (though one species is common around the Canal Zone in Panama) and little is known about their habits in the wild. They are sometimes kept as pets, and they are easier to have around a house than other monkeys because of their small size and timid natures. But any pet monkey is liable to be a nuisance.

Tropical rain forest
structure.

There are twelve genera of American cebid monkeys, and each is distinctive both in appearance and character. Capuchins—the monkeys of the organ grinders—are among the brightest of all animals. There is no good way of comparing the intelligence of, say, dolphins, elephants, chimpanzees, and capuchin monkeys; but they are all very bright; they learn quickly and remember well. Chimps and capuchins are less cooperative with men than dolphins and elephants are, but psychologists and animal-trainers have managed to teach all of them some astonishing tricks. Capuchins have been called "monkey mechanics" because of their ability to manipulate tools. They are at least as good at this as the apes; they are able, for instance, to reason well enough to use a wire hook to get a short T-stick to knock down a long T-stick with which, finally, they can reach a desired banana. They can even "make" tools; for example, they will roll a newspaper to enable them to rake in something they want but cannot otherwise reach.

Then there are the spider monkeys, whose only rivals as acrobats are the gibbons of the Malayan forests. Gibbons have no tails, but spider monkeys have a long, prehensile tail which serves them as a fifth hand. Despite their gentle nature, they are impossible to keep around the house because of their habit of regarding every piece of furniture as a possible trapeze. Other appealing primates are the charming saimiris or squirrel monkeys, each face freshly out of some inkpot, and *Aotus,* the owl or night monkeys, that spend the days sleeping in tree hollows and the nights roaming through the treetops.

The noisiest member of the animal kingdom is the howler monkey, *Alouatta.* The hyoid bone of its throat is enlarged into a boxlike resonator, and when one of them starts to roar the sound can be heard for miles. They regularly greet the dawn with noisy choruses, and in regions where they have not been hunted, their roars at any intruder can be terrifying. Where they have been shot at, however, they rapidly become shy and hard to see—as is true of all of these monkeys. Monkeys are able to get along in the forests much better than scientists, which makes the study of their habits difficult.

All of the New World monkeys are strictly arboreal, coming to the ground only rarely. Among the Old World monkeys, the baboons have taken to life on the ground and in open country. The macaques of the Asiatic tropics may also spend considerable time on the ground, so that they are not as sharply distinctive of the deep

forest as are the American monkeys. But the majority of monkey species, every-where, are characteristically inhabitants of the rain-forest canopy.

The great apes also are forest animals, but of the four kinds, only the Asiatic gibbons are truly arboreal. The African gorillas and chimpanzees and the East Indian orangutans are too heavy to be real acrobats, though they are all good climbers. For that matter, man himself is a pretty good climber, if he is brought up in an environment where climbing is important: the agility of a Micronesian youth shinnying up a coconut palm is astonishing.

There are many traces of arboreal background in our heritage. We—and the monkeys and apes—live in a world that is primarily visual. Eyesight is important to a climbing animal, especially depth perception if he is to leap from limb to limb—hence the placing of the eyes forward on the face to give binocular vision. Men, apes, and monkeys also have color vision, which they share with birds and at least some of the fishes. Other mammals, as far as we can tell, see only varying shades and intensities of light. Man's grasping hands with opposable thumbs are also left-overs from life in the treetops. Our feet, adapted for walking and running, are quite different from the feet of the great apes, which still can be used for holding onto things. But those manipulative human hands, now freed by the walking feet, are fundamental to the human condition—hands, and the brains to use them with.

Life on the Forest Floor

The floor of the rain forest is relatively open, carpeted with the richly variegated browns of many different kinds of fallen leaves, and sometimes brightly spotted with blue, red, or yellow flowers that have fallen from the unseen heights above. The carpeting is easily scuffed away to show the reddish lateritic soil characteristic of the equatorial regions. The processes of decay are rapid: bacteria and fungi flourish in the continuous warmth and moisture, so that there is no thick accumulation of leaf mold or humus like that of northern forests. Here among the leaves, under logs, and in the soil is a complex world of small animals—insects, mites, worms, spiders, and centipedes—living on the dead organic material or on each other, inconspicuously playing their basic roles in the maintenance of the forest economy.

There are larger animals, too, in the forest floor zone, but not many very sizable ones. Of the host of large African mammals, for instance, only the elephant, buffalo, okapi, wild hog, and leopard occur in the forest. In the American forest, only the tapir and jaguar could be called "large." The ground-dwelling mammals tend to be small, stealthy, and inconspicuous. The smallest of the hoofed mammals, for instance, is a tiny deer, *Tragulus*, of the Oriental forests, not much larger than a rabbit. There are dwarf forest antelopes in the Malayan and African forests, and dwarf deer in the American forest.

Characteristic mammals of this habitat are the various kinds of pigs of the Old World and the peccaries of the New. These are well equipped with snouts and tusks for rooting in the soil and debris of the forest floor, and their digestive tracts are able to cope with a wide variety of the animal and vegetable morsels to be found

A jaguar, the New World version of the leopard. (Tom Lark: Western Ways)

Rare and shy, the okapi of the Congo forest was not discovered until the turn of the century. (Weldon King)

there. American peccaries travel in bands, as do some of the African and Oriental pigs. The African bush pigs are particularly good at ploughing through the forest debris; it is said that numbers of them, working cooperatively, can push aside the largest of fallen logs to get at all of the food, from snakes to fungi, lurking there.

The American peccaries are anatomically different from the true pigs, but they fulfill the same role in the forest. There are two types, the white-lipped and the collared. Both travel in large bands, which gives them protection against possible predators. Because of its ferocity and intolerance, the white-lipped peccary is generally considered to be the most dangerous animal in the American forests. In a region where these beasts abound, it is always a good idea to have a tree picked out for possible climbing.

There are many ground-living rodents in the forest, but since they are largely nocturnal we know little about their habits. Some of them, like the agoutis of tropical America, are rabbit-sized, but most are much smaller. Among the diurnal mammals of the American forests, the coatimundis are conspicuous and particularly fascinating. They are expert climbers and spend much time foraging for fruits and insects in the canopy, but when alarmed they take to the ground. They are relatives of the raccoons, and though they poke their long, sensitive noses into everything, they make even more charming and intelligent pets. Coatis generally go in small bands and are quite capable of defending themselves; hunters dislike them, for instance, because they sometimes kill dogs that show too much interest in their activities.

Reptiles and Amphibians

Tropical forests and snakes go together in the minds of many people. Snakes are there, to be sure, but they are never conspicuous. One can pass many days in the forest without seeing a snake; and even expert herpetologists are never sure that they will be able to find any. Forest animals in general are good at concealment—except for those that advertise themselves safely in the treetops—and snakes in particular are apt to be colored in ways that blend marvelously with the environment. Many types of snakes have taken to the trees in the rain forest, some of them incredibly slender and agile.

The ground-dwelling species of snakes are mostly active only at night. The heavy-bodied vipers which live mostly on the forest floor are apt to be marked in bold, diagonal patterns of grays and browns that blend perfectly with the litter of leaves in which they live. They depend on this concealment for getting their food, lying in wait until some unwary beast has come within striking distance, whereupon swift death and a leisurely meal follow. Snakes that have to chase their food are less ponderously built.

The largest of the American vipers, and one of the most dangerous of poisonous snakes, is the bushmaster, said to reach a length of twelve feet. The fer-de-lance and its various relatives of the genus *Bothrops* are smaller but still terrifying inhabitants of the forest floor zone. There is a considerable variety of forest vipers in the Old World tropics. A few of the vipers in both hemispheres have taken to the trees; they remain unusually thick-bodied for tree snakes, but make up for this by developing prehensile tails. Most arboreal vipers are green—as are most tree snakes.

Right: These walking leaf insects from Borneo are difficult to distinguish from the leaves on which they sit. (Sven Gillsater)

Far right: The armor-plated pangolin, another of nature's surprises, lives mostly on ants. (Pierre Pfeffer)

There are many lizards in the forest, too, some scrabbling about among the litter of the floor but most of them highly adapted to arboreal life. Among these are the chameleons of tropical Africa and Madagascar (the lizard sometimes called "chameleon" in America is a different animal), known for their ability to change color. In these lizards the toes are greatly modified to form strong, clasping tongs capable of supporting the animal in apparently precarious perches, and the tails are highly prehensile. Chameleons and some of the arboreal lizards of the American forests stalk their prey with agonizingly slow-motion deliberateness; in the case of chameleons, the final capture is made with a lightning-like protrusion of the tremendously extensible tongue.

The warm, moist air of the tropical rain forest is an ideal environment for frogs and toads, and there are numerous species everywhere. Again the arboreal forms—the tree frogs—are the most striking. They are hardly ever seen by day, but the choruses of the males after sundown indicate their abundance, and they can be readily located at night by the brilliant shining of their eyes in the beam of a flashlight.

The greatest problem for a tree frog is water for the tadpole stage, and this problem has been solved in a variety of ways. Some of them climb down out of the trees to lay their eggs in water in the normal way. A few take advantage of the "treetop marshes" of the rain forest—the water in epiphytes and rot holes. Some lay their eggs in sacs on branches overhanging water, so that on hatching the tadpoles fall into their proper habitat. Others, however, have managed to skip the free-living tadpole stage entirely; metamorphosis takes place within the large, watery egg and the animal that hatches out is already a tiny frog. These eggs usually are deposited in some protected, moist spot among the trees, but in a few cases they are carried about by the adult frogs, glued to the back of the female.

Forest Insects

There are undoubtedly more kinds of insects in the rain forest than in any other type of habitat; they are incredibly abundant and varied, occupying every possible sort of niche. Statistics are difficult to get because the insect fauna of the forest is so incompletely known—a good collector will turn up new and undescribed species in the course of a day's work in any of the continental rain-forest areas. Some students estimate that only 10 per cent of the existing species have been named and described; whatever the figure, the task of classification still ahead is enormous. Mostly these undescribed species are small and obscure animals, not noticed by the usual visitor to the forest. New species of butterflies are rarely encountered, and groups prized by collectors or important in the welfare of man (like mosquitoes) are pretty well known. But the diversity remains overwhelming, and what is still unknown about rain-forest insects is far more impressive than what is known.

In the rain forest, as in the coral reef, animal coloration reaches its greatest development. The bright, contrasting colors are mostly flaunted by animals living high in the canopy, and one cannot help but wonder whether there is some relation between the gaudy butterflies and the clear light of the habitat. In the American rain forest, one sees the startling metallic blues of the huge Morpho butterflies, their wings flashing in the sun, tantalizingly out of reach for the collector below, who must resort to baits to attract them, or depend on his luck near forest margins, where the fauna of the treetops comes nearer the ground. In the East Indies and especially in New Guinea, there are the even more magnificent bird-wing butterflies, Ornithoptera. The numerous treetop butterflies of the Orient and Africa are only slightly less spectacular. In all of these cases the females are relatively plain and dowdy; the bright colors are obviously a sexual phenomenon.

The forest has its share of wasps—some species of considerable size—and they too are brightly colored. This serves to advertise their sting, to warn possible predators that they are not to be tampered with. It is interesting that the wasps are conspicuously colored, while the poisonous snakes have concealing coloration; the

Tropical Forests

37 Monkeys that can hang by the tail come only from tropical America; this *Cebus*, or capuchin, is the cleverest of the South and Central American monkeys. (Carl Rettenmeyer)

38 Left: A chimpanzee in the Congo forest. (George Holton)

39 Right: Like owls, the African bush baby or night ape (*Galago senegalensis*) has large, staring eyes and loves the night. (W. T. Miller)

40 Below: The coatimundi, a relative of the raccoon, is equally at home on the ground and in the trees of tropical American forests. (John H. Kaufmann)

41 Above: A three-toed sloth in Brazil, an archaic animal that has somehow survived in the modern world. (James R. Simon)

42 Right: A tree-living anteater uses his powerful claws and long snout on a termite nest in the Panamanian forest. (Carl Rettenmeyer)

43 Above: A tiger in India. Originally Siberian, tigers have spread far into the Oriental tropics. (Ylla: Rapho-Guillumette)

44 Right: The tayra, a member of the weasel family, preys on small animals in the tropical American rain forest. (John H. Kaufmann)

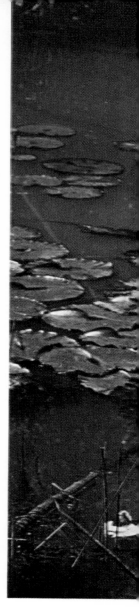

45 Facing page, above: The parasol ants of tropical America carry home fragments of leaves to mulch their fungus gardens. (Ross E. Hutchins)

46 Facing page, below: The Brazilian tree boa, like many snakes, takes to the trees in the tropics. (James R. Simon)

47 Above: A tapir in the Amazonian forest; these odd relatives of the elephant have survived only in tropical America and the East Indies. (James R. Simon)

48 Left: Although the iguanas of the tropical American forest look like miniature dragons, they are good to eat. (Paris Match: Photo Researchers)

difference lies in the fact that the wasps get their prey by force and agility, so that color does not matter in food-getting, while the snakes get theirs by lurking in concealment.

Many of the forest butterflies in both the Old World and the New have developed acrid body juices which give them a nasty flavor. This has been tested by feeding them to monkeys, birds, or other possible vertebrate predators; such butterflies are promptly rejected as food. These protected butterflies, like the wasps, are conspicuously colored—they advertise their inedibility. It is interesting that a good many other butterflies and some day-flying moths, without this protection, have come to copy the markings of a protected species, sometimes quite exactly. A variety of other insects—moths, flies, even bugs and beetles—have taken on the form, colors, and postures of the wasps. The similarity of these quite unrelated insects is sometimes startling, and even the experienced collector may be fooled.

In all of these cases, the insect protected by sting or bad taste is called the model, the insect imitating it, the mimic; and the phenomenon is termed mimicry. The mimic gains protection from predators, but at the cost of existing as a relatively rare species. If the mimic became abundant, the system would lose all meaning, since it depends on possible predators learning about the danger through experience with the model.

49 A squirrel cuckoo, inhabitant of the forest margin in Panama: like its smaller North American relatives, but unlike the European cuckoo, it builds its own nest. (John H. Kaufmann)

Mimicry can be regarded as a special case of concealing or protective coloration. We have noted how frequently forest vertebrates show this, but the most fantastic examples are to be found among the insects. Species of the floor zone take on the shapes and colors of dead leaves, and a gaudy butterfly flying through the forest may simply disappear when it alights, folds its wings, and shows its leaflike undersides. Beetles, bugs, and moths copy the patterns and form of bark and branches. The greatest extreme in detail of copying is reached by members of the order Orthoptera—crickets, katydids, walking sticks, and praying mantises—living in the canopy of the rain forest. They sometimes imitate not only the shape and venation of leaves, but even the details of fungus spots and frayed edges nibbled by some caterpillar.

No account can be written of animals in the tropical rain forest without some mention of ants. Of course these insects occur in every sort of habitat on land, but they reach their greatest profusion in number of species and individuals, and in variety of habits, in tropical forests. One can discount the hazards of the forest from poisonous snakes, leopards, jaguars, or even biting insects, but the ants are always there, some of them with stinging powers that make wasps seem relatively innocuous.

50 The Brazilian macaw, a member of the parrot family. (James R. Simon)

A great many ant species live entirely in the canopy of the forest. Some of them live in association with epiphytes like orchids and bromeliads, some nest in tree holes or other protected spots, and some build paper carton nests. A few species in both the Indo-Malayan and South American forests build nests by sewing leaves together, using their larvae to spin silk for this purpose, which is often cited as one of the cases of tool-using among animals. But there are a variety of special ant-and-plant relationships. In the American forest, trees of the genera *Cecropia* and *Triplaris* have hollow stems inhabited by special species of fiercely stinging ants; and a number of other trees and shrubs have hollow thorns in which ants live. Such trees often have glands at the bases of the leaves which secrete sap used by the ants as food; this is regarded as an example of symbiosis, in which the plants provide home and food for the ants and the ants in turn protect the plants from marauding animals.

The most notorious of the forest ants are the driver ants of Africa and the army ants of tropical America. These insects travel through the forest in bands that may include 100,000 or more individuals, foraging everywhere through the floor zone and lower canopy, killing and dissecting any animal life that cannot escape.

Among the most fascinating ants are the agricultural *Attas,* the leaf-cutting ants of tropical America. Long columns of these insects are often encountered in the forest, each homeward-bound worker carrying a large piece of green leaf or flower like an umbrella. The trails, protected by scurrying individuals of the soldier caste, lead to huge mounds where hundreds of thousands of ants live together in a complex, ramifying system of chambers and passages. The leaves are used to form a matrix on which is cultivated a species of fungus which serves as food. A special caste of tiny workers maintains these fungus gardens.

Termites as well as ants abound in the rain forest, playing a basic role in the decomposition of dead wood. But while termites are predominantly tropical, the species that live in open country are sometimes even more conspicuous than those of the forest, and for this reason termite habits will be discussed in the next chapter.

9

Open Country

Within the tropics, forest gives way to grassland in regions with less rainfall or where there is a long and pronounced dry season between the rains. Sometimes the division between forest and grass is sharply defined, with forests forming galleries along the watercourses in otherwise open country, or with systems of savannas or marshes breaking the solid cover of the interminable forest. In such cases, the sharp boundaries are apt to be determined by the limits to which the annual fires can burn: savanna people everywhere have the habit of firing grasslands regularly to foster fresh growth. More usually the division is not sharp. As the country becomes drier, it becomes more open; the trees become smaller and more scattered, and there are only a few species instead of many. Frequently the trees bear thorns, and in many parts of the world there is a special "thorn scrub" vegetation covering drier lands. Finally there are no trees, only a sea of grass stretching out to the horizon.

Grassland of course is not limited to the tropics. It covers a good part of the land area of the southern hemisphere—the pampas of Argentina, the veldt of South Africa, the great plains of Australia. To the north, there is a broad belt of grassland across Europe and Asia and central and western North America.

The varied character of these open landscapes is reflected in the list of words we use for them: prairie, steppe, veldt, savanna, pampas, campos, llanos. This is partly a matter of different languages in different regions; but the words have been taken into English because this open country does vary in appearance and in fauna in different parts of the world. "Prairie" in general implies tall grass, "steppe" short grass, and "savanna" the tropical grasslands that so often alternate with forested country—though attempts to give precise meanings to the various words have not been generally successful. All of these landscapes have one thing in common: they are dominated by members of that curious family of plants, the grasses.

Grass and Grazing

The grasses make up one of the largest families of plants, with something like ten thousand described species. The daisy family (Compositae) has more species, as does the orchid family, but while there are more kinds of composites or orchids, these families include far fewer individual plants growing around the world. The grasses are the commonest of seed plants by a wide margin; and they are also the most widely distributed, being found in every sort of situation from arctic regions to tropics, from marshes to deserts, and from lowlands to high mountains.

The grass way of life, then, is eminently successful. Grasses seem, furthermore, to be specially adapted to being eaten by animals. In perennial grasses, the stem (rhizome) is usually underground or closely pressed to the ground surface, and the leaves can be eaten without serious damage to the plant itself. Even where there are no underground runners, the leaves can be cut without killing the plant—as anyone who mows a lawn knows.

Grasses and grazing animals appear at about the same time in the geological record, and they have been getting along together ever since. There is a positive advantage for the grasses that are grazed: other types of plants are stunted or killed by being chopped off, leaving the grasses in full possession. Where shrubs or young trees manage to become established and to shade the ground, the grasses tend to give way. There is, of course, a point of overgrazing; but as far as we know, such cases have always involved human interference in one way or another. Without man around, the balance of nature—grass, herbivores, carnivores—seems to work nicely.

The bulk of vegetation per acre or per square mile of grassland is obviously far less than the bulk for a similar area of forest; yet one gets the impression that there is a greater mass of animal life in a given area of grassland than of forest. There is nothing in the forest that corresponds with the great herds of grazing animals on the African plains, or the uncounted millions of bison that once roamed the North American prairies. If one could collect and weigh all of the insects and other invertebrates in a given area of forest, they would surely add up to a considerable mass, but the grasslands also teem with insects. Moreover, in the forest there is never anything comparable with the great swarms of locusts that sometimes develop in open country. In ecological terms, it looks as though the first-order consumers live nearer to the limit set by the producing system in grassland than in any other type of land community.

The Problem of Eating Leaves

These first-order consumers, numerous though they are as individuals, represent a small part of the great range of animal diversity. It is remarkable, when you come to think of it, how few kinds of animals can digest leaves: some of the mollusks (such as snails), various orders of insects, and the grazing mammals. There are odd cases where certain species have found some way of living on leaves: certain turtles and land crabs; among the mammals, pandas eat bamboo, koala bears eat eucalyptus, and sloths in the tropical American forests browse on the foliage. But these are the exceptions. Many kinds of animals eat other vegetable products—fruits, seeds, tubers, nectar, and the like—but not leaves.

The difficulty with eating leaves is the cellulose of the cell walls. To digest them, an animal must either have an enzyme in the digestive juices capable of breaking down cellulose or have a symbiotic relationship with cellulose-digesting microorganisms, or have some method of reducing the leaves to a fine pulp. Most herbivorous animals combine at least two of these methods. The grazing mammals, for instance, have teeth built for grinding and also have cellulose-digesting organisms in their stomachs or intestines. In the ruminants, like cattle, the chewed-up leaves go through a fermentation process in the "first stomach," and the whole sequence of digestion becomes quite complicated. In the horse family, much of the digestion

In open country, giraffes can browse on trees and shrubs that are out of reach of other animals. (Weldon King)

is carried out by bacteria in the intestines. In the hippopotamus and in grazing kangaroos, special pockets in the stomach hold cellulose-digesting organisms. The digestive tract of herbivores is in general longer than that of animals living on other sorts of diets; and rabbits and hares increase this effect by eating their own feces and thus running vegetable food through their digestive systems twice.

Even with these special adaptations, herbivores must spend most of their time eating; they have to consume a great bulk of vegetation per individual to get needed food elements. The digestive problems of a carnivore are much simpler, but the carnivore has to face the special difficulty of catching his food. Grass may be hard to digest, but at least it doesn't run away. The problem for a herbivore is not to find food but to avoid becoming food for the second-order consumers.

Life in Open Country

In open country there is no place to hide unless you are very small: the adaptations of animals that live in the open thus tend to be different from those of forest dwellers. One possible way of hiding is to burrow, and we find the burrowing habit well developed in various kinds of grassland animals in different parts of the world. Keen eyesight is useful, and again animals in the open tend to depend on vision more than do those of the forest. Sheer toughness and bulk can be protective, as is shown by elephants and rhinoceroses. Speed in open plains is important for both pursuer and pursued; it is significant that the fastest land animals live in open country. Togetherness gains a special value in the open; many eyes are better than one, and there is safety in numbers. Herding characterizes grassland animals everywhere.

There are various combinations of these possibilities. The tough and ill-tempered rhinoceros is solitary, and has poor eyesight as well but he manages to get along. Elephants, though tough enough, are also gregarious. Many of the burrowing rodents, like the "prairie dogs" (really ground squirrels) of the North American plains and the viscachas of the Argentine pampas, are social. Gazelles, antelopes, and the like combine sociability with fleetness.

Sheer toughness and bulk, as in elephants and rhinos can be a protection in open country. (George Holton)

It is an interesting example of parallel development that three quite different types of birds—the rheas of South America, the ostriches of Africa, and the emus of Australia—have developed large size, high running speed, and flightlessness in the tropical and southern grasslands of the three continents. All three birds are powerful animals, quite capable of defending themselves from attack, and all three are to some extent gregarious or at least polygamous. The ostriches frequently herd with the grazing mammals, like zebras and wildebeests. There is a mutual advantage: the ostriches, with their keen vision and seven-foot stretch, are helpful sentries; and the mammals, trampling through the grass, flush out tasty small animals to add to the ostrich diet.

Social Behavior in Animals

Social behavior is particularly striking among animals living in the open, but it is by no means limited to such habitats. In the forest social monkeys, flocking birds, and mammals like peccaries and coatis herd together. And the similar phenomenon of schooling among fishes has already been discussed. As for social insects, there are more kinds in the forest than in the open, if only because there are more kinds of insects of all sorts. Even so, in tropical savanna country termites and ants make an impressive showing: their societies often seem bigger and more complex than those of forest species.

When examining the different kinds of relations that exist among individuals of the same species, we find a wide variety of patterns, and come face to face with the nice question of which to call "social." This has a special significance because man is so social, and we cannot but wonder about the animal origins of his sociability.

With any sexually reproducing animal, there are three different categories of individuals within the species—males, females, and young. This allows for six possible major classes of relations—male-female, female-young, young-young, female-female, male-male, and male-young. Except in the case of animals like oysters,

where eggs and sperm are simply released into the water, reproduction always involves some sort of male-female relationship. Interaction between individuals of the two sexes may be limited to the act of fertilization, or there may be a longer association involving courtship, or the relationship may persist through raising the young, or in some cases it may last for life. The differences among species in this regard are interesting from many points of view, but they are better regarded as degrees of family rather than social cohesion.

With birds and mammals, female-young relations are universal, except for a few birds like the phalaropes, where the female has managed to leave all family responsibility to the male. It is interesting that there is no known case among mammals where the female has managed to avoid nursing the young: physiologically, one can imagine that in some instance the male might have developed functional mammary glands and been left with the young by the absconding female. It is no more absurd, after all, than the male sea horse with his brood pouch. But it has not happened, except that the modern human male sometimes comes close, with bottles and diapers. Parent-young relations, however, are still at a family rather than a social level.

Where more than one young is born at a time in birds and mammals, there are always young-young relations. Where births (or egg clutches) are single, one juvenile may still be with the family when the next appears; at least, this happens with gibbon families. With warm-blooded animals, then, we are still dealing with usual, with normal or ordinary, relationships. But persistence of family relations with amphibia, reptiles, fishes, or invertebrates is exceptional, and perhaps because of this the behavior of such animals may be classed as social.

Where the family group consists of a single adult male with two or more females, there are inevitably female-female interactions. Is such a polygamous grouping a society? It is the sort shown by many grazing animals—parrot fish in the sea as well as herbivores on prairies. With grazing fishes, the young do not stay with the herd, but they must with herding mammals. In the grasslands females (and young) sometimes herd together for at least part of the year, with the males either herding separately or becoming solitary.

All of these groupings that are larger than or different from the simple nuclear family are probably best classed as "social." The most complex cases are those in which several males, along with females and young, herd together. Here all of the possible classes of cooperative interaction within the species must occur—we are dealing not with a nuclear family but with a nuclear society. Of the open-country animals with this sort of pattern, baboons have received the most attention—though our knowledge of them is still woefully inadequate.

Baboons

Baboons have a special interest because they are primates, and we are always curious about our relatives. But baboons also have a particular relevance to our attempts to understand our own prehuman background because of the presumption that our ancestors started on the road toward humanness when they came out of the forest into open country. Except for the baboons, the living monkeys and apes are mainly forest animals. In baboons, perhaps, we can see something of ourselves.

The most widely quoted studies of baboon behavior were made many years ago on a "monkey island" in the London Zoo. The animals in a sense were "free," but their range of movement was still extremely limited, and the group was abnormal in having many more males than females. From the London studies, it was concluded that baboons were preoccupied with sex; that they were extremely jealous of sexual prerogatives, the males ready to fight to the death over a female. They seemed almost equally preoccupied with status, with who could lord it over whom. This fitted nicely with some of the more dismal psychological theories of human behavior. But it always seemed to me that trying to understand baboons from their actions in the London Zoo would be like trying to understand people by watching what happened after a few females had been turned loose in a model prison. The results might be interesting, but they would not help much in understanding life outside the prison.

Studies of baboons in the wild have been curiously neglected, considering their possible psychological interest. A South African naturalist, Eugene Marais, spent many years watching baboons, but he published in Africaans, and even though his book *My Friends the Baboons* was translated into English in 1940, it has never received much attention. Recently two American anthropologists, S. L. Washburn and Irven DeVore, carefully observed baboons in the African park reserves. It turns out, understandably, that baboon life in the African wild is very different from that in the London Zoo.

Plumed in the middle but bare at both ends, the ostrich is a ridiculous sight prancing across the plains. (Ylla: Rapho-Guillumette)

Right: The emu of Australia (shown here), the rhea of South America, and the ostrich of Africa offer striking parallels in their flightlessness, large size, and high running speed. (Sven Gillsater)

Baboons live in troupes that may include as few as ten or as many as two hundred or more individuals. Each band ranges over a fairly definite territory of several square miles, and different troupes do not often come in contact with each other. Washburn saw no signs of a troupe defending its territory against intrusion by neighboring bands, and there was often considerable overlap in the range areas of different bands. The baboons thus differed from the howler monkeys observed by Carpenter in the Panama forest, which defended the boundaries of their territories by roaring at neighboring bands when they came into view. On one occasion Washburn saw more than four hundred baboons around a water hole at the same time—members of three troupes that had come together. There was no intermingling, but no fighting either, though smaller bands tended to give way to larger ones.

Within a given troupe there was a definite dominance hierarchy (or "pecking order") among the males, subordinate individuals giving way to dominant ones. This status was presumably established by fighting, but fighting or bickering was not often observed. When it did break out among younger animals, the dominant males would move in to put a stop to it. Interestingly enough, fighting over females in heat was never observed, and the dominant males showed no sexual jealousy. In fact, the females tended to go first to the subordinate males to mate, only later to the dominant ones. As with the monkeys that Carpenter observed in Panama, initiative in sex seemed to lie entirely with the females. The dominant males were, however, groomed much more often. The baboons spent a great deal of time grooming each other. In part this is simply friendly interaction, but it does serve to keep their fur remarkably clean in tick-infested country. Individuals formed small friendship groups within the troupe, but neither individuals nor groups ever strayed away from the main band.

Baboons are primarily vegetarian, eating many kinds of fruits, buds, plant shoots, and grass. They also eat insects, eggs, and bird fledglings when they can find them, and occasionally they kill and eat the very young of other mammals. The baboon troupes sometimes associate with herds of grazing animals, especially the impalla antelopes. There is a mutual advantage here, because the keen noses of the impalla and the keen eyesight of the baboons complement each other in detecting possible danger.

The baboon troupe is an effective organization for defense; the adult males, working together, can discourage any attack except from the biggest cats. When a lion appears, the baboons immediately take to the nearest trees, barking fiercely enough once they are safe but making no attempt at defense on the ground. Night is the dangerous time for animals that depend on eyesight, and as dark approaches, baboons climb into the trees to sleep.

The success of the baboon way of life is clearly due to the close and cooperative social organization. The South African farmers regard these animals as first-class pests; but the baboons manage to hold their own even against this opposition. They occupy a secure and conspicuous niche in the complex fauna of the great stretches of open country in Africa.

Herding, as in these zebras in Kenya, characterizes grassland animals everywhere. (Weldon King)

The Herbivore Complex

The grasslands of Africa support a fantastically varied and numerous fauna of herbivores. It is curious that the open country of no other continent supports so

The baboons are primates that have taken successfully to life on the ground in open country. (Sherwood L. Washburn)

many species, at least of mammals. The great plains of North America were grazed by vast hordes of bison, but they and the pronghorns had this niche to themselves. The tropical savannas of South America have an even more limited fauna, with deer the sole native grazers; the pampas, farther south, have only the camel-like guanacos. In the immediate past, the grasslands of Europe and Asia supported a more varied fauna of horses, cattle, and antelopes; and Australia has a number of kinds of grazing kangaroos. But these are still hardly comparable with the African situation.

The varied African herbivores, however, are by no means all in direct competition with one another; they occupy a diversified set of niches in the open-country landscape. The giraffes, most obviously, are adapted to browsing low trees and shrubs, out of reach for the others. Elephants frequent both forest and less wooded country, and in moving between the two they serve as pathmakers for other species by breaking and uprooting trees and trampling vegetation. The hippopotamus also occupies a special niche, being always closely associated with water. These animals generally spend the day in rivers, pools, or lake margins, and come out at night to graze in nearby grasslands; during seasons of heavy rains, they may wander quite far from their usual aquatic haunts.

In general, grazing mammals show considerable differences in their preference

for wet or dry conditions. Within a given region, species tend to shift their pastures with the changing seasons, some avoiding marsh conditions, others preferring them. The ecological studies that are now being made in the African game reserves show a nice balance among these various animals in the utilization of the habitat, which accounts in part at least for the great numbers of herbivores that can be supported without apparent overgrazing. But the balance between the herbivores and the pastures depends also on the predators.

Open-Country Predators

The herbivores find safety in numbers; only a few, like the misanthropic rhino, walk by themselves. One would expect that social cooperation, or ganging up, would also be advantageous for the predators. A few, like the jackals and hyenas, do hunt in packs; and many members of the dog family in various parts of the world have developed a social way of life. Members of the cat family, on the other hand, are generally solitary; but lions have discovered the advantage of at least a certain amount of cooperation.

As all crossword-puzzle addicts know, a group of lions is called a "pride." It is generally presumed that prides constitute a family organization, an adult male with associated females and young. It is said, however, that sometimes larger groupings of thirty or so lions will hunt cooperatively, though it may be that such super-prides have little permanence. A large group of lions would make a powerful aggressive force; but such a group would also be faced with provisioning problems, since the animals would need a steady and considerable food supply. Perhaps the usual family-size pride is the most efficient unit.

Apparently the lion prides are strongly territorial, roaming over an area with a radius of six miles or so, and defending this territory against intrusion by neighboring prides. Lions are a major factor in preventing overpopulation in the herds of grazing mammals. And this thought always leads to the question of what controls the size of the lion populations. The answer may lie in territory and territorial squabbling. Territorial behavior, at least, seems to be important in limiting numbers in many animal species. But reports of lion behavior by different observers often conflict, and it is difficult to know what to believe.

Lions, tigers, and cheetahs, among the large cats, are chiefly open-country predators. The lions hunt in cooperative prides, tigers rely on ambush, and cheetahs on speed. Of other big cats, the Old World leopards (and the corresponding New World jaguars) and the panthers sometimes hunt in the open, but they are just as much at home in the forest.

One tends to think of the big cats as living on the larger grazing mammals, but they do not scorn smaller prey. The grasslands are home for a wide variety of small- to medium-sized rodents, and many kinds of amphibians and reptiles, as well as swarms of insects. This lesser prey is also food for lesser predators, especially hawks and snakes. Among these small herbivores, members of the grasshopper family are everywhere abundant, playing their part as key-industry animals in the economy.

Wildebeests resting on the open plains of Kenya. (Weldon King)

Locusts

Among the insects, grasshoppers go with grass, as the hoofed animals do among the mammals. They are characteristic animals of all sorts of open country—beaches, deserts, marshes, scrub, and grassland. Their mouth parts are beautifully adapted to grinding up tough leaves, their long hind legs give them a quick start in escaping danger, and they are small enough to depend on their coloration to hide them.

Ordinarily grasshoppers are solitary creatures, each individual going about his business of eating the foliage in his immediate vicinity. Some kinds of grasshoppers, however, occasionally undergo a complete change of character, becoming gregarious instead of solitary and migratory instead of stay-at-home. They form into vast swarms that darken the sky when they move, and they strip the earth of every green thing when they briefly settle down. The visit of a locust plague is truly a catastrophe. In the face of the unbelievable numbers of invaders, modern man with his poisons and flame throwers and helicopters and tractors seems just as helpless as primitive man frantically beating on drums.

There are several species of migratory locusts in the grasslands of the different continents, and in each case the swarming form is slightly different in color and in body proportions from otherwise similar solitary grasshoppers. For a long time the swarming and solitary forms were thought to be different species and were given different names. Then in 1921 the English entomologist B. P. Uvarov proposed the theory that these forms were simply different phases of the same species of animal. The theory has been fully confirmed by subsequent work, though it is still not completely understood how the phase transformation comes about.

The locust of the Bible is a species called the desert locust, *Schistocerca gregaria*. This occurs in Africa both north and south of the Sahara and across southern Asia into northwest India. Individuals of the solitary phase can be found almost everywhere in this region, ordinarily not causing any striking damage to crops or landscape. Then suddenly, at irregular and unpredictable intervals, vast hordes of the slightly darker and differently marked migratory phase move out of the wilderness to devastate the countryside. Sometimes they pause long enough to leave the ground packed with the pods of eggs that will carry the migration through another generation. Eventually the momentum of the swarm is lost. Sometimes the hordes head out to sea and end in a sort of mass suicide; sometimes they simply peter out, the offspring turning again into individualistic, stay-at-home, solitary grasshoppers.

In one sense the mechanics are simple enough. Whether an individual is solitary or migratory depends on how crowded the conditions are under which it grows up. If the young hoppers are crowded together, in the laboratory or out in the field, they become darker and more restless as they grow; they tend to seek the sun rather than the shade; and they respond to each other, becoming gregarious. These tendencies—and here is one of the mysteries—are transmitted to the next generation, which starts out in life darker and with gregarious tendencies. As population increases, gregariousness increases, until eventually the swarm is built up to pour irresistibly from its homeland into the outer world to eventual destruction.

It is thus clear that the locust plague is a consequence of overpopulation in the grasslands. But what leads to the overpopulation; what starts the sequence from solitary to migratory phase? It happens mostly in remote parts of the Sudan or Arabia or along the margins of the Sahara, with no scientists around to watch. Presumably it is related to climatic conditions—the result of a series of years particularly favorable for grasshopper multiplication. But from the meteorological reports, no one has been able to predict when a locust outbreak might start.

The desert locust has a relative, *Schistocerca paranensis,* which lives as a solitary grasshopper over most of tropical America and which, at irregular intervals, develops a destructive migratory phase in Mexico and Central America and, far to the south, in the pampas of Argentina. Other species of grasshoppers show similar periodic outbreaks in southern Russia and Siberia, in South Africa, and in Australia. In the past, a few grasshopper species in the great plains of North America sometimes formed locust plagues, but there have been no major outbreaks in recent years.

Why should so many kinds of grasshoppers, in different parts of the world, show this great change in behavior under overcrowded conditions? It is tempting to look at it as a sort of mass suicide, as "nature's way" of dealing with overpopulation. One always thinks of overcrowded man; will he develop some similar frenzy and solve his problems through blind mass suicide?

More likely the change in behavior of the grasshoppers in some way promotes the survival and dispersal of the species, with the occasional mass suicide an incidental accident. The locusts live under semiarid conditions, where the environment is never stable for long. The phase change provides a way in which the species can occasionally burst out of one kind of habitat into others, giving the animal two ways of life instead of leaving it chained to one. But this is only a guess.

Termites

Grasshoppers are almost as ubiquitous as grass, and, like grass, they are most obvious in open country. Termites, on the other hand, are primarily tropical

animals, and within the tropics they are found in almost every kind of situation. It is in tropical grasslands, however, that their nests often form a prominent part of the landscape. The earth-cemented termite mounds of the African veldt may be twelve feet in diameter at the base and twenty feet high—each mound a city with millions of bustling, soft-bodied, industrious inhabitants. Termite mounds in the savannas of tropical America, Asia, and Australia never get quite this big, but they may be conspicuous enough. It is curious that quite different termite species in different parts of the world should have developed similar mound-building habits. Presumably it is a response to the frequency with which grasslands are flooded, making underground nests impractical.

In Africa and Asia, but not in America or Australia, some of these termites live by cultivating fungus gardens within their mounds. The other species live on the general vegetable debris of the savannas; judging by their abundance, they must play an important though little-appreciated part in the grassland economy. The mounds are toughly constructed of earth cemented with special secretions, and they may be very hard to break open. Yet a number of quite different animals, like the giant anteater of America, the aardvark of Africa, and the pangolins of Africa and Asia, specialize in tearing open termite nests and eating the inhabitants. One of the Australian parrots digs into termite mounds to make its nests, and in Africa there are species of toads that live in the termitaria.

Termites are "social insects." Yet in terms of our analysis of social behavior, the huge termite colony is really a gigantic family, its members all offspring of the "queen" and "king," better called "primary reproductives." This, of course, is also true of the various social ants, bees, and wasps, which makes the basic structure of an insect society quite different from that of larger-than-family groups among the vertebrates. Among the social ants and bees, the worker castes are composed of sterile adult females. In the termites, the soldiers and workers include individuals of both sexes but with full sexual development suppressed. Essentially, the worker termite castes are composed of perpetual adolescents, which has led someone to remark that termite society is based on child labor. (The work of the ant colony, using this analogy, could be said to be carried out by old-maid sisters.)

The complex termitaria, with their elaborate superstructures and extensive underground passages, provide more than a refuge for their inhabitants from the danger of floods: they serve as a protection against that other hazard of the grasslands—fire.

Fire

There is much discussion among ecologists about the role of fire in maintaining grasslands. In most parts of the world the savannas and prairies are fired regularly by local people during dry seasons, both to herd game and to provide cattle with fresh pasture from the newly sprouting grasses. The human practice of setting fire to grasslands is undoubtedly ancient, and certainly important in maintaining and extending present landscapes. The discussion turns largely on the possible importance of fire in the geological past, before human activities became a special influence on nature.

The growth habit of grasses makes them resistant to destruction by burning, just as it makes them able to withstand grazing, and the trees and shrubs that now grow in open country are also fire-resistant species. In many parts of the world, it appears that the grasslands would gradually change to some other, more stable type of vegetation, if they could be protected from fire and from heavy grazing. Yet clearly vast prairies must have existed on earth for a very long time, in order to allow for the evolution of the host of grass-associated mammals. If fire is a necessary factor in maintaining grasslands, then "natural" fires must have a long history.

There is remarkably little direct evidence about the frequency with which fires may be started by lightning in different parts of the world. One of the best studies has been made in Everglades National Park in Florida; in this case it seems clear that fires do result from lightning, and that they have been a basic factor in determining the vegetation (and the fauna) quite apart from possible human action. If this is true for the Everglades, it may well be true for other grassland areas also. But fire by itself cannot make lasting grassland in a geological sense: it must be fire in an appropriate climate, which brings up the problem of water.

Water

As we have noted, open country is generally characterized by lower rainfall than neighboring forested regions. In tropical grassland regions, there is generally a sharp contrast between rainy and dry seasons, so that the land often alternates between being flooded and parched. As a consequence of this, water is always an

Open Country

51 The onetime lords of the western plains—
bison. (Andreas Feininger: *Life*)

52 Above: These topi in Nairobi Park, Kenya, are a kind of antelope. (George Holton)

53 Left: Rhinoceroses in Ngorongoro Crater, Tanganyika. (George Holton)

54 Right: The bored kings—lions in Tanganyika. (George Holton: Photo Researchers)

55 Below: But zebras, being lion food, can't afford to relax. (George Holton)

Right: Lions are an important factor in keeping down overpopulation in herds of grazing mammals. (Weldon King)

56 Left: In Africa, nature makes strange mixtures—elephants and pelicans, forest, grassland, and marsh. (Emil Schulthess)

important factor in the ecology of open-country animals—sometimes because there is so little, sometimes because there is so much.

The various kinds of grasses are adapted to a wide variety of drainage situations. There are species that grow on land that is always flooded as, for example, the grasses of permanent marshes, whether fresh water or salt. Then there are species that are adapted to the various possible alternations of dry and wet conditions; and species that grow in upland savannas, where the ground is always dry.

The animals run a parallel gamut, from the hippos to the upland antelope. Especially in Africa many of the mammals migrate with the changing seasons, staying with wet conditions or with dry as the case may be. In the dry savannas, water holes become important as a focus for animal life for miles around; and here elephants inadvertently play an important role because of their habit of digging "wells" in dry stream courses. Sometimes the rains fail, and drought strikes the grasslands with disastrous consequences for the fauna.

Among open-country animals we begin to find special adaptations to conserve water. Many kinds, especially insects, pass the dry season in a state in which normal life processes are suspended, comparable to the way in which animals in high latitudes pass the unfavorable winter: in the one case estivating, in the other hibernating. When the rains come, frogs and toads suddenly appear everywhere, noisily rejoicing as they come out of estivation and feeding on the swarms of insects that also suddenly appear. But some of the grassland toads have managed to dispense with water entirely, passing their whole lives underground and going through the tadpole stage in large and specially provisioned eggs.

As we shall see, in regions of lower rainfall, the conditions of life become more special and more difficult, and in the desert water becomes the paramount problem for all forms of life.

IO

Deserts

The desert has a great fascination for many people, including naturalists. For the latter the attraction may in part be the relative simplicity of its organization—in which respect the desert is like the subarctic. The observer is not overwhelmed by the number of species or of individuals: he can see particular things and recognize them. He can guess at many of the adaptations, whether they be to the rigors of the environment or among the various animals and plants. In the desert man has some hope of understanding what is going on, as compared with his groping in the bewildering complexity of the rain forest or the coral reef—though this complexity has an equally powerful, if different, appeal.

The fascination of the desert has another side. It is one landscape that man has not yet dominated and altered. To be sure, large desert areas have been irrigated and planted and this has been going on since the days of Babylon and before. But even larger areas are still untouched, still innocent of axe and plough. The peninsula of Lower California today fits the descriptions of the first Europeans who saw it; man has tried to impose himself on it, but so far without much success. The visitor from cities finds a new, strange, and often exhilarating perspective in the vast desert areas. Here is sun and sand and thorny scrub; life that is fierce, perhaps, but natural. There are other kinds of wilderness, but they are more remote, more difficult to get into. Perhaps none will last, but we can savor them now and hope, in the case of the desert, that harnessed solar energy and desalted sea water will leave some room for dunes and desert foxes and jumping mice.

A desert, in its original sense, is a place where no one can live—no people, that is. In this sense, Antarctica is a desert as well as the Sahara. But as the word is generally used, it means a place where life is limited by the scarcity of water, by dryness rather than by coldness. This still leaves the problem of distinguishing between desert and not-desert, which involves quibbling about a definition that perhaps can never be settled to the satisfaction of everyone.

An easy definition is to describe as desert any region with an average of less than ten inches of annual rainfall. A slightly different approach is to say that where evaporation exceeds rainfall, desert conditions prevail. From another point of view, one can look at deserts as blind alleys in the network of water circulation of the earth, regions in which no streams arise to contribute to the reservoir of the sea. A few rivers, like the Nile in Africa and the Colorado in North America, flow through deserts on their way to the ocean; but they lose water rather than gain it during the desert passage. Sometimes the desert blind alley in water transport takes the

Swift terns lay their eggs on the desert sands of Juraid Island off Saudi Arabia. (Arabian American Oil Company)

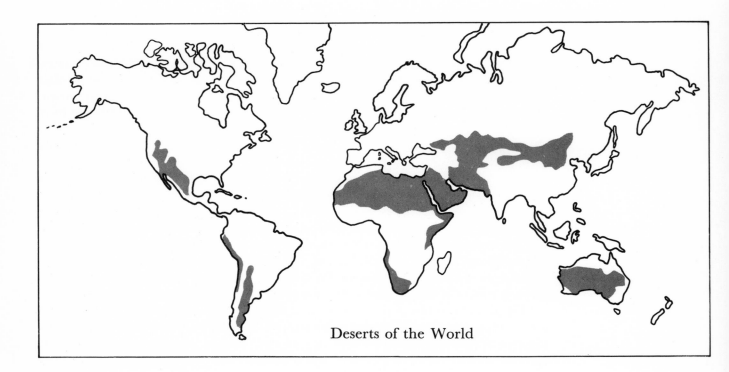

Deserts of the World

form of a lake, salty because it has no outlet, such as the Great Salt Lake of Utah.

It is impossible to draw a line and say there is desert on this side, and semi-desert, scrub, or some other landscape type on the other; yet there is a general agreement about the major desert areas of the planet. For the most part they lie near the lines of the tropics in both the northern and southern hemispheres. In the northern hemisphere, there are the deserts of the southwestern United States and northern Mexico, lying just above the tropic; in Africa, the Sahara; farther east, the Arabian Desert, straddling the line of the tropic; still farther east, the great Asiatic deserts with most of their area quite far north of the Tropic of Cancer. In the southern hemisphere, the large desert region of Australia is crossed by the Tropic of Capricorn, as is the Atacama-Peruvian desert of South America and the Kalahari Desert of South Africa.

The relation of the deserts to the lines of the tropics is due to the general pattern of wind circulation of the atmosphere, which results in descending and drying air masses in the region called the "horse latitudes." The details of the continents and seas, of course, greatly modify the pattern of air circulation and consequently of climates: the Rocky Mountains, the Andes, the Himalayas all play a role in determining the shape and extent of the desert areas.

Desert Vegetation

A botanist is apt to think of a desert as a region where the vegetation is widely scattered, not forming a general covering for the soil as it does in grasslands, and one where highly specialized plants are able to grow under dry conditions. There are, of course, considerable areas of desert with no plants at all, as in the case of

Right: The sacred scarab, here shown in Kenya scrub country, buries its ball of dung to provide a nest and food for its larvae. (Arthur Christiansen)

Far right: Small desert animals, like this tarantula of the southwestern United States, can meet the problem of scorching midday temperatures by burrowing or by hiding under rocks. (Mervin W. Larson)

the unending sands of the Libyan Desert. But complete deserts are far from necessarily sandy. The Eastern Desert of Egypt is rocky and mountainous—a spectacular exhibit of naked geology—as is the Painted Desert of the western United States. But completely lifeless areas are a rather small part of the regions of the globe that are ordinarily called "desert." For the most part there is some rain, however irregular and slight, and some plants can grow. Where there are plants, animals too have found a means of withstanding the rigors of the environment.

Desert plants have to have some special way of dealing with the water problem; if water is available in any normal or regular way, we do not have a desert situation. Botanists class plants in three general groups in this regard, according to whether they are drought-escaping, drought-evading, or drought-resisting. The plants that "escape" are the ones that grow very fast, that spring up after the occasional rains, bloom, and then disappear until rain comes again. Those that "evade" have some way of closing up shop between rains, of persisting through unfavorable periods, as the deciduous trees of a northern forest pass the winter by shedding their leaves. Those that "resist" must have special means of collecting or storing water, as well as some way of cutting down ordinary water loss through evaporation.

The drought-resisting plants are apt to be the weird-looking ones like cacti that are so often associated with desert landscapes. The cactus family is native only on the two American continents and neighboring islands, though in modern times various species have been planted—and have gone wild—in many of the warm, dry

The spines of cactuses protect not only the plants, but also animals, such as this roadrunner, that nest among them. (Mervin W. Larson)

regions of the Old World. The cacti have no functioning leaves; photosynthesis is carried out by the swollen, water-storing stems, and the leaves have been reduced to spines. Quite unrelated plants of the spurge family (Euphorbiaceae) have developed a very similar structure and appearance in the South African deserts, in adaptation to dry conditions.

Thick, spongy stems have been developed by many different desert plants as a method of conserving water, and this contributes to their odd appearance. Oddest of all is the boojum of Lower California (properly called *Idria columnaris*) which has been described as "like an upside-down carrot improbably provided with slender, spiny and usually leafless branches which seem to be stuck helter-skelter into the tapering, carroty body." Joseph Wood Krutch, who has spent a great deal of time tracking down boojums through the deserts of the Lower California peninsula, considers the carrot analogy too mild. "They often," he points out, "branch in an absent-minded manner towards the upper end, and sometimes, as though embarrassed by their inordinate length, curve downward until the tip touches the earth and thus become what is perhaps the only tree which makes a twenty-foot-high arch like a gateway into a wizard's garden."

It is difficult to write about the desert without getting involved with the plants, which are often so peculiar. But our concern is with the animal world, in which plants are simply something to eat or to hide in. Desert animals are rarely quite as bizarre in appearance as many of the plants, but they are interesting and they face many special problems.

Because of the heat of day, the desert comes to life at night, as shown by this bobcat in Arizona. (Bob Clemenz)

Animal Life in Deserts

The desert during the day is a world of bright, clear skies and hot sun, with the temperature dropping rapidly as night sets in. To be sure, the skies over the deserts of coastal Peru are often overcast with fog because the air has been chilled by the cold Humboldt current, but no rain falls from this fog. And the Gobi Desert of Asia, stretching farther north than any of the others, can be bleak and cold all day. But in most deserts, day is hot and bright, night cold, and the difference in temperature may be as much as 60 degrees or 70 degrees F. The problems of desert animals, then, include temperature extremes as well as water scarcity.

A surprising number of different creatures have managed to meet these rigorous conditions. It would hardly be correct to say that any desert "teems" with life, though desert enthusiasts sometimes sound that way. But wherever plants have managed to grow, some animals have found a way of living—often a considerable variety of animals. Dung beetles have even been reported in connection with camel droppings far out in the Sahara, distant from any plant, and with the dung supply uncertain and irregular.

Desert animals tend to be small. We associate camels with the desert, but this is a special case. When camels are found in country without any available water, there are always men along too, and both camels and men are on their way to some place where there is water. Lions, too, are sometimes called desert animals, but again this raises the question of how "desert" is to be defined. No desert, by any ordinary biological definition, would have enough prey to support an animal as big as a lion. The various desert foxes are about the biggest predators in the truly desert areas of the world.

Characteristic desert animals are rodents of various sorts, a number of birds with special habits, snakes and lizards, and of course insects and such relatives as centipedes, spiders, and scorpions. All of these animals are apt to meet the problem of scorching midday temperatures either by burrowing or using someone else's burrow, or by hiding under stones and rocks—another reason why any very large animal would find desert life inconvenient. In general, animals meet the problem of temperature extremes by regulating the timing of their activities, and desert life tends to be night life. Since sound becomes more important than vision with nocturnal animals, many desert inhabitants like the jack rabbits and kit foxes of the American southwest have big ears.

The water problem is something else. In many desert areas, the air is so dry that there is rarely or never dew, despite the cool nights, so that there is not even this possible source of free water. Animals that live on fleshy plants get water enough for their needs from the plant juices. Predators get their water from the blood and meat of their prey. In both cases, the animals have to be very economical in their use of water to get along without drinking, but they do get along. Most puzzling are the rodents and insects that live on completely dry materials like seeds, and that yet manage without drinking. They have as much water in their blood and tissues as other animals that are able to drink freely. How do they do it? The studies of physiologists are beginning to give us at least some of the answers.

The Remarkable Kangaroo Rats

The most detailed studies of water economy have been made on the kangaroo rats (*Dipodomys*) of Mexico and the southwestern United States. These animals are true rodents, but their tiny forelimbs and greatly developed hind legs give them much the look of miniature kangaroos. They are another instance of the frequency with which quite different animals in open country have developed adaptations for jumping or leaping, from grasshoppers to kangaroos themselves. Various rodents in the desert regions of the world have this kangaroo look, like the jerboas and gerbils of Africa and Asia. Some of the native desert mice of Australia have acquired this form, as well as some of the small desert marsupials.

The American kangaroo rats are found in the semiarid grasslands as well as in more truly desert country. They live in small colonies that dig extensive burrows marked by low mounds, often with a number of surprisingly large entrance holes. The theory is that the big holes allow the rats to make for the safety of home at high speeds, without having to pause to squeeze in. Once inside, they are fairly safe because the burrows are intricate, with many different chambers for nests and for storing food and with complex tunnel systems in between.

In the laboratory, kangaroo rats have been kept for months on a diet of dry barley or rolled oats, without any water whatsoever, yet they have remained perfectly healthy. The obvious answer is that these rats must somehow "manufacture" their water out of their food; they must live on what is called "metabolic water." The trouble with this answer is that there is no evidence that kangaroo rats are any better at manufacturing water than any other mammal. When food such as starch is "burned" (oxidized) in the body to produce energy, some water is always formed as a chemical by-product. This is also true of our own metabolism.

Deserts

57 Vultures sunning themselves on cordon cactus in the Sonoran Desert, Mexico. (Mervin W. Larson)

58–59 Above: Camels making their
way over the Sahara Desert. (Emil
Schulthess)

60 Right: Although coral snakes are
usually nocturnal, this one emerges in
the morning. (Mervin W. Larson)

61 Far right: The kangaroo rat, like
some other desert animals, has met the
water problem by making do with less.
(Willis Peterson)

62 Above: A Gila monster, one of the poisonous creatures of the desert. (Willis Peterson)

63 Left: A collared lizard in southeastern Arizona. (Willis Peterson)

Knut Schmidt-Nielsen, a physiologist working at Duke University, has been particularly interested in this matter. He calculates that a man doing a moderate amount of light work and living on an average diet of 2800 calories per day manufactures about 340 grams of this "oxidation water" daily—something like half a pint. This is far from sufficient for a human being, losing water by evaporation from his lungs every time he breathes, needing water to control his body temperature through sweating, and using water to carry away the waste products concentrated in his kidneys and large intestine. Ordinarily our kidneys alone use at least three times as much water as could be produced by the oxidation of our food every day; for this reason we have to drink. The kangaroo rat, and other desert animals, have met the water problem by cutting down on use and loss.

Kangaroo rats have no sweat glands. They spend the day in their cool burrows and come out only at night, so that they never have to use water to control their body temperature. Inevitably, they do lose water by evaporation when they breathe, and this is their greatest loss. Their faces are very dry, and, most remarkably, their urine is extremely concentrated. Its salt concentration is nearly four times that normal for man and twice that of ordinary rats. It is twice as salty as the oceans, which led Schmidt-Nielsen to suspect that they could drink sea water without danger. He succeeded in making some of his laboratory animals very thirsty by feeding them soybeans (the high protein content of the beans caused large amounts of urea to be formed, thus requiring extra water for excretion), and sure enough they were able to meet this water need with sea water!

The kangaroo rat, then, meets the water problems of desert life chiefly through the unusual way in which its kidneys function. This is probably the way marine mammals like whales, dolphins, and manatees get along without fresh water. Probably it is also important for sea birds, though some of these have special glands for secreting salt. There is still much to be learned about the water and salt problems of all of these animals.

Of all animals with the ability to go without water for long periods, camels are the best-known example. The stories about these animals are various and conflicting. Schmidt-Nielsen, fresh from his kangaroo rat experiments, decided that someone ought to get some facts and measurements about camels, and he went to North Africa to study camels.

Camels

As everyone knows, there are two living species of camels: the larger, one-humped dromedary of North Africa and Arabia; and the two-humped, hairier Bactrian camel of central Asia. These are geographically widely separated from their nearest relatives, the llamas of South America. Many kinds of fossil animals of the camel type, however, are known from Europe and North America, showing that at one time they were a common and widely distributed group of grazing animals. Our present camels and llamas, then, are relics surviving from the geological past. Why they survived, or why all of the others became extinct, is anyone's guess.

One can argue as to whether any of the present-day camels are truly wild. Or on the contrary, one can maintain that no camels are truly domesticated. The latter line of reasoning, used by many people experienced with camels, is that camels are simply stupid enough to allow men to use them—up to certain limits. The stories of camel stupidity and obstinacy are endless enough, and maybe it was this low I. Q. that led to their extinction in all parts of the world where no one bothered to look after them. There are, to be sure, herds of two-humped Bactrian camels wandering over the plains of central Asia, but these wild animals look no different from those raised by men, and the two interbreed freely. In the case of the African dromedaries, any apparently wild animals are supposed simply to have wandered off from some camp or caravan.

Stupid or not, camels have been very useful to the peoples of the Old World desert areas, carrying considerable loads for days across waterless terrain. How large a load they can carry, and how many days they can go without water, depend on who is telling the story—and probably also on the camel and on the weather conditions. Camel facts are scarce, which is what led Knut Schmidt-Nielsen to study their physiology.

Schmidt-Nielsen found that in the cool winter months in North Africa, grazing camels were not watered at all; they got all of the water they needed from the plants they ate. He decided to see what would happen if a camel were put on a very dry diet; for this purpose he tried thoroughly dried dates stuffed with peanuts. Camels, it developed, do not take to new food easily, but he finally got one animal to eat this diet, until the oasis where he was conducting the experiment ran out of peanuts. It turned out that in cool weather a camel could go for several weeks without drinking even on this dry food, but it steadily lost weight. Camels, Schmidt-Nielsen discovered, could lose up to 25 per cent of their body weight without apparent ill effect. When offered water, however, they would rapidly drink enough to bring their weight back to normal: one animal drank twenty-seven gallons of water in ten minutes.

The water is not stored in any particular place—not in the hump, which is pure

fat, nor in the stomach, though this always has digestive juices. Like the kangaroo rat, the camel manages by being very economical in its use of water. The urine is highly concentrated, and sweating is greatly reduced. Camels meet the sweat problem by not trying to maintain a steady body temperature. On a warm day, body temperature will rise up to 105 degrees F. before sweating starts; during the cold night, body temperature drops, so that it may be as low as 93 degrees F. at dawn, which gives the animal a head start in meeting the heat problems of the day. Body temperature fluctuations, however, are much smaller in the case of animals with free access to water. The camel's hairy coat also serves as insulation against the heat of the day, an animal that was shaved produced 60 per cent more sweat to control body temperature than animals with normal protective hair covering.

Donkeys are also fairly successful animals in dry country, and Schmidt-Nielsen decided to compare them with camels. He found that under similar conditions, a camel could go for seventeen days without drinking, a donkey for only four days. The donkey maintained a much more constant body temperature and had to use sweat for this. Both could lose up to 25 per cent of the body weight, but the donkey could get it back much faster by drinking—in two minutes instead of the camel's ten. It would take a man several hours to drink an amount of water equivalent to a quarter of his body weight.

Snakes and Lizards

Deserts and lizards somehow seem to go together. Lizards scamper over rocks or hot sands, finding their living in the most barren country if it is warm enough. Of course lizards are not particularly desert animals any more than are, say, rodents. They are found in a wide variety of habitats in the tropics and nearby regions, and there are fewer species in deserts than in forests. But in the desert lizards are at least conspicuous. For that matter, there is no large group of animals that is characteristically desert inhabitants, as one might say that cacti are characteristically desert plants. The desert fauna is made up of representatives of many animal types, species that somehow have managed to adapt to the special conditions of water scarcity, scattered plant cover, and temperature extremes. Many lizards meet these conditions nicely, as do many snakes.

The desert snakes are far less noticeable than the lizards, some of them because they hide by day and come out at night, like so much of the rest of the fauna. The snakes that are abroad during the day are well camouflaged, often lying partially buried in the sand. Snakes and lizards do not have acute water problems because, as predators, they get the blood of their prey—for the most part insects in the case of lizards and rodents in the case of snakes.

When frightened or attacked, this Arabian toad-headed agamid in Saudi Arabia can bury itself in the sand by vibrating its body. (Arabian American Oil Company)

Lizards and snakes are "cold-blooded" animals, which may seem to suggest that they have no control over body temperature. Desert lizards have been especially studied in this regard, and it turns out that they do regulate their body temperature to a considerable extent by their behavior. They expose themselves to the sun to warm up and retreat to shade or burrows when they get uncomfortably hot, thus maintaining a surprisingly steady internal temperature throughout their period of activity.

Quite different species of desert lizards in various parts of the world have devel-

175

Although not so good at economizing water as camels and kangaroo rats, these wild asses in the Sahara live quite successfully in dry country. (Emil Schulthess)

oped fringes of scales on their toes. These apparently help them in scampering across sand, as "snowshoes" do animals that live on snow. Various lizards and snakes have also developed the ability to burrow into sand with remarkable speed. The burrowing lizards tend to have reduced legs, and a number of skinks with this habit in different parts of the world have lost their legs entirely.

Lizards everywhere are apt to have a mythological look; perhaps they served as models for the dragons of folklore. At least this seems more likely than that any of the dinosaurs survived to enter into human tradition. Desert lizards on the average are probably no more fantastic than those of any other habitat, but there are some odd ones. Among these is the "horned toad" of the North American deserts.

There seems to be no particular explanation for the spined armor of this lizard: its skin is said to be quite sensitive to the bites of ants, for instance. In the similarly well-armored but unrelated girdle-tailed lizards of South Africa, the heavily spined tail makes a good defensive weapon.

Popular beliefs notwithstanding, the only poisonous lizards in the world are the Gila monster and its relative, the beaded lizard, of the North American deserts. But this does raise the question of whether there is any higher incidence of poisonous animals in the desert than in other types of habitat.

Poisonous Animals

One can say that desert plants tend to have acrid juices, thick, leathery leaves, spines, or some combination of these three protective devices. Perhaps this is a consequence of the physical environment, in which leaves tend to be reduced to spines or to become leathery to cut down evaporation, and in which there is not enough water for much sweet sap. Or maybe it has biological meaning in that the few plants able to grow have to have special devices to resist possible herbivores, though they all get eaten to some extent by some animals.

With animals, it would be difficult to say whether a higher proportion of desert species than of others have some poison apparatus for offense or defense. It is easy to be impressed by scorpions and Gila monsters. But poisonous snakes, for instance, occur in a great variety of environments, and include sea snakes, water moccasins, arboreal vipers, forest bushmasters and cobras, as well as desert species. It is probably sheer chance that the most powerful venom of all is that of a desert snake, the saw-scaled viper *(Echis carinatus)* of North Africa and southwest Asia. It is a small snake, at most two feet long, but highly nervous, quick, and aggressive, and it is treated with great caution by people within its area. Quite a few other Old World vipers live in arid or semiarid regions, and in the New World some of the rattlesnakes and coral snakes prefer dry country. But there are also many desert snakes that are not poisonous.

Scorpions and centipedes, including some big ones that can give powerful stings, turn up in deserts, but there are equally venomous species in rain forests. There are stinging ants, wasps, and bees in the desert, but some of the tropical forest species are even more venomous. There are so many more species in the forest, though, that it is not surprising that some of them achieve superlative force. Perhaps the most that can be said is that venom is no handicap in the desert and that in this harsh environment it possibly has somewhat unusual advantages for its possessors.

But let us turn from the deserts to the forests of the temperate zones. There bees and wasps and some of the snakes have venom; and during the winter the conditions of life may be as harsh as those in any desert. During the summer, however, moisture and temperature conditions are favorable, and a rich animal life has developed, capable of meeting these alternating seasons of heat and cold.

11

Forests of the
Temperate Zones

Since the days of the Greeks, geographers have divided the earth into the torrid, temperate, and frigid zones, according to the apparent movements of the sun. Within the torrid zone, the sun will be directly overhead at noon twice during the year (or once on the exact line of Capricorn or Cancer). Within the frigid zone, the sun will not appear at all on at least one day and will be above the horizon for twenty-four hours six months later. Length of day thus varies in regular fashion from the equator (where day and night are always twelve hours each) to the semi-annual twenty-four-hour day and twenty-four-hour night at the poles.

This variation in light has important effects on both animals and plants, but the related temperature differences are even more obvious and important. The Greeks' vocabulary, however, is not very apt. They may be forgiven "torrid" because they knew the tropics only where the line of Cancer crosses the Nile at Aswan, where it can be very hot. "Frigid" too is understandable, since the Greeks had only heard vague rumors of frozen Ultima Thule. And the land they knew around the Mediterranean could reasonably be called "temperate." We now commonly use more neutral words like "tropic" and "arctic" or "polar," instead of torrid and frigid, but we are still stuck with "temperate." It is obvious that a region in which you were liable to sunstroke in July and frostbite in January would be more appropriately called "intemperate," but the word has become a part of our vocabulary.

The regional temperature differences within the two temperate zones may be considerably modified by geographical features of the continents and oceans. The British Isles and Labrador lie in the same latitude, but their climates, vegetation, and animal life are quite different because of the Atlantic currents. The patterns of continents, oceans, and mountains result in rainfall as well as temperature differences, which are reflected in plant and animal life. The grasslands and deserts already discussed lie largely in the dry regions of the horse latitudes near the lines of the tropics. The remaining area of the temperate zones was originally largely covered with forests, but of many rather different types.

Most of the land of our planet is in the North Temperate Zone. There is more than six times as much land there as in the corresponding South Temperate Zone (twenty-seven million square miles as compared with four million). Furthermore, the northern land mass is continuous except for the narrow break at Bering Strait—which often has been dry land in the geological past—and the wider break of the north Atlantic. On the other hand, the land of the South Temperate Zone includes

Badgers, usually nocturnal, venture boldly out by day along a stream in Sweden. (Sven Gillsater)

parts of the widely separated continents of Australia, South America, and Africa. This difference gives the two temperate zones a quite different character, despite their similar seasonal changes in length of day and temperature.

The main vegetation type of the North Temperate Zone—at least before man started his drastic alterations—was a great forest of broad-leaved trees that spread across western and central Europe and, except for interruption by the grasslands of central Asia, continued in eastern Asia to Japan. The eastern half of North America was covered by a similar growth. Because most of the trees drop their leaves during the winter, this is generally known as the "temperate deciduous forest." To the north of this, across Scandinavia, Russia, Siberia, and Canada, stretch the great evergreen coniferous forests, which will be discussed in the next chapter.

In the region of the deciduous forest, there is rain all through the summer growing season. Around the Mediterranean the summer is generally quite dry, with most rain falling during the mild winter months, and this results in a rather different type of vegetation. This Mediterranean climate also characterizes California in North America, as well as part of the Chilean coast and southwest Australia in the southern hemisphere. These regions are sometimes grouped together as a single major "Mediterranean biome."

In the southern hemisphere there is no large area of vegetation comparable with the northern deciduous forest. In southeast Australia, Tasmania, New Zealand, southern Chile, and Tierra del Fuego, a heavy rainfall results in luxuriant forests which are sometimes classed as "temperate rain forests." The only similar areas in the northern hemisphere are around Puget Sound in the state of Washington, and in southern Japan.

Left: The opossum gets along well in the North American forest, making up in fertility for whatever it may lack in animal intelligence. (William Vandivert)

Bears, such as these in the Great Smoky Mountains, are common in the United States national parks. (Tennessee Conservation Department)

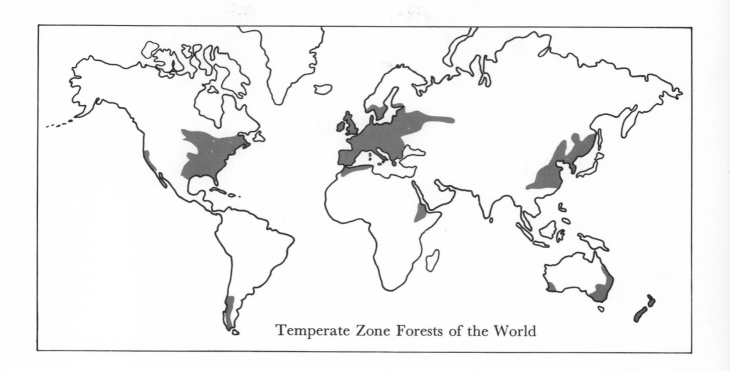

Temperate Zone Forests of the World

The Deciduous Forest

The primary landscape type of the North Temperate Zone is the deciduous forest, or at least it was until man began long ago to clear it away. Now the cities, villages, and fields of Japan, China, Europe, and the United States have replaced most of the forest, and it is difficult to imagine what it might have been like before man came, or rather before man became highly civilized. In Asia and Europe the forest, except for modified fragments, disappeared long ago. But in North America the early settlers and visitors found the forest pretty much intact, and they have left us descriptions of what they saw.

The forest was the enemy of the early settlers, and it was not always appreciated by visitors. Mrs. Frances Trollope (mother of the novelist Anthony) lived in the United States between 1827 and 1831 and wrote a book entitled *Domestic Manners of the Americans*. She was not impressed by the people or the landscape.

Walking out from the Tennessee town of Memphis into the surrounding forest, she noted that "the great height of the trees, the quantity of pendant vine branches that hang amongst them; and the variety of gay plumaged birds, particularly the small green parrot, made us feel we were in a new world." A few days later, staying at a little settlement in the woods, she reported that "I found no beauty in the scenery round Nashoba, nor can I conceive that it would possess any even in summer. The trees were so close to each other as not to permit the growth of underwood, the great ornament of the forest at New Orleans, and still less of our seeing any openings, where the varying effects of light and shade might atone for the absence of other objects."

Mrs. Trollope had some unpleasant experiences when she attempted picnic excursions into the forest near Cincinnati:

Left: Fauns are a sign of spring in the northern forest. (Leonard Lee Rue III: Annan Photo Features)

Right: Deer such as this European species are probably the best-known inhabitants of the forests in the temperate zones of the world. (Julius Behnke)

"Still we were determined to enjoy ourselves, and forward we went, crunching knee deep through aboriginal leaves, hoping to reach some spot less perfectly air-tight than our landing place. Wearied with the fruitless search, we decided on reposing awhile on the trunk of a fallen tree; being all considerably exhausted, the idea of sitting down on this tempting log was conceived and executed simultaneously by the whole party, and the whole party sunk together through its treacherous surface into a mass of rotten rubbish that had formed part of the pith and marrow of the eternal forest a hundred years before.

"We were by no means the only sufferers by the accident; frogs, lizards, locusts, katiedids, beetles, and hornets, had the whole of their various tenements disturbed, and testified their displeasure very naturally by annoying us as much as possible in return; we were bit, we were stung, we were scratched; and when, at last, we succeeded in raising ourselves from the venerable ruin, we presented as woeful a spectacle as can well be imagined."

Descriptions like these of the primeval North American forest in the summer often remind me of the undisturbed rain forest that can still be found in parts of the tropics. The thick canopy of tall trees, the heavy growth of vines, the dark gloom of the forest floor—free of underwood because of the heavy shade—all sound like the present Amazonian or Congo forest. But even aside from winter, the differences between the two forests are vast; even in summer the northern forest differed

greatly from that of the tropics. There were not very many species of trees in any given area of deciduous forest, and only a few kinds of vines—nothing like the variety of the tropics. Animal life was abundant enough even though not always obvious, but again there was nothing like the variety of the tropics.

Some of the animals of the deciduous forest have disappeared completely, like the small green parrot (the Carolina parakeet) noticed by Mrs. Trollope. Others, once common, have become rare. And many species that are now found commonly around clearings and woodlots were presumably much scarcer in the old days because suitable habitats were less common. The animals of eastern North America are chiefly species that have managed to survive the onslaught of civilization on the deciduous forest. This is equally true of the animals of Europe, Japan, and much of China.

Forest Mammals

In general, the animals of the deciduous forest are less strictly arboreal than those of the tropical rain forest. In the case of mammals, Ernest Thompson Seton considered that thirteen of the species of the eastern American forests were mainly arboreal, eighteen ground-living, whereas in tropical forests the majority of mammals are arboreal. This same general tendency toward more emphasis on ground living is true also of birds, reptiles, and insects. With its few species of trees, the temperate-zone forest offers less varied opportunities for life in the canopy; and in the winter, when the leaves have fallen, the treetops have few attractions.

Squirrels are the conspicuous arboreal mammals of the forest. There are tree squirrels in all of the forested areas of the northern continents, and something like two hundred species have been described, all of them looking much alike—sleek, alert, and bushy-tailed. Many of these tree squirrels are tropical, but in the tropics they never seem to form as conspicuous an element in the landscape as they do in the north; and some of the species of Europe and North America, at least, have succeeded very well in getting along with man. This was not due to human encouragement; the early settlers in America regarded the gray squirrel as a pest because of its habit of raiding fields and gardens, and the colonies paid considerable sums as bounties in an effort to kill it off. But squirrels are adaptable and breed fast, and they won out in the long run to gain toleration and even affection.

The squirrel habit of storing food is notorious, but there is disagreement among students of behavior about whether the animals remember where they have hidden food, or whether they locate these supplies again with their keen noses. If they depend on memory, it seems that they often forget, or perhaps they store more food than they need; as a result, their habit of carrying nuts and acorns around and burying them is an important factor in the dispersal and reproduction of forest trees. The American red squirrel is fond of mushrooms and stores quantities of these during the summer. The mushrooms are carefully dried by being laid out on branches high in the trees, and then are gathered to be put away in a dry place, whereas the same animal storing pine cones would pick a moist situation. But the squirrels don't have to learn which mushrooms are poisonous; they are immune even to the deadly amanitas, which they eat in some quantity.

Flying squirrels are also common inhabitants of the deciduous forest. Most species are Asiatic, but there is one genus in Europe and another in North America. "Gliding" would be a more appropriate adjective than "flying," since they depend on the parachute effect of large skin flaps stretched between the fore and hind limbs; but they are remarkably skillful in maneuvering in the air. They are quite common in some settled areas but are hardly noticed because they are nocturnal.

Some of the forest mammals are equally at home on the ground or in trees; this is the case with the opossums and raccoons. Like the squirrels, these animals have also adapted well to the human alteration of the landscape. Both are omnivorous and will eat almost anything, so that human garbage offers rich possibilities. By any method of testing animal intelligence, opossums turn out to be pretty stupid animals, but they make up for this by prolific breeding. Raccoons, on the other hand, show a great ability to learn and to modify their behavior, and this intelligence and adaptability have contributed to their survival. Both belong to groups that are typically South American. Outside of the Americas, the closest relatives of the opossums are the marsupials of Australia; and of the raccoons, the pandas of Asia.

Surely the bears are as bright as the raccoons, and the species in the deciduous forests are just as miscellaneous and adaptable in their food habits. But they are too big and too uncertain of temper to survive with civilization. The brown bear probably disappeared from the British islands in Roman times (the animals used for "bearbaiting" in Elizabethan days were imported from the continent). The few bears that still survive in Europe are limited to the wilder mountainous areas of Scandinavia, Spain, Italy, and the Balkans, though they are still fairly common in

The owl, here attacking a mouse, is typical of the night activity in a deciduous forest. (Hermann Schunemann: Annan Photo Features)

parts of Russia and Asia. The American black bear, once common everywhere, is holding its own in the mountain forests of the Appalachians and in various wildlife reserves. This bear nomenclature, incidentally, is confusing because "black bears" may be brown, and "brown bears" black; the words are used to distinguish two genera, *Ursus* and *Euarctos*. *Ursus,* the brown bear genus, is represented in America by the "grizzlies" of the northwest.

Different species of deer inhabit the forest in various parts of the world; and Virginia deer in the North American woods are probably more numerous now than they ever were. Once, however, there was a forest race of the bison in eastern North America, and wapiti (called elk in America; the animals that Europeans call elk become moose in America) formerly ranged all through the eastern forest.

The forest predators have been hardest hit by civilization. Only the foxes and some of the weasels are managing well. Wolves and cats, even the small bobtailed lynx, are either gone or rare in Europe and North America. The Asiatic tiger, it appears, is basically a deciduous forest predator that has extended its range into tropical open country, and it is still at home in many parts of Siberia.

Forest Birds

The woodpeckers are as conspicuous and distinctive among the forest birds as are the squirrels among the mammals, and like the squirrels, they are found through all of the Temperate-Zone forests. The large ivory-billed woodpecker of the southeastern United States has not been able to adapt to the increasingly limited and modified forests, nor has its relative, the pileated, but most woodpeckers seem to be doing quite well. Their feet are beautifully adapted for maintaining a firm grip on tree trunks, and most species have their bills and tongues constructed for getting at the insects that live in dead wood. They locate their prey, it seems, chiefly through their keen sense of hearing. Since the supply of wood-boring insects is pretty constant through the year, most woodpeckers, unlike many northern birds, do not migrate.

The turkeys that were once such a characteristic part of American forest animal life almost disappeared along with the original forest. They have, however, been able to adapt to life in the remnants of the Appalachian forest and in some Florida forests, and now seem to be in no immediate danger of extinction. The turkeys encountered by the first settlers were bold, curious, and easily shot; but their descendants somehow have learned better and have become extremely shy. Wild turkeys spend the night in trees, but they forage and nest on the ground. They are the most arboreal of the gallinaceous birds except for the curassows and their relatives of tropical America, some of which nest in trees. Most birds of this order are ground dwellers even when, like grouse and pheasant, they move into the forest.

Hawks and owls are among the lesser predators in deciduous forests everywhere, living on the numerous rodents and not disdaining insects. However, most of the birds that are now most abundant in Europe and eastern North America were probably less common when the land was covered by forest, since they prefer woodland margins and relatively open habitats. This is particularly true of the songbirds, though some of the thrushes are true forest dwellers.

Forest Insects

Like the birds, the common butterflies of our gardens and roadsides were probably much less common before man started his clearings. Butterfly-collecting in a European or North American forest is not a rewarding experience—at least in number of species likely to be caught. The rather small brown or gray wood nymphs (Satyridae) are common almost everywhere among the dead leaves and scattered grasses and herbs of the forest floor, and sometimes a bright blue Lycaenid will flash its wings in a thicket. There are a few striking species that may be glimpsed tantalizingly high in the trees, but nothing comparable with the bright life of the canopy of the tropical forest. Forest Lepidoptera in the north are predominantly nocturnal —moths in endless variety, mostly dull-colored to match tree trunks or dead leaves, but often with bright hind wings that are concealed while the moth is at rest. The big and quietly beautiful moths of the silk family (Saturnidae) are well represented in the North American forests—the green luna, the velvety cecropia, the elegant brown polyphemus, and the like. This family is very poorly represented in Europe, and over most of the world it is predominantly tropical.

Among the Orthoptera, the katydids and relatives with their long antennae are as characteristic of the forest as are the grasshoppers with their short antennae ("short horns") of the open country. The katydids and tree crickets are apt to have concealing coloration, matching the green leaves among which they live. As a group, they also go in for sound production, sometimes turning the forest into a

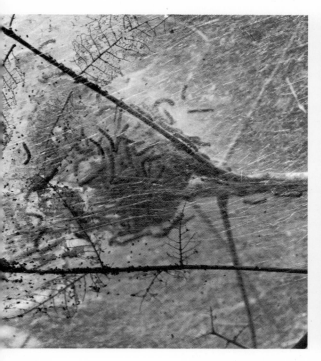

Webworms find protection in their nest, coming out to feed at night. (Andreas Feininger: *Life*)

Right: The Australian koala lives only in forests where it can feed on the leaves of certain species of eucalyptus. (Grant-Thomson: Annan Photo Features)

fairly noisy place toward evening and night. The unrelated forest cicadas also are great noisemakers, sometimes filling the forest with their loud, strident rasping toward the end of the summer.

The cicadas breed in the forest soil, which is home also for many other insects, especially larval forms. Many beetles and their larvae live in the soil or in the leaf litter, and beetles are by far the most numerous, though not the most conspicuous, of forest insects. Some of them live in bark, some bore into growing wood and others into dead wood; some are found in fruits, nuts, and seeds, others in mushrooms. Every conceivable forest niche seems to have been found and occupied by some species or other of beetle. Like the moths, they often hide during the day, going abroad only at night. Night life is a common characteristic of many of the inhabitants of the deciduous forest.

Night Life

The human animal is essentially a daytime creature, and night, for us, remains eerie and mysterious. For the most part we have to guess about the behavior of nocturnal animals, or judge indirectly by watching them in the laboratory or by trapping them in the forest. It has long been known that man can see farther into the red of the spectrum than can most animals, and red light has been used for studying nocturnal behavior in the laboratory. A few years ago, the British naturalist H. N. Southern wanted to study the feeding behavior of owls in the wild. He found that if he lit up the area around an owl's nest with his automobile headlights covered with red filters, the owls would go on about their ordinary business as though quite unaware of the illumination. Southern could hide quietly at a little distance and watch the birds comfortably with his binoculars. Wood mice, badgers, and foxes also seemed quite unaware of being in a red spotlight. Southern thus found a solution to the problem of animal-watching at night, which presently may enable us to learn a great deal more about the habits of some of our common neighbors.

Nocturnal activity seems to be especially developed in the very different environments of the desert and the forest. In the desert it is an avoidance of the unfavorable daytime temperatures. Perhaps in the forest the limited usefulness of daytime vision has led many animals to depend on other senses which function as well by night as by day. But of course there are many nocturnal animals in every kind of habitat. Taking the animal kingdom as a whole, it would be hard to tell whether there is more activity at night or by day. One is tempted to say that most animals are nocturnal. Among the Lepidoptera, for instance, there are about six hundred species of butterflies in North America, all with diurnal habits; but there are nine thousand or so species of moths in the same area, almost all of them nocturnal. Of course this is not a typical sample of insects, because most flies, bees, ants, wasps, and the like are diurnal.

In the case of mammals, there are more kinds out at night than during the day, chiefly because of the many species of nocturnal rodents and bats. Birds are mostly daytime animals, which gives owls an unusual prominence. Reptiles are probably about half and half, but amphibians—frogs and salamanders—are apt to be nocturnal.

Whatever the exact figures, there is plenty of activity in the animal world at night. The kinds of activity are no different from those that go on in the day: foraging for food, finding mates, raising families, or just playing. Animals that are active at night must find some place to hide during the day; but this is hardly different from the problem of diurnal animals, which must find some safe way of passing the night. In both cases, some species burrow into the ground, others construct nests, others hide in crevices of trees and rocks, and some just sleep wherever they can without taking any special precautions for safety. The difference between night and day is not a matter of kind of activity but of kind of sense perception—of how the animal finds its way around.

There is almost always some light, except underground, and one adaptation to night life is the development of eye structures capable of functioning in very dim light. Our own eyes are quite remarkable in this respect: with our iris fully expanded, we can make out objects in a dark forest where the light intensity is perhaps a billionth of the intensity of that on a bright beach. In dim light, only the rod cells of the retina function; since we see color with the cone cells, we are all color-blind in the dark. In animals with night-adapted eyes, the rod cells predominate.

Many nocturnal animals have developed a special glistening opaque layer in the eye called the tapetum, which underlies the retina and reflects light back through it for greater efficiency. Light reflected by this tapetum causes eyeshine—the bright glow of animal eyes seen in your car's headlights. The principle is the same as that of the reflectors placed on highway markers. Most nocturnal mammals show it, as do frogs and reptiles. The deep ruby eyeshine of a crocodile is unforgettable, and the eyes of spiders in the beam of a flashlight make glistening jewels scattered over the forest foliage.

But sight, understandably, is less necessary for most nocturnal animals than other senses. Sound takes on a new importance in the dark: think of all of the strident insects, the croaking frogs, the hooting owls, advertising their presence to

Temperate
Forests

64 Deciduous beech woods
in New Hampshire. (Eliot
Porter)

65 Left: A fawn of the white-tailed deer. (William Vandivert)

66 Above: Young bobcats on a ledge in the Adirondacks. (William Vandivert)

67 Right: A long-tailed deer mouse. (Jack Dermid)

68 Above: A Rocky Mountain orange-crowned warbler. (Eliot Porter)

69 Left: Raccoons are found only in the New World; their nearest relatives elsewhere are the Asiatic pandas. (Willis Peterson)

possible mates or warning trespassers off their territories. Owls have extremely sensitive ears and can pounce unerringly on a mouse that gives away its presence by incautious squeaks or rustlings. In the daytime, the swooping hawk depends on speed; there is no point in its trying to be inconspicuous or silent. But with owls, the feathers of the wings are arranged in such a way that the fatal plunge in the dark is completely soundless. The stealth of cats is another case of "adaptive silence" fitted to the night world where ears take over from eyes.

The ultimate in night dependence on sound is the echo-location system of bats. In flight, these animals constantly emit very-high-frequency squeaks—far above the sound range audible to us—and they guide themselves through black caves or dark forests by the echoes of these squeaks from surrounding objects. The echoes give the bat an extremely accurate picture of the environment, enabling it to fly swiftly and surely without recourse to either sight or smell, both of which are rather poorly developed in these animals. With this echo-location system, bats hunt the night-flying insects on which they live. If a pebble is tossed in front of a hunting bat, it will dive, but stop short of catching it, apparently because the echoes are not quite right.

Many moths have a highly developed tympanum or "ear." This is curious because moths are not known to use sound in any way in their ordinary lives. It has been suggested that this may be an adaptation to the bats, that with the tympanum moths can hear the noisy squeaks of approaching bats and get out of the way. It sounds farfetched, but so far no one has come up with a better explanation.

Moths and other insects, as well as many other kinds of animals, depend chiefly on smell to find their way around at night. This is a world that is closed to us, with our poor noses, and man has great difficulty in imagining what it may be like. What are the ecstasies that a dog, taken for a Sunday drive, finds in the wind? What is the shape of the odor trail left by a rabbit that passed by hours ago? The complex plumed antennae of a moth are organs for odor perception; they tell the moth the direction of the smell, the kind of object giving it off, and even perhaps some estimate of distance. We see the shapes, colors, and perspectives in a forest, but can hardly imagine these translated into a three-dimensional world of smells.

There is for each kind of animal a characteristic daily rhythm of activity, and both the sense organs and way of life of the species are fitted to this rhythm. The contrasts between day life and night life discussed above are oversimplifications. Some animals are most apt to be active at midday, others late in the afternoon and early in the morning, still others only at dawn and dusk. Similarly, nocturnal species may be abroad for only part of the night.

In addition to the daily rhythm, each species has an annual cycle of activity, especially in environments where there are strong seasonal contrasts. In the tropics, as we have seen, seasonal adaptations are apt to turn on the changing availability of water through the year. In the temperate zones, the overwhelming problem becomes that of surviving the winter.

Survival in the Winter

The problem of winter turns on the physical properties of water, which freezes at 32 degrees F. (0 degree C.). Protoplasm is an aqueous solution—that is, the chemistry of life depends on water in a liquid state—and if the water in the body of an animal freezes or forms ice crystals, the whole system is disrupted and the animal dies. But winter temperatures in the north and south drop below this freezing point and frequently stay below for long periods of time; so animals, in order to live, must have some way of keeping the water within their bodies from freezing. Different animals have found different ways of meeting this problem.

In the first place, there are great differences between "cold-blooded" and "warm-blooded" animals. Birds and mammals are called "warm-blooded" because they have developed a physiological means of keeping the temperature inside their bodies fairly constant, despite the normal temperature fluctuations of the outside world. Species differ considerably in the amount of variation that they can tolerate in body heat, as we saw in the comparison between camels and donkeys under desert conditions, but the problems of warm-blooded animals are quite different from those of cold-blooded kinds.

In the case of cold-blooded animals, there is generally some special stage in the life cycle adapted to the cold conditions of winter. This is especially striking in the insects, where the life history is in any event divided into a series of distinct stages. All insects grow by means of a series of moults of the skin; their skin is really an external skeleton, which does not itself grow but can only expand to the extent allowed by softer membranes between the hard plates. Periodically, then, the growing insect has to develop a new and larger armor.

In some instances, the insect that hatches from the egg changes gradually with succeeding moults to attain the size and form of the adult. Such insects are said to have an "incomplete metamorphosis." In other cases—the caterpillar and the butterfly, the maggot and the fly, the grub and the beetle—the organism that hatches from the egg is very different from the adult. In such cases all growth takes place in the larval stage, and there is a special resting stage, called the pupa, during which the body is completely reorganized to take on the adult form.

In general, cold-blooded animals cannot be active when temperatures fall below freezing. Therefore it is not surprising that with insects the winter is generally passed in one of the inactive stages—egg or pupa. In such a stage the protoplasm may have a greatly reduced water content, so that its freezing point is much lower than usual. Often, too, the egg and pupal stages are spent in the soil, where temperatures do not get as low as in the air above. Sometimes the hibernating pupal stage is given some sort of a special protection, like the cocoons of the silk moths. There are, however, insects that have developed ways of hibernating as larvae or as adults. In general, any insect or other invertebrate that inhabits regions where temperatures for part of the year are below freezing has developed some special way of passing the cold season in an inactive stage. Where winters are longer and colder, fewer species have developed such special adaptations, so that as one goes north from the tropics, the number of kinds of insects that are able to meet the conditions becomes smaller and smaller.

This is true also of the reptiles and amphibians. These too enter a special inactive hibernating state, which is frequently passed in the soil or in some other protected place where temperatures are less severe than in the open. Only the warm-blooded animals can be active when temperatures are below freezing.

Many mammals hibernate—but there is a delicate question of exactly what is meant by "hibernation." Biologists now generally agree that a mammal can be truly said to hibernate only if the body temperature drops greatly and the whole metabolism, including respiration and heart rate, is reduced. This is what happens with such small animals like woodchucks, hamsters, hedgehogs, and many bats. Bears are not considered to hibernate in the strictest sense of the word. They pass most of the winter sleeping, but their body temperature drops only a few degrees, and they can wake up without going through a slow process to do so. This was demonstrated by a physiologist who entered the den of a hibernating bear in Alaska and tried to take the animal's rectal temperature. The sleepy and grumbling bear obstinately sat on its tail, like a dog, frustrating the attempt. A woodchuck or dormouse in a hibernating state would be completely torpid and manageable. With bears, the young are born during hibernation, the animals depending on fat reserves to keep them going.

Migration

Many birds and some bats solve the seasonal problem by avoiding winter—by migrating. Their ease of movement through the air makes this possible; a bird can fly from Michigan to Florida or South America and back each year without much trouble, whereas for a land mammal such a journey would be out of the question. Many mammals make seasonal migrations, but over relatively short distances. Marine mammals and fishes often have migration patterns, possibly because swimming involves even less work than flying, though it is not so rapid. Bird migration is certainly understandable from a practical point of view, but in other ways it is one of the most remarkable phenomena in the animal kingdom. Though it has been the subject of many books and articles, it is full of mysteries.

Generally, birds that migrate breed in the warm season in the temperate zones and pass the rest of the year in or near the tropics. This habit must have some definite biological advantage. The majority of birds—something like 85 per cent of the species—are purely tropical. The ones that make the long migratory flight to breed thus escape competition within the overcrowded tropical environments. In the Temperate-Zone summer they find hordes of insects and large supplies of seeds and fruits—rich food stores for their growing families. As winter comes and food supplies fail, the birds move to warmer and more favorable regions. Apparently most birds could easily enough withstand winter temperatures if they could find sufficient food. Many birds have learned to remain near cities and suburbs where they are regularly fed, and caged tropical birds like parrots often seem better able to stand the cold than their owners.

Nevertheless, it is difficult to understand why some birds undertake the fantastic journeys that they do. The upland plover makes a nonstop flight from North America to winter in Argentina, Paraguay, and Bolivia; so does the Hudsonian godwit. Some sea birds make long migrations to winter at sea and to return to some particular island or bit of coast each year to nest. Each bird species has a characteristic route which is followed generation after generation, and we are still far from a clear understanding of how birds manage their often precise navigation.

One of the curious things is the way these birds, obviously capable of flying almost everywhere, return year after year to the same neighborhood to nest, sometimes to exactly the same tree or chimney or field. This is related to a rather general phenomenon of animal behavior: territory and home range.

Territory and Home Range

Most of our knowledge of animal behavior has been acquired by observation and study of the animals of the deciduous forest. This is natural enough, because most biologists live in the centers of Western civilization; and these are located in areas once covered by this forest, where fragments of the vegetation and representatives of the animal life remain. Our knowledge of territorial behavior, for instance, dates from studies which an English naturalist, Eliot Howard, made in his garden and orchard, and published in 1920 in a little book called *Territory in Bird Life*.

One can find all sorts of allusions to territorial behavior in older literature, but somehow the idea was never developed and did not really affect the thinking of biologists until Howard published his book. Now scientists notice territorial behavior in all sorts of animals in many kinds of environments; but it all started with British birds.

Howard observed that male birds were apt to turn up in his garden first, and that each picked some particular spot where day after day he proclaimed his presence with song. Other males of the same species that tried to establish themselves nearby were driven off. Presently the male would acquire a mate and the whole business of nesting and family raising would start, but any birds of the same species that still tried to intrude into an area around the nest were driven off. Howard

Below, left: The Atlantic golden plover is unusual in that it flies south in fall by one route but in spring returns by another. The Pacific golden plover flies from Alaska to the South Pacific and returns by the same route.

Below: The European stork, which breeds mostl in northern Europe and western Russia, migrates to Africa mainly through the Gulf of Suez or Spair

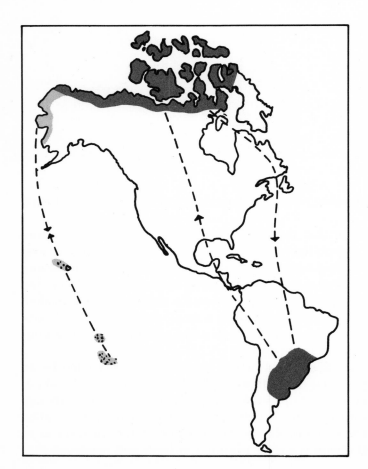

Many birds, such as these wild geese, solve the problem of winter by migrating. (Stan Wayman: Rapho-Guillumette)

made a map of his garden showing neatly the boundaries of the territories of each nesting pair.

Subsequent work has shown that there are many different kinds of territories among animals. Sometimes, as with the birds first observed by Howard, the territory covers the mating, nesting, and feeding ground. Sometimes no more than the mating and nesting area is defended against the intrusion, with many individuals sharing the feeding grounds; sometimes only the mating area or the nesting area is defended. To social birds like gulls that nest in large groups a small area around each nest may be reserved as a territory by each pair, though other activities are carried out in areas shared by all members of the colony.

Territory in animal life has thus come to mean an area that is defended by an individual, a pair, or a larger social group from any intrusion by other individuals of the same species. Often animals will stay for long periods in a limited area, though there is no evidence that the area is actively defended; in that case the area is called a "home range." The difference gains significance because of the question as to whether defense of a limited region is a strong instinct in birds and mammals that carries over into human behavior. Thus, as noted earlier, Carpenter found that his howler monkeys in Panama defended their territories against invasion by other howler groups; whereas Washburn, observing baboons in Africa, found that each group had a definite home range but did not actively defend against intrusion.

There is no question that a great many mammals have a definite home range within which they stay under ordinary circumstances. In studies with live traps, the same individual may be caught over and over again within a limited area, but the ranges of several individuals often overlap, without any evidence that there is conflict among them over space. In birds, active defense of at least the area around the nest is widespread, and similar behavior has been observed in at least some reptiles and fishes.

Since most birds are diurnal, their behavior is relatively easy to observe. It is much more difficult to know what goes on among nocturnal mammals. For that matter, it is hard to watch mammals that are active during the day, because they are apt to be shy and to be able to detect a hidden observer through their keen sense of smell.

Special Kinds of Forests

We have been writing about the temperate deciduous forest as though it were a rather uniform habitat. This, of course, is far from true. The species of trees making up the forest differ from region to region, and this inevitably affects the kinds of animals living in the forest. Climate varies, too, with consequences both for vegetation and animal life. One landscape type generally treated as a distinct unit by ecologists is the Mediterranean forest, which is developed in regions with winter rains and summer droughts—a kind of climate that characterizes not only the Mediterranean, but the California coast and parts of South Africa. The trees retain their leaves throughout the winter, when most growth occurs, and survive the dry summers because deep root systems reach underground water.

In a few places—particularly in New Zealand and in the United States around Puget Sound—heavy rainfall results in what has been called a Temperate-Zone rain forest.

The eucalyptus forests of Australia and the pine woods of the southern United States form two more landscapes that cover extensive areas and present special problems for their animal inhabitants. Insects in particular are often strictly limited by the range of the plant species on which they feed. Mammals, birds, and reptiles are less apt to be restricted to a single type of forest, though there are many exceptions. The Australian koala, prototype of the teddy bear, is one example—it feeds on the leaves of certain favored species of eucalyptus and lives only in the forests where those grow. This special diet presents zoo-keepers with difficulties in parts of the world where eucalyptus will not grow.

In many parts of the Temperate Zone there are forests of evergreen conifers, but the great coniferous forest extends across the northern part of the zone and is best treated in a separate chapter.

12

Taiga:
the North Woods

The geratest of the world's forests is the taiga of Siberia, the vast sea of fir and spruce that stretches interminably across Asia. Second only to this in area is the Canadian forest, the North American wilderness that remains hardly affected by man despite the insatiable demands for lumber and pulpwood, for furs, and for the "sport" of shooting its animal inhabitants.

The trees are conifers—fir, spruce, pine—which means that they are green all year round, with stiff needles instead of broad leaves. Willows and birches grow along the streams, and there are stands of poplars, usually marking a region where the forest has been burned in the recent past. But overwhelmingly the trees are evergreen, growing in dense stands with little undergrowth of shrubs and herbs. The ground is covered with a mat of slowly decaying needles which produce a special type of soil known by its Russian name of *podsol*. Lakes, ponds, and bogs are numerous in many regions, providing a variety of habitats.

The growth of trees northward is limited by the longer winters and by ever lower temperatures. Trees are smaller, stunted, and scattered, and as the conditions of life become more severe the taiga gradually gives way to the treeless expanse of tundra. To the south where summers become longer and warmer, the taiga blends with the hardwood deciduous forests; but the transition zones here have been greatly altered and blurred by the activities of civilized man. In mountainous regions, the conifers extend far south, making intrusions of taiga conditions into lower latitudes. These mountain habitats, however, have special characteristics and will be dealt with separately.

There is a gradual decrease in the variety of animal life northward from the deciduous forest through the taiga to the tundra. Yet life in the taiga is abundant and surprisingly varied. Birds, of course, can take advantage of the summer and avoid winter's harshness by migrating; therefore, the number of birds resident all year round decreases steadily northward. With mammals, the problem is similar to that which faces mammals farther south, except that winter is longer and colder. This is somewhat offset by the greater protection of the evergreen trees and the abundant food supply provided by coniferous seeds. Few reptiles and amphibians can adapt to the long winters, though some frogs get quite far north. Insects adapt better; there are far fewer species, but individuals may be incredibly abundant during their brief season, providing plenty of food for insectivorous animals.

The Problem of Snow

Animals of the taiga must adapt not only to the low temperatures of winter but also to the long period during which the ground is covered with snow. Of course, snow covering is not limited to the taiga; it occurs in the deciduous forests and grasslands to the south and in the tundra to the north. But snowfall is generally heavier in the taiga than in the drier tundra areas, and of course it forms an uninterrupted cover over the ground for a longer period than in the habitats to the south.

Some animals apparently cannot adapt to such conditions for any length of time, and this rather than temperature may limit their northward distribution. Opossums, pronghorn antelope, and wild turkeys are examples of this. Other animals, like shrews, foxes, and various kinds of deer, seem to tolerate snow easily, though without any strikingly unusual adaptations for life in snow.

Snow is an excellent insulator, and ground temperatures under its cover rarely drop below about 20 degrees F., even under Siberian or Alaskan conditions when air temperatures drop to 50 degrees below zero. A host of small rodents thus find snug conditions for passing the winter under the snow. They make runways and nests, and live on roots, buried vegetation, or stored seeds. It is a dark, silent world under the snow, and the inhabitants are even protected from many of their usual predators. But sometimes they have to construct ventilating shafts because of the accumulating carbon dioxide, and they may be seized by passing owls at the openings of these shafts.

Only larger animals are able to withstand the cold above the snow surface. Red squirrels remain active in the trees until temperatures drop to about 25 degrees F. below zero, when they take cover under the snow. Hares and ptarmigan in both the New and Old World taiga regions have developed large "snowshoe" feet that enable them to get about on the snow, much as some desert animals have developed large feet for locomotion on loose sand. The Siberian ptarmigan has feet three times as large as similar grassland species, and the American snowshoe hare has feet more than twice the size of those of a Kansas jack rabbit, which is a much bigger animal.

Stilts are an alternative to snowshoes, and the long legs of the moose are an example of this sort of "adaptation." But when the snow is more than three feet deep, even these long legs are useless, and moose have the habit of making winter "yards" where the snow is kept packed down. In the fall some caribou migrate from the tundra into the tree-covered taiga, where the snow is relatively soft, light, and thin, so that they can paw through it to get at food below. This discussion of the habits of caribou and moose raises general questions about the behavior of members of the antlered tribe.

A moose in the Canadian forest. Its long legs or "stilts" are helpful during the prolonged periods when snow covers the ground. (Canadian National Film Board)

The Antlered Tribe

Numerous species of the deer family are found on all of the continents except Australia and Africa south of the Sahara, and they have adapted to a wide variety of habitats, from tropical forests to arctic tundra. But nowadays they are most prominent in the taiga, chiefly because the big species have been able to survive man's depredations only in this wilderness. Moose, elk, and caribou are all animals that we associate with the north. Unfortunately, the names of these animals have

been given to different species in the New World and in Europe. For instance, the animal called "elk" in America is quite different from the one called by the same name in Europe, and each author finds a somewhat different solution for this vocabulary problem. Perhaps it would be easier and clearer to use the Latin generic names for all members of the deer family, and it would be useful to know the names before discussing the habits of the animals.

Cervus is the red deer of Europe, the elk of America. A subspecies in eastern Siberia is called the wapiti, and many authors use this name for the American animal as a way out of the elk dilemma. The extinct Irish deer with its fantastically developed antlers is sometimes classified as *Cervus* but is more often put in a separate genus, *Megaloceros.*

Dama is the fallow deer of Europe. Probably originally wild in the Mediterranean and Asia Minor, in Europe it has been maintained for centuries only in parks.

Elaphurus is the genus of Père David's deer, that odd animal that was saved from extinction in the last century by the Duke of Bedford, who surreptitiously built up a herd on his estate at Woburn Abbey. This deer has been described as looking like a shaggy ox with goat's ears, a stag's antlers, a donkey's tail, and reindeer's hooves. This animal was discovered in Peking by the French missionary priest Abbé Armand David in 1865, when he bribed Tartar guards to allow him to peer over the wall into the Emperor's park, where a herd had been kept for many centuries. The French government succeeded in persuading the Chinese government to give them some specimens, and presently other European governments secured specimens too. The Chinese herd disappeared at the time of the Boxer Rebellion, when European soldiers camped in the Emperor's park and according to conflicting accounts either ate the deer or sold them to the starving peasants. The animals in the European zoos presently died, and it was only then that the Duke of Bedford's thriving herd was discovered, since the Duke had been notably reticent about the animals he had acquired. The species now seems well established in several zoos.

This animal is remote from the taiga, since no one has ever seen a wild *Elaphurus,* and ideas about its original habitat are pure guesses. *Elaphurus* does demonstrate both the dangers facing wild deer species because of expanding civilization, and the ease with which some species can be "preserved."

Odocoileus is the genus of the common American deer: the white-tailed deer of the east and the mule deer of the west. These animals are not closely related to any of the Old World deer, though they are represented in South America by a number of different forms.

Alces is the genus of the elk of Europe—called "moose" in the New World. These are the largest of the surviving members of the deer family, though the extinct Irish *Cervus*-like species was even bigger. Both the European and American *Alces* species are taiga animals.

Rangifer includes reindeer and caribou. The American caribou come in a number of shapes and sizes, variously classified as species and races, and they once ranged rather far south—to Michigan, for instance. The European and Siberian reindeer are smaller, and have long lived in close association with man.

Capreolus (roe deer) is the genus of the common wild deer of Europe and temperate parts of Asia. It seems to be getting along well with man, as does the different *Odocoileus* of North America—though both species are protected by a variety of game laws and reserves.

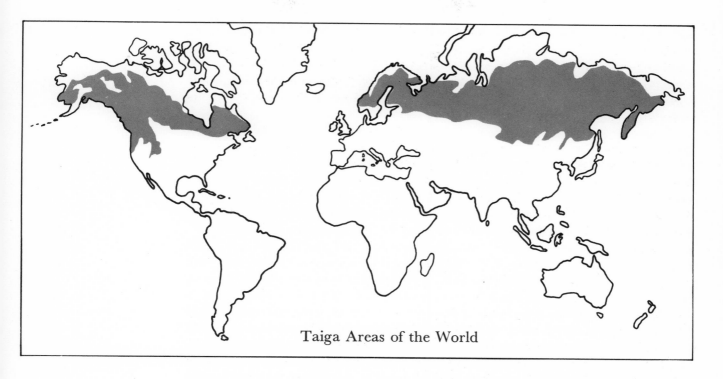

Taiga Areas of the World

These animals all have a curious anatomical feature in common: the males (and the females in the case of *Rangifer*) have deciduous antlers. Horns on the head, sometimes large and bizarre, occur in many groups of mammals and reptiles, and it is often difficult to explain their function, if any. In some instances the horns are clearly weapons, and, as with wild cattle, very effective in defense. When the horns are found only on males, as is so often the case, they are presumed to have some sexual function, either to impress the females or as a weapon among competing males. But the horns sometimes develop such odd shapes, as in some of the antelope, that they seem absurd as weapons. In many kinds of deer, the great, many-branched antlers would seem to be much less efficient weapons than the simple, sharp horns of cattle—as Charles Darwin long ago observed. Besides, why are they grown over and over again every year as they are in the deer family, at what must be some physiological cost to the animal?

Antlers reached the height of absurdity in the extinct Irish deer, in which they had a spread of as much as twelve feet. Perhaps the overdeveloped antlers were the direct cause of the animal's extinction, though it seems more likely that they survived well enough until the human species came along.

There are many accounts of fierce combat among males of various species of the deer family during mating season, and photographs have been taken of deer found dead with antlers interlocked. But the American naturalist Olaus Murie, one of the ablest observers of wildlife, thinks that actual combat may be rather rare; in his long observation of American "elk" *(Cervus)* he has never seen such a contest. The old bulls certainly spend a great deal of energy rounding up a herd of females and protecting them from the attention of rival males. But in all cases observed by Murie, intruding males retreated without actually putting up a fight. The antlers, then, may function for intimidation. But Murie also suspects—and this sounds reasonable—

that the old and large-antlered bulls are so preoccupied with status that the young bulls may really be responsible for most of the breeding through surreptitious copulation. If so, the big antlers would not be a genetic advantage. Murie has seen several cases in which cows were killed by being accidentally wounded by antlers, which again hardly sounds genetically advantageous. Altogether, antlers are an evolutionary puzzlement.

The social life of deer can be somewhat complicated, and it has been the subject of some careful studies, like Fraser Darling's *A Herd of Red Deer,* and Olaus Murie's *The Elk of North America.* In general, males and females are apt to lead segregated lives except during the breeding season, when single males try to round up private harems. From reports, it seems that the migrating herds of caribou and moose sometimes include animals of both sexes, but that occasionally the females with young move separately from the males.

Birds of the Taiga

Bird life in the taiga is surprisingly rich, at least during the summer months when the teeming insects serve as key-industry animals to support the consumer complex. There are not nearly as many different kinds of insects as in the hardwood forests to the south, but the bark beetles, caterpillars, flies, and the like may add up to just as great a bulk of food per acre. The birds don't care about variety; it is the quantity of food available for the growing young that counts. And the long days of the northern summer give the birds more time for hunting food.

Roger Tory Peterson, who probably knows more about American birds than anyone else, has remarked that at least half of the birds in the Canadian summer woods are warblers. "Warbler" is another of those English terms that have different meanings on the two sides of the Atlantic. In America it means birds of the family Parulidae, a purely New World group of about 125 species. Some dozens of species breed in the northern coniferous forests and migrate to the tropics for the winter. For this reason, bird watchers in thickly settled country may see them only twice a year, that is, in the course of the spring and fall movements, when identification of the various species presents a true test of expertness.

There is a general principle in biology that no two species can occupy the same ecological niche in a particular region; in other words, that two species in the same place cannot have identical habits, at least if both are to survive indefinitely. The presence of many warblers in the north woods would seem to challenge this principle, but studies have shown that the various species do have distinctive habits. Some forage only among litter on the ground, others in low shrubby growth, still others high in the trees, so that each exploits the insects in a slightly different habitat.

The New World warblers for the most part have rather weak and uninteresting songs, while the members of the different Old World family (Sylviidae) are generally excellent songsters. Several of these warbler species breed in the taiga of Europe and Siberia, though in the Old World the niches of insect-eaters of the northern forests are more commonly occupied by thrushes. There are thrushes in the American taiga too—the American robin, which is a thrush, breeds as far north as trees grow in Alaska and Canada.

In addition to the summer visitors, there are a number of permanent bird

A mule deer wading in the Athabaska River, Alberta. (Annan Photo Features)

residents of the taiga. The most curious of these are the crossbills, with species in the pine forests of North America, Europe, and Asia. With their awkwardly crossed bills, these birds look like one of nature's mistakes, badly handicapped by some freak of development. But the crossed bills, it turns out, are extremely efficient instruments for prying open pine cones to get at the seeds which are the birds' chief food. The crossbills move about the forests in flocks that may include several hundred individuals.

Most of the eighteen species of the grouse family are inhabitants of the far north, extending, in the case of the ptarmigan, through the taiga into the tundra. During the summer, a varied diet is available to the northern grouse, but apparently they get through the winter mostly by living on the buds of plants like spruce or willow. How they get stones for their gizzards to grind this food up when everything is covered with snow remains an ornithological mystery.

The birds of the taiga include a number of predatory hawks and owls. Characteristic of the coniferous forests all around the northern hemisphere is the great gray owl, called the Lapp owl in Europe, where it is lighter colored than in North America. Like the snowy owl of the tundra farther north, this bird is forced to do much of its hunting by day simply because the summer nights are so short. It feeds on rodents and small birds, and in times of food scarcity in the north it sometimes turns up as far south as Germany or the Adirondack region of New York. It lays its eggs in deserted hawk nests.

Left: Despite how awkward they may look, the beaks of these crossbills are efficient tools for prying open pine cones. (Patricia Witherspoon)

Bird life in the taiga is surprisingly rich during the summer months. Here a male wood grouse is "displaying" in the Swedish taiga. (Sven Gillsater)

The taiga food web includes among the predators not only hawks and owls but a considerable variety of mammals. Several members of the weasel family live there, including the famous ermine. The largest of the bobtailed cats, the lynxes, range over Canada and Siberia. And the original home of the tiger is thought to be the Siberian taiga, where it seems better adapted than in the jungles to the south. Wolves are now also chiefly taiga animals. They were once common in the deciduous forest, but man's activities in North America, Europe, and Asia have driven them back into the remaining wilderness of spruce, fir, and pine.

Wolves

Wolves have a special interest for us because of their relation to domestic dogs. The exact relationship is far from clear; one can argue that dogs are simply domesticated wolves, or that they are descended from some wild animal species now extinct, or that they represent a mixture of several species of wild canines. Certainly wolves and dogs interbreed easily and show many similar patterns of behavior.

Our knowledge of wolf behavior in the wild is understandably limited, since it is not easy for man to watch wolves in their native habitat. The best study known to me was made by Adolph Murie in Mount McKinley National Park in Alaska. He spent over three years observing wolves and other animals under the relatively undisturbed conditions of the park and was able to accumulate a considerable amount of information about their habits. His studies were mostly made in open country above tree line, where he could use field glasses. Thus the conditions were

closer to those of the tundra than of the taiga, but wolves all over the world range out from the taiga into tundra.

Wolves normally live in social groups known as packs. These sometimes consist of a single family, male and female with pups, but all sorts of combinations have been observed. One pack at Mount McKinley had two adult males along with a female and her young, all living in harmony; another pack included two females with young and three adult males. Packs of as many as fifty individuals have been reported, but the more usual number is somewhere between six and ten. Lone wolves are also fairly common, and Murie had a chance to watch one such wolf unsuccessfully attempt to join a pack. Twice the strange wolf approached the den, and despite fawning and begging behavior was driven away, badly wounded before it finally became completely discouraged and disappeared.

The reaction of the wolves to a strange member of the species is thus like that often shown by dogs. Whether a wolf pack defends a definite territory against other wolves is, however, unclear, though it does seem certain that lone wolves are at least not allowed near the dens. Murie found that the wolves in hunting ordinarily ranged a distance of a dozen miles or so from the den, but that they would sometimes go twice this far—to prey, for instance, on a large band of caribou that had calved some twenty miles away. During the winter months, when the dens are abandoned, it may be that the wolves range widely, though Murie felt that around Mount McKinley, at any rate, particular packs tended to stay in a given general area.

In that region, caribou formed the chief food of the wolves, followed by mountain sheep and moose. Big game was definitely preferred, and smaller animals were eaten only when nothing else was available. Murie was able to watch the wolves hunting on a number of occasions, sometimes in packs and sometimes alone. The objective generally was to get caribou calves: a caribou band with calves would be chased, the wolves and the caribou managing about the same speed, until one of the calves started to fall behind, which would be the end of that particular calf. Relatively weak or sickly calves were thus the first to be eliminated from a band— a nice illustration of the force of natural selection. It seems likely that the only adult caribou killed are those already crippled or weakened in some way.

In no case observed by Murie did caribou attempt to defend themselves from wolf attack; they simply fled. The larger moose with their sharp hooves, on the other hand, are able to put up a vigorous defense. Under favorable circumstances, mothers can successfully protect their calves and sometimes even kill attacking wolves. Wolf attacks on moose generally occur within the forest during times of deep snow, when the movements of the moose are greatly handicapped; it is adults that then fall victims to attack.

A pair of wolves face into a blizzard in Mount McKinley National Park. (Marcel Cognac: Annan Photo Features)

Weasels and their Relatives

Weasels and their relatives form a family of carnivores, called the Mustelidae, that is found all over the world except in the Australian region and on oceanic islands. Therefore the group can hardly be considered typical of the taiga or of any other particular landscape. Yet no account of this region can leave the mustelids out. Sable, ermine, mink—these are all taiga mustelids that have, to their own mis-

Primarily tree-living and nocturnal, martens are fierce both in hunting and in defending themselves. (Sven Gillsater)

fortune, achieved fame among men because of the thick, rich fur that serves so beautifully to protect them from the rigors of taiga winters. Fishers, martens, and wolverines, which once ranged through the forests farther south, are now also virtually limited to the remaining wilderness of the northern woods.

Sable, marten, and fisher are all names applied to species of the genus *Martes*. The true sable is an Old World species that once ranged through the forests of Russia and Siberia. The demands of the noble and wealthy for sable cloaks led to its extinction west of the Ural Mountains long ago, and it can be argued that the pursuit of sables was one of the reasons for the Russian conquest and settlement of Siberia. In the years around 1800 the Kamchatka region alone produced some ten thousand skins a year, and in 1881 the output was still nearly three thousand skins. For a while sable were apparently doomed to extinction, but the U.S.S.R. has enforced protective laws and established reservations within its territory. The variety found in northern Japan has also been protected. Sables now could probably not be called common anywhere, but in a few places in the vast reaches of Siberia they are at least not rare.

Sable, marten, and fisher are all considered primarily arboreal animals, though the sable is probably more given to ground hunting than the other two. Like all mustelids, they are fierce and fearless both in hunting and in defending themselves. They live on mice and other small rodents, squirrels, rabbits, birds, eggs—anything they can get. They are chiefly nocturnal, and nest in hollow trees or logs. They are also apparently antisocial, the males associating with the females only for the mating period. All of them seem to require wilderness for survival.

The wolverine or glutton, such as this one in Sweden, persists only in remote forests of Scandinavia, the Baltic states, Russia, and the American Rockies. (Sven Gillsater)

The wolverine or glutton is also a wilderness animal. In prehistoric times it ranged all over Europe south to the Pyrenees, but it has long disappeared except in remote forests of Scandinavia, the Baltic states, and Russia. In North America it has disappeared from the United States except for remnant populations in a few regions in the Rocky Mountains. Now it is really an animal only of the Canadian and Siberian taiga, and not common there. The wolverine has been prized for its fur, but beyond that, it has generally been regarded as a pest because it combines mustelid ferocity with a respectable size (the males weigh thirty pounds or more). The European form is said to kill cattle, sheep, and reindeer, and various countries have long paid bounties to speed its extermination. It is also said to be clever, and trappers maintain that it will not only follow a trap line to kill and devour the catch, but that it will remove the bait from a trap without getting caught.

Wolverines are the largest and the weasels the smallest of the mustelids. Several species of weasels live in the taiga, and of these the least weasel—which occurs over much of Canada and Alaska and ranges into the United States—is only six or seven inches long, including two inches of tail. It can enter mole tunnels only an inch in diameter in the ground, and old mole runs may be used as den sites. The numerous weasels of the taiga depend chiefly for their food on the even more numerous small rodents, though they eat anything they can catch. In their white winter fur, weasels become "ermine," and range not only through the forested taiga but out into the open tundra, where so many of the inhabitants acquire white winter coats. But the tundra inhabitants deserve a separate chapter.

13

Far North
and Far South

The Arctic Circle is a line drawn around the globe at 66 degrees 30 minutes north latitude. Another line, the Antarctic Circle, is drawn at 66 degrees 30 minutes south latitude. At any point on the Arctic Circle the sun is above the horizon for twenty-four hours on June 21, and on December 21 it never appears at all. Midnight sun at the Antarctic Circle falls on December 21, and midday night on June 21. From these circles north—or south—the length of the period of light or of darkness increases to reach its limit of six months of day and six of night at the poles themselves.

These arctic lines, like the tropic lines, thus reflect the neat geometry of the astronomical universe—the tilt of the planet on its spinning annual swing around the sun. From this comes the climatic zonation that in turn governs the zoning of life, but not with any astronomical precision. Palms are not precisely limited by the lines of the tropics, nor spruce by those of the arctics. Patterns of land and sea, of winds and ocean currents, blur the boundaries.

The way in which geography modifies the astronomical zones is particularly striking in the case of the lines limiting the two polar regions. The Arctic Circle crosses land almost all of the way around the globe. Half of its circumference falls on the Eurasian land mass: northern Scandinavia, Russia, and Siberia. Across the narrow Bering Strait it cuts off the upper third of Alaska and of the Canadian Northwest Territories. Most of Greenland lies above the circle, and Iceland is just below where the line crosses the North Atlantic. These arctic lands marked off by the circle form the shores of the almost landlocked Arctic Ocean.

The Antarctic Circle, on the other hand, falls almost entirely on the seas surrounding the isolated southern continent. In the north, then, we have land surrounding a polar sea; in the south, seas around a polar continent. This makes the conditions of life in the vicinity of the two poles completely different.

The Tundra

The Arctic Circle corresponds in a very general way with the tree line—the region where the taiga gives way to the open tundra. The tundra is essentially an arctic grassland, and the vegetation includes a considerable variety of grasses, sedges, herbaceous plants, lichens, and mosses. The subsoil is permanently frozen—this is the region of the permafrost—and since decay is greatly slowed by the low temper-

The fauna of Antarctica consists primarily of penguins, and the skuas that pester them. (Fritz Goro: *Life*)

atures, level ground becomes covered with a thick, spongy mat of live and dead material. Precipitation in the tundra is low, but so is evaporation, and the melting ice and snow form numerous bogs and ponds in low areas during the summer.

The conditions of animal life are severe in the tundra, and the number of different species that have been able to meet these conditions drops off rapidly from the margins of the coniferous forests toward the permanently frozen north. The growing season is short, averaging perhaps sixty days, but the long sunlight means that growth during this brief warm season can be very rapid.

The arctic vegetation, including the lichens, seems to be particularly nutritious for the animals able to eat it. Thus, while there are few kinds of animals, those that have been able to adapt may be supported in large numbers. During the summer, herds of caribou and reindeer graze there, but some of them retreat to the taiga during the winter. Musk oxen, however—once common in both the New and Old World arctic, but now found only in remote parts of Greenland and Canada—live in the tundra all year around. And not long ago the tundra had two other spectacular inhabitants, the wooly mammoth and the wooly rhinoceros.

Giants of the Past

The tundra mammoths have attracted popular attention ever since the first frozen carcass was discovered in Siberia in 1692, and over the passing years a great deal has been written about them. Recently William R. Farrand, a paleontologist, sifted through the accounts and summarized his conclusions in the journal *Science*. According to Farrand, there has been a total of thirty-nine discoveries of frozen mammoth remains, all from northern Siberia except for two fragmentary carcasses found in Alaska. But only four of the Siberian discoveries were reasonably complete animals. It is extraordinary, though, that any frozen mammoth flesh should be found, and it raises the question of what could have happened to these animals.

It is natural to think first of some sudden catastrophe, some abrupt change of climate that trapped these animals and left them frozen during many thousands of years to be disclosed again with present thawing. But after carefully reviewing all of the evidence, Farrand finds no evidence of cosmic catastrophe. It is clear, in the first place, that the animals were not abruptly frozen. The flesh had decomposed to a considerable extent in all cases, and it appears that the decomposition had set in before freezing. The autopsies on the fairly complete bodies indicate that death was caused not by freezing but by asphyxiation.

Only mammoths and rhinoceroses have been found frozen, yet we know that many other animals were living on the tundra along with these—stag, reindeer, musk oxen, and the like. The heavy, awkward animals were trapped, perhaps by a collapsing river bank or by becoming mired late enough in the year to be frozen before they had completely rotted, and then were preserved by the permafrost.

Only a few of these frozen carcasses have been discovered, but many thousands of mammoth tusks have been collected by ivory hunters in Siberia over the centuries. One cache of more than a thousand tusks has been found, and it has been estimated that more than fifty thousand tusks in all have been taken from Siberia. It would appear, therefore, that the mammoths were once common animals on the tundra. When did they become extinct—and why?

When under attack by men or wolves, musk oxen in remote Greenland and Canada form a tight circle with the calves in the center.
(Vitalis Pantenburg)

Evidence of various sorts indicates that the frozen animals died somewhere between twenty and thirty thousand years ago. From the stomach contents, it appears that they ate plants of the same sort that grow on the tundra today, and it seems most likely that the climate then was not greatly different from the climate today. If this is so, mammoths and rhinos could still be living on the tundra—perhaps, like the reindeer of today, migrating seasonally between tundra and taiga.

The extinction of these tundra animals coincides with the disappearance of other kinds of mammoths and elephants from Europe, Asia, and North America, along with many other species of large mammals. They all became extinct at about the same time that men became prevalent, and we know that the Stone Age hunters of both Europe and America killed mammoths. It is difficult to dismiss the idea that perhaps the human species had something to do with this extinction, though it is impossible to prove one way or another. It is easier to believe that man killed off the mammoths of Germany and Kentucky than to imagine him decisively affecting survival in the far north. But if these hairy pachyderms survived the advances and retreats of the ice through the previous glaciations of the Pleistocene, it is hard to see why they should not have survived the last retreat of the ice and lived on into the present. Whatever the cause of the extinction, it is apparent that in the geologically recent past the tundra supported a more varied fauna than it does at present.

Musk Oxen—Prehistoric Holdovers

In the case of the musk ox, we can watch the process of extinction, whether we understand it or not. This species disappeared from the tundra of the Old World in prehistoric times, or at least before historians took any notice of events that far north; but it still retains a precarious foothold in remote parts of the New World. It disappeared from Alaska about 1865, though it has recently been reintroduced on Nunivak Island. There is also a protected band in a game sanctuary north of Great Slave Lake in the Northwest Territories, and there are scattered bands across the islands east to Greenland.

Musk oxen are year-round inhabitants of the open tundra. They are large, cow-sized animals, with heavy, long, shaggy coats; short legs; large, splayed hooves adapted for support on snow; and backward-curving horns that lie close to the skull. The curiously short legs of the musk ox illustrate a general principle— that all appendages of animals living in cold climates tend to be smaller than those of related species living in warmer regions. Thus the tails, legs, and ears of arctic mammals tend to be reduced in size, and the bodies tend to be rounded and bulky. This serves to cut down the rate of loss of body heat.

Under attack by men or wolves, musk oxen form a tight circle with calves in the center. This habit, which presumably makes for an efficient defense against wolves, is of no avail against men with rifles, since the stolid animals can be picked off one at a time until the whole herd has been killed. For once, however, Europeans cannot be blamed directly for the recent great reduction in the numbers of an animal species, since shooting musk oxen has never been a major sport—though it is said that some six hundred of them were killed for food by Admiral Peary's arctic expeditions. Eskimos with guns are responsible for most of the modern decline in the animal's numbers. The animals are not easy to protect in their isolated habitat, and it is difficult to explain conservation measures to hungry Eskimos. But the circular defense of the musk oxen also makes them an easy target for men with spears, and this is probably the explanation of the disappearance of the animals from northern Europe and Siberia long before rifles had been invented.

At least, the musk-ox herds are a convincing demonstration that the lichens, mosses, and skimpy vegetation of the arctic barrens is rich and nutritious enough to support large herbivores all through the year, if the animals are able to resist the cold. This also makes the wooly mammoths and rhinoceroses seem a little less improbable, and if scattered bands of men in these remote lands are able to reduce the numbers of musk oxen so rapidly because of the animal's habits, the disappearance of other animals becomes more understandable. Perhaps mammoth behavior too was not adapted to resist the tactics of that curious new creature, man.

Lemmings—and Animal Cycles

Lemmings are the key-industry animals of the tundra. They are small, fat, compact rodents with thick fluffy coats, short legs, short tails, and tiny ears almost concealed in the fur—neat illustrations of the principle of reduced appendages in cold-climate animals. There are several species in the American and Eurasian arctic.

Lemmings have become famous because of their recurrent population crises

Taiga

70 An elk, here shown in Yellowstone Park, is the red deer of Europe and the wapiti of Siberia. (Ed Park)

Left: A long-tailed
weasel in winter coat: the
weasels that turn white in
winter become the ermine
of fur traders. (C. G.
Hampson: Annan Photo
Features)

Left, below: Cape
May warblers in the
Minnesota woods: at least
half of the summer birds
of the American taiga are
warblers. (Eliot Porter)

Tundra

73 Right: Moose
browsing on shrub willow
near Anchorage, Alaska.
(Steve McCutcheon)

74 Above: Caribou crossing a frozen lake in the barrenlands of Canada. (Fritz Goro: *Life*)

75 Above, right: A sand crane in the barrenlands of northern Canada. (Fritz Goro: *Life*)

76 Right: Adélie penguins at Wilkes Land on Antarctica: they return annually to the same rookeries, walking as much as sixty miles over trackless ice. (John R. T. Molholm)

77 Left: The outsized feet of the snowshoe rabbit help him cope with snow. (William W. Bacon III)

78 Below: Pacific walrus in the Bering Sea. (Steve McCutcheon)

79 Right: A polar bear running across a snowfield. (Steve McCutcheon)

which seem to result in mass suicide. The stories of jostling masses of crazed rodents streaming down from the Norwegian mountains to take to the sea, swimming out to an inevitable death, are apparently farfetched. But the lemming population of both continents does grow to enormous size every three or four years, and at the population peak they are apt to move out from their habitat in all directions, showing erratic behavior that is suicidal for most of them. There is a population "crash," after which the survivors start building up in numbers again—toward the next crash.

Other arctic and subarctic animals show periodic fluctuations in numbers, and these cycles have attracted the attention of many students. The Hudson's Bay Company of Canada has kept records of the furs brought in each year since about 1800. Over this long stretch of time, lynx furs have shown a regular peak in numbers every 9 or 10 years (the average is every 9.6 years). Snowshoe hare records show the same cycle, but with the peak every 7 or 8 years. Since the lynx feed largely on hares, this looks like a prey-predator cycle.

The shorter three- to four-year cycle of the lemmings is similarly related to short-term cycles in the foxes and snowy owls that feed on them. Snowy owls turn up quite regularly in the United States every three to four years, apparently forced south by the failure of their lemming food supply after a population crash. Since it seems likely that the snowy owls never find their way back north and fail to survive in the warmer latitudes, this is suicidal behavior for them too.

The cycles of the predators are explained as a result of the cycles in their prey, the lemmings or the hares. But what causes the cycles of the prey? There are many

The effect of cold climate: an arctic fox, a common or red fox, and a desert fox, showing how ears— along with all other appendages—of animals in cold climates tend to be reduced.

people who are convinced that somehow all natural events tend to follow cycles, that cycles are a sort of cosmic principle of the universe. Such people can find cycles everywhere, in human events as well as in the forests and the seas and in the circling of the stars. This has led to a reaction on the part of others who have become suspicious of all alleged biological cycles, regarding them as fictions of the human mind rather than natural events. Sometimes this suspicion seems justified, but the cycles of lemmings, hares, lynx, and owls seem to be real enough, and a considerable challenge to understanding.

Attempts to relate the animal cycles to changes in climate, or to cosmic events like sunspots, have not been very satisfactory or rewarding. It seems more fruitful to search for explanations within the biological system itself.

An American ecologist, Frank Pitelka, has spent several years now studying the

lemming cycles in the region around Point Barrow, Alaska. He finds that the lemmings breed most rapidly during the winter months, under their snug cover of snow. With the coming of summer, when predators can get at them more easily, their numbers decline somewhat, but they are still usually more numerous than the year before. By the third winter, however, they have become so abundant that they destroy much of the vegetation, removing a good part of what little protection they have from summer's predators. Disaster strikes, if not that summer, then in the following fourth year.

Obviously the whole cycle is much more complicated than this. There are possible psychological effects of overcrowding, possible effects from diet, and much yet to be learned about predator relations. But it seems entirely likely that the cyclical effect can be explained within the biological system, without recourse to such outside factors as sunspots. It also seems that these fairly regular cycles, with great fluctuations from year to year in the numbers of animals, are characteristic of relatively simple biological communities. Where there are many different kinds of animals living in the same habitat, relationships become more complex and the numbers of individuals of the various species are less apt to show regular changes. But when lemmings become scarce in the tundra, there is no other common prey for snowy owls and foxes—so they decline in numbers too.

The simplicity of the tundra community is real enough. Northeast Greenland is considered to have one of the richer tundra faunas, with eight species of mammals: hare, lemming, musk ox, reindeer, ermine, wolf, polar bear, and fox. Spitzbergen has three species of mammals. In contrast, the state of Michigan, at the margin between the taiga and deciduous forest, has sixty-seven species of mammals; and the Republic of Panama, within the tropics, has one hundred and fifty-two species.

These arctic hares on the snows of Greenland are a classic example of protective coloration. (Alwin Pedersen)

Left: The ptarmigan is unusual in having three seasonal changes of plumage—brown in summer, gray in autumn, and white in winter. (Alfred M. Bailey)

226

Tundra Bird Life

During the brief summer the tundra acquires a considerable bird population, but it is mostly water birds like ducks, geese, swans; shore birds like sandpipers and plovers; and sea birds. The nearest thing to a permanent bird resident of the tundra is the rock ptarmigan; but in the worst weather even this species retreats to the margin of the taiga, where it makes small shelters in the snow. The ptarmigan is unusual among birds in having three seasonal changes of plumage: during the summer it is brown; in the autumn, gray; and in the winter, white.

Among the summer bird residents are the rapacious skuas and the smaller but equally fierce jaegers—the hawks of the seas. The skuas mostly breed in the antarctic and the jaegers in the arctic, where they are among the chief summer predators on the lemmings when those animals are abundant. But the skuas and jaegers are best known as thieves. They watch gulls, terns, and other sea birds from on high until a catch is made, and then swoop down to pester the owner into dropping the fish, which they expertly catch in mid-air. They also prey on the eggs and young of other nesting birds; the great skuas of the antarctic are said to be the chief enemies of nesting penguins.

The skuas and jaegers nest as isolated pairs in remote polar lands, and roam widely over the seas during the rest of the year. Many species of gulls and terns also nest on arctic islands and coasts, but in social groups. One of these, the arctic tern, which breeds in the far north, moves to antarctic waters during the period of northern winter, so that most of its life is spent in the continuous daylight of the summer periods of the two polar regions.

Many species of geese, swans, and ducks also go far north to nest, finding rich summer feeding grounds in the marshy tundra. Since the ducks on their migration south in the fall are favorite targets of American and European sportsmen, the maintenance of the duck populations has become a prime conservation interest. Laws have been passed protecting them during the breeding season in the north, which seems reasonable, except that Eskimos like ducks too. With guns, the Eskimos can wreak considerable havoc among the nesting birds; and they don't see why they should be prevented from eating duck just so people farther south can shoot them a little later. This also seems reasonable, making one of those dilemmas that are so frequently encountered in game management.

Arctic Color

The snowy owl of the arctic is white all year, whereas the ptarmigan develops white plumage only in the winter. Among mammals, the polar bear is white all year, and so is a form of the caribou, named after Admiral Peary, that lives on that northernmost of islands, Ellesmere Land. The hares, foxes, ermines, and some other weasels have white coats in the winter, brown or gray in the summer. These would seem to be classic cases of protective coloration, blending with the snow background. Yet the raven gets along all year, though black.

Alternatively it has been suggested that the white coat is an advantage to warm-blooded animals in cold climates because white does not radiate away body heat,

Among the summer bird
residents of the tundra
are the fierce jaegers—the
hawk of the seas.
(Fritz Goro: *Life*)

as do darker colors. The white color would serve, along with thick fur and layers
of fat under the skin, as an adaptation to the cold.

Among the lemmings, some species turn white in the winter and others, living
in apparently identical circumstances, stay brown. And of course musk oxen, reindeer, and caribou (except for the Ellesmere Land form) seem to get along all right
through the arctic winter without white coats. But these facts are equally difficult to
explain on either the protective-coloration or heat-adaptation theory.

Antarctica—and Penguins

There are small areas of tundra-like conditions on some of the southern islands, but
these are too limited and too fragmented to allow for the development of anything
like a tundra fauna. The area climatically natural to tundra is covered by the sea.
The further fact that the south pole is in the middle of a continent and the north
pole in the middle of a sea also makes for great differences in the conditions of life.
The accumulated ice on the antarctic continent has turned the whole land mass
into a vast deep-freeze. This is not possible with a sea because the continuously
circulating water limits ice accumulation to a relatively thin surface layer.

Vegetation could hardly be said to exist on Antarctica. Only two kinds of seed
plants have been found on the continent, while something over four hundred kinds

grow north of the Arctic Circle—which is plainly due to the moderating effect of the polar sea. True land vertebrates are absent from Antarctica. The penguins and seals depend on the seas for their living. The few insects either live in the penguin rookeries or are parasites on seals. The fauna of the continent, then, consists essentially of penguins, and the skuas that pester them.

Yet of the seventeen living species of penguins, only two, the Adélie and the Emperor, breed on the antarctic continent. All of the others, however, live in the southern hemisphere, on the coasts of the southern reaches of New Zealand, Australia, South Africa, South America, and the southern islands, except for one that inhabits the Galapagos Islands astride the equator.

The various kinds of penguins differ in the details of their markings, but all have white breasts and dark backs. This appears to be an adaptation to their aquatic life, since animals in the sea are generally light-colored below and dark above. The black-jacketed penguins thus violate the rule about cold country whiteness. Apparently the advantages of a dark back at sea more than compensate for the disadvantage of heat loss on land. And the penguins are truly marine animals. It is said that with their streamlined bodies they can attain speeds of thirty miles per hour swimming, which is equal to that of the fastest fishes.

Unused to enemies on land, penguins are easy to catch and hence to mark. In fact Adélie penguins were among the first birds to be banded; a member of the French Antarctic Expedition of 1908 tied green celluloid bands on some of them and discovered that they came back the next year to the same breeding area.

Much of our knowledge of the Adélie penguins comes from Dr. William Sladen, a British medical officer and antarctic explorer, who has come to know their habits quite well over several years. These birds spend the antarctic winter at sea, living on the planktonic krill that also serves as food for the whales. With spring the penguins head for the coast; sometimes they have to walk for as much as sixty miles across the sea ice to reach their rookeries. Since they have to depend on the sea for food, this means that they must be ready for a long fast. They build nests with stones in order to keep the eggs and young above melting snow water; and the building goes on continuously, since the birds are much addicted to stealing stones from each other's nests.

Three weeks after arrival at the rookery, the female lays two bluish white eggs. The male then takes charge of the nest while the female goes back to sea to feed, returning for a change of guard in about two weeks. The parents take turns in going for food until the young are ready to go to sea themselves. It appears that the mated pairs recognize each other and identify their own young even when the chicks have all herded together in large bands as a defense against the predatory skuas. Penguins illustrate another one of those mysteries of bird navigation. How do they find their nests, waddling over interminable miles of rough sea ice, with no apparent landmarks of any kind?

The Emperor penguins build no nest; they carry the eggs and chicks on their feet, and they undergo even longer periods of fasting than do the Adélie penguins. The Emperors arrive at the breeding grounds about the middle of March, at the beginning of the antarctic winter, and the males alone incubate the eggs for some two months. Then, at hatching time, the females come back to take over, again finding their own mates and chicks, even though there is not even the marking of a nest.

Going North is like Climbing a Mountain

As we go north or south toward the poles, conditions become colder and more difficult for life, until we reach the frozen antarctic continent or the ice-covered Arctic Ocean. But anywhere on land—as in a mountain system, for instance—temperatures also become colder as we climb to higher altitudes, until finally a zone is reached in which trees no longer grow and we have tundra-like conditions. If the mountains are high enough, we presently reach perpetual snow and ice, conditions similar to those near the poles.

Yet latitude and altitude are not the same. For one thing, the length of day changes as we go poleward but not as we climb. A new factor, air pressure, comes into operation as we leave sea level. But mountain systems have so many special characteristics for animal life that they are best dealt with separately.

At home in the sea as well as on ice, polar bears swim to an iceberg. (Vitalis Pantenburg)

I4

Mountains

So far we have been considering the animal worlds of the continents, from forests to deserts and from warm tropics to cold poles—broad landscapes in which the conditions of life are largely governed by climate. The patterns of these biomes, we have noted, are greatly modified by the positions of the mountain chains on the different continents, but nothing has been said about the mountains themselves. Mountain life could hardly be considered until these major climatic zones had been examined, because within mountain systems the zones all come together. Permanent snowfields may be within a few miles of tropical forests; one side of a ridge may be desert and the other covered with lush vegetation; rocky barrens may alternate with rich bottom lands. Mountains clearly present special conditions of life for their inhabitants.

The World's High Places

Each of the great mountain systems of the world has different characteristics which are reflected not only in its own animal life but also in its influence on the lands around. The greatest of the mountain masses is that of the Himalayas and the vast, bleak Tibetan plateau to the north. This forms a massive barrier between the Asiatic tropics and the Temperate-Zone biomes to the north, a barrier which continues with outlying ranges eastward into China and westward through the mountains of Iran and the Near East. On a world map, even the Alps and the mountains of Spain and the Balkans look like outlying fragments of this great east-west system.

In America, on the other hand, the major mountain system runs north and south, with the Rockies extending from Alaska into Central America and, after the interruption of the narrow isthmus of Panama, continuing in the Andes to form a western border for the whole South American continent. Thus, instead of being a barrier between the tropics and temperate conditions, the North American mountains form a highway along which animals from the north can extend their range on the cold uplands right down into the geographical tropics.

The African continent has much more high plateau country than does South America but no single great mountain range comparable with the Andes. The high mountains of Ethiopia and central and south Africa form isolated patches, so that there is no large area over which cold-loving animals can range. But Africa's highest peak, Kilimanjaro, reaches 19,565 feet, well into the region of permanent snow.

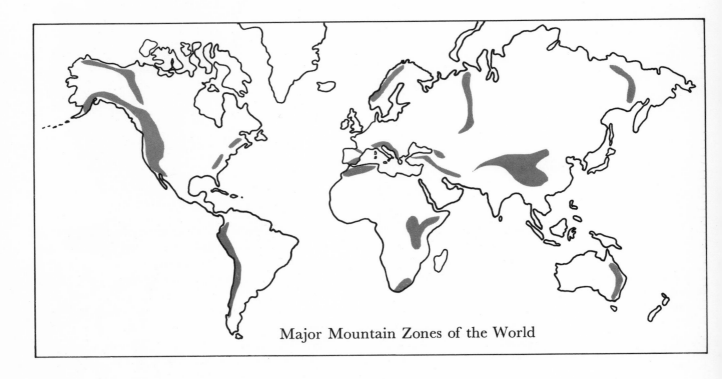

Major Mountain Zones of the World

The mountains of Australia also form isolated patches, in the eastern, central, and western parts of the continent. Few peaks rise above 5000 feet, and the highest elevation on the continent (Mount Kosciusko in New South Wales) is only 7328 feet. New Zealand is much more mountainous, with Mount Cook reaching up to 12,349 feet. New Guinea, with a high mountain system forming the backbone of the island and peaks reaching over 15,000 feet, has developed a special and characteristic mountain fauna.

Effect of Altitude

Because the geography of mountain systems is different in each of the continental areas, there are important differences in the conditions of animal life. Yet in some ways mountains everywhere are similar, presenting comparable problems of adaptation for their inhabitants. The similarities are consequences of the effect of altitude, especially on air pressure and temperature.

As everyone knows, air pressure drops steadily with increasing altitude. For animals, this means less and less oxygen available for respiration. At about 18,000 feet the oxygen pressure is half that at sea level, and under such conditions animals may need special adaptations for survival. The highest permanent human settlements are at 16,000 feet in Tibet, though herdsmen with their animals range at times 2000 feet higher. Wild sheep and ibex in the Tibetan mountains live up to about 19,000 feet; wolves and foxes get almost as high, and yaks get even higher.

The effect of great altitude on the human animal was demonstrated in 1875 when three French aeronauts, Gaston Tissandier, H. T. Sivel, and J. E. Croce-Spinelli, made an ascent in the free balloon *Zenith*. Tissandier kept notes on his

The thin air of high altitudes makes for flight problems, but the white-tailed eagles (right), vultures, and condors generally manage great heights easily. (Svante Lundgren)

sensations. At 24,600 feet he began to feel an extraordinary torpor. There was no sensation of pain or suffering; on the contrary, there was an inner joy (which sounds like the "rapture of the depths" encountered in the opposite act of deep ocean diving). He lost consciousness at 26,200 feet. The recording barometer on the *Zenith* marked 27,950 feet before the balloon began to sink. When it reached ground, Tissandier was alive and sitting up, but both Sivel and Croce-Spinelli were dead.

Mountain laboratories for studies of the effect of altitude have been established in several places, most notably in Peru, where a physician, Carlos Monge, has been making observations for many years. Despite careful studies of the effect of altitude on human physiology, it is still not clear whether mountain people like the Tibetans and Andean Indians represent special "genetic races" adapted to high altitudes. Certainly they are different. Mountain people, for instance, have a much greater lung capacity than lowlanders. Peruvian Indians living at 14,000 feet have an average chest measurement of 36.2 inches, while coastal Indians of the same height average 30.6 inches. There is also an increase in the total number of red blood cells. Such adaptations may be acquired by long residence at high altitude, but there is also evidence that some of the high-altitude traits are inherited.

233

It has long been noticed that domesticated animals, when first taken to high altitudes, tend to be sterile. This is true of people too, and Dr. Monge, going through Spanish colonial records, found that it was usually many years before the first European children were born in the mountain settlements.

With birds, the thin air of high altitudes makes for flight problems, though the largest of living birds, the Andean condor, seems perfectly at home soaring among the highest peaks. Vultures, condors, and eagles in general manage great heights easily, and so do some members of the crow family, like the Alpine chough. The chough has been seen to alight and take off at an altitude of 27,000 feet in the Himalayas. The take-off was made by running downhill, however, and this height is probably about the ceiling for bird flight.

Cold-blooded animals are less susceptible to low air pressure than are warm-blooded ones. In the laboratory, frogs have survived much lower air pressures than those found on the highest mountains. But the most spectacular experiments were made with insects by the late Frank Lutz of the American Museum of Natural History.

Lutz first tried taking an ordinary cricket on a laboratory version of a balloon ascent. He put the cricket under a bell jar and with a vacuum pump reduced the air pressure in two minutes to somewhat less than that at the top of Mount Everest. Any mammal would be killed by such a rapid change in pressure. The cricket,

Lutz reported, was rather quiet for about fifteen minutes, but then began to clean its legs and to behave normally. After forty minutes, Lutz broke the vacuum, which would be equivalent to an instantaneous descent to earth from six miles up. The cricket "gave a little twitch as though a bit startled" but aside from that showed no discernable ill effect.

This led Lutz to try a whole series of experiments with insects in vacuums. He tested flies, ants, butterflies, beetles, and the like, and found that none of them showed any ill effect from exposure to air pressures equivalent to those at an altitude of about seventeen miles above the earth. He could not get a lower pressure than this because of the water problem. Water, of course, evaporates rapidly from the body of any animal in a vacuum. This in itself might bring death directly by drying, or indirectly by causing the remaining water in the tissues to freeze because of the cooling effect of the water evaporation. To avoid this, Lutz kept a dish of water under the bell jar with the insects, but of course the resulting water vapor set a limit to the extent to which the pressure could be lowered. Lutz decided to ignore the water factor and to see what would happen in the most complete vacuum he could obtain.

He tested three bees, two ants, a beetle, and a grasshopper in an apparatus that could attain a practically complete vacuum—equivalent to conditions in interstellar space. It took two minutes of pumping to reach this point, and the insects were held there for another minute before they were suddenly returned to earth by the breaking of the vacuum. Not an insect moved for a while, but in two hours all were active and behaving normally. Next day one ant was dead, but the other insects seemed unaffected by their excursion into space. In an experiment with a bumblebee and two butterflies, Lutz tried exposure to four minutes of complete vacuum. The bee survived, and it seems likely that the butterflies were killed only by the rapid and excessive drying rather than by the lack of air.

The Zones on a Mountain Slope

Lutz's experiments show that insects are remarkably resistant to low air pressure. Yet there are few kinds of insects, or of animals of any sort, at great mountain heights. The problem is not pressure but temperature. Mean annual temperature decreases quite regularly with elevation above sea level, though the rate understandably varies with the latitude. In the Alps, average temperatures drop about 1 degree F. for every 255-foot increase in elevation; in the Caucasus, the rate is 1 degree F. for every 300 feet; in the equatorial Andes, 1 degree F. for every 350 feet.

The change in temperature encountered in climbing is thus similar to the change in moving from the tropics to the poles, and climate on various mountain levels tends to be comparable in many ways with the geographical climatic zones of the continents. The same words are often used to label altitudinal and latitudinal changes; one can speak, for instance, of the "subtropical" and "temperate" zones of tropical mountain ranges.

In North America the relation between mountain zones and biomes is particularly striking. The grasslands, deserts, or deciduous forests of the lowlands give way on the mountain slopes to taiga-like forests of pines and other conifers, and these give way in turn, above tree line, to open tundra-like conditions. Since the moun-

Far left: A chamois, master mountaineer of the Swiss Alps. (Pierre Didier)

Left: The ibexes of European mountains are wild but interbreed freely with domestic goats. (Gerard Vienne: Images et Textes)

tains extend southward from the arctic, northern animals and plants are also able to extend south, finding appropriate conditions at ever greater elevations. The relationships are less neat, however, in other parts of the world, and in general it would seem to be desirable to use a special vocabulary for the vegetation zones of mountainous regions. One such vegetation zone, of wide occurrence on tropical mountains, has been aptly called "cloud forest."

Cloud Forest

Vegetation changes on mountain slopes are apt to be gradual, without precise boundaries. In the wet tropics, rain forest thus imperceptibly changes character as one climbs, until at elevations somewhere between four and six thousand feet it can more appropriately be called cloud forest. The rainfall at these heights may be even greater than in the valleys below, but the appearance of the forest is determined not so much by the rain as by the frequent fog, for this is the elevation at which the clouds meet the upthrusting land. The forest is always wet and dripping; in Honduran Spanish, it is called *la montana llorona*, the "weeping woods." Everything—tree trunks, rocks, ground—supports a thick covering of moss, and the trees are loaded with epiphytes of many kinds. Most of the elegant, gaudy, and delicate orchids of our hothouses come from this fog zone of tropical mountains, and in the American tropics the bromeliads—the plants of the pineapple family—here reach their greatest development.

The cloud forest is always cool, but the temperatures are not low enough to have an inhibiting effect on either animals or plants. It is not known whether anyone has made a count, but one could guess that there are almost as many different kinds of animals living in a given area of cloud forest as in a similar area of lowland rain forest. Of course the cloud forest, as a zone on mountain slopes, is far more limited in extent than the forests of the equatorial plains and valleys. Cloud forest is also difficult to reach. Many major tropical cities are located in this zone because of the pleasant, healthful climate, and the forest has been destroyed wherever it can be easily reached, to be replaced by gardens and coffee estates. In most parts of the tropics, it requires a mountaineering expedition to get to undisturbed cloud forest.

Flowers, like the orchids, are often startlingly bright against the damp and mossy background of the cloud forest. It also seems to be the home of the most brilliantly colored birds and butterflies. The only competitor is the rain forest below, and there the gaudy inhabitants are more apt to be lost in the treetops.

Hummingbirds, as an example, are most numerous both as individuals and as species in the cloud forest of the American tropics. Some 319 species have been described, and a few of these are found in all sorts of situations from Tierra del Fuego to Alaska (where one species, the rufous hummingbird, turns up in the summer). But the great majority are tropical; only 18 species have been recorded in the United States, mostly in the southwestern mountains. One species, the rubythroat, is found in the eastern states. There are no Old World hummingbirds, though their relatives, the swifts, are world-wide. Hummingbirds must have followed an independent course of evolution in the western hemisphere over a long stretch of geological time.

The mountain sheep of the Canadian Rockies are now limited to protected herds. (Annan Photo Features)

They are the smallest birds, the tiniest being the bee hummingbird of Cuba, two inches long, with a bill and tail that take up about half of this length. The largest, called the giant—one of the Andean species—is about eight inches long. They are the most expert fliers of all animals. They can hover, helicopter-like, in mid-air; back up; dash in any direction; perform all sorts of aerial acrobatics. In these maneuvers, the wings may beat as fast as two hundred times a second, which requires special bone and muscle arrangements. But hummingbirds present physiologists with many puzzles, not only in explaining their speed and agility but in understanding how they maintain body temperatures with their very small size, and how they get energy for the long flights that some species make in migrating.

Hummingbirds are extremely pugnacious, and everyone who has watched them in the tropical mountain forests where they are most abundant is impressed with the amount of time and energy that they spend in quarreling. As the Florida naturalist Archie Carr has expressed it, "They are peevish and generally ornery and are no comfort either to themselves or to anyone who lives with them."

Carr's comments in his book *High Jungles and Low* on the hummingbirds of the cloud forest of Honduras illustrate this.

> *"If you lie on your back and stare upward at the level where the treetops interlace high above, you may see pairs of buglike hummingbirds zipping over and under the green canopy like dogfighting planes diving into and out of cloud banks. One such pair may suddenly plunge downward in a breathless spiral, the hind bird following in machine-like detail every intricacy of the mad course of the pursued. They collide in mid-air in front of your face and then fly separately away to sit on twigs and preen and await the fine new surge of anger that will tune their incredible little muscles for more joyous combat."*

Hummingbirds are brilliantly and beautifully colored as well as nasty-tempered. But cloud-forest birds tend generally to be brilliantly colored. Many of the trogons, for instance, live in mountain forests, including the Central American quetzal, national bird of Guatemala. This bird, iridescent green except for its bright red belly, and with three-foot-long tail feathers in the male, is as astonishing in appearance as the famous birds of paradise, which are also mostly cloud-forest inhabitants in the mountains of New Guinea.

Butterflies of tropical mountain forests seem also to be particularly bright, though usually they are of the same general types as those found in the rain forests lower down. But collections from the foothills of the Andes or the Himalayas or the mountains of the East Indies are especially colorful. A walk along a cloud-forest trail is a particularly exciting experience for a butterfly collector, perhaps in part because life here tends to be nearer to the ground than in the lowland forests.

Mountain Heights

In general, life comes closer to the ground as one climbs upward through mountain forests. Since higher slopes are apt to become more and more precipitous, soil deep enough to support great trees is less likely to accumulate, and of course temperature steadily decreases. Fog and rain usually continue to be abundant up to the altitude where rain turns into snow.

There is no general agreement among biologists about names for the different zones of mountain life. This is partly because every mountain system is somewhat different from every other; even each slope has its own peculiarities. In general, the nature of the vegetation is apt to change noticeably with every one- or two thousand-foot increase in elevation. Faunal changes are less conspicuous, yet a great many animals have quite restricted altitudinal ranges. The animals of mountain peaks—or mountain valleys—thus tend to be as isolated from those of other peaks or valleys as are the inhabitants of different islands. In the case of both mountains and islands, these isolated populations tend to develop distinctive traits so that each can be classified as a different race or even species. But one can turn this around and say that mountain species tend to have restricted ranges.

It is possible, however, to recognize a few very general classes of mountain habitats. At somewhere between seven and nine thousand feet in most tropical mountain systems, the cloud forest gives way to a much more stunted and limited sort of vegetation. This higher zone has been aptly called "elfin woodland." The

A member of the camel family, vicuñas (shown above at 15,000 feet in southern Peru) occupy the sheep niche in the high Andes from Peru southward. (O. P. Pearson)

persisting fog continues to allow a rich growth of mosses and lichens, but the shallow soil, the cold, and the wind result in a twisted growth of shrubs and small trees which often give the effect of a Japanese garden or of the illustrations used for fairy tales. Gnomes, leprechauns, and elves would be fitting inhabitants for such a landscape.

This presently gives way to completely open country. Tree line varies greatly in different mountain systems. It may be as low as six thousand feet on some tropical islands, more than thirteen thousand feet in some parts of the Andes and Himalayas. Above tree line, the vegetation is tundra-like, yet the conditions of life differ in many ways from those above the geographical tree line of the subarctic. There is no permafrost—often there is very little soil on the rocky heights—and in mid-tropics there is little or no seasonal change in the course of the year. But in both the far north and mountain heights, temperature becomes the limiting factor for life, and this results in many similarities. Because of the differences, it would be misleading to call the open country of great heights "tundra" or even "mountain tundra." I prefer the Spanish word *paramo,* which could be used not only for the Andes but for the landscape above mountain tree line everywhere.

Finally, at about fifteen thousand feet, snow begins to persist all year round even in the mid-tropics, so that snowfields and glaciers become the permanent landscape. Of course there are great differences in the elevation of snow line, depending, like the tree line, on local conditions.

Insects and spiders reach the greatest heights. L. W. Swan, an American ecologist who has studied paramo conditions in both hemispheres, found immature spiders at 22,000 feet in the Himalayas, though he had no idea what they could find to eat at that height. He also found that ants, bees, wasps, butterflies, moths, beetles, and bugs—a considerable variety of insects—were fairly common at elevations up to 16,000 feet. Insect life at that altitude is easy enough in the warm radiant heat of the sun, but as everyone who has climbed to high altitudes knows, the contrast in warmth between sun and shade is abrupt and great. This means that insect activity in cloudy weather is greatly restricted. Of butterflies, Swan noted that "they not only come to earth during cloudy weather but lie on their sides in a manner most unbecoming to butterflies." Insects disappear at night, probably into places like rock crevices; at high altitudes they have to face a daily problem comparable to hibernation in the far north. High-altitude mammals like mice, foxes, and snow leopards also pass the night in underground lairs.

The Goat Habit

There may be considerable areas of level or gently rolling country in the paramo zone—high valleys and plateaus. But there are also precipitous slopes and rock-strewn landscapes that present special locomotion problems for animals, especially mammals. To get about in such terrain, a mammal must be agile and sure-footed. These are the outstanding characteristics of one group of antelope-like grazing mammals, the caprines—goats, sheep, ibex, and the like. There are mountain species of this family on all of the continents except South America and Australia, and many of them show incredible mountaineering skills. To be sure, the group also includes such exceptions as the stolid musk oxen of the tundra and the peculiar cowlike takins of high Himalayan valleys, which hardly look agile or fleet.

Among the members of the goat family are the chamois and ibex of the mountains of Europe. Our common vocabulary is confused by classification problems here, as in so many cases. The ibex is a "true goat" while the chamois belongs to a subgroup called "rock goats." The Rocky Mountain goat of North America belongs with the chamois; it is not a goat in the most narrow meaning of that word. But in the larger sense of the word, all caprines are goats, which, incidentally, makes sheep a kind of goat too, for they share the goatlike mountain skills.

The chamois seems to be maintaining its position fairly well on the higher and more inaccessible mountains of southern Europe from Spain to the Caucasus, but the wild ibex is apparently doomed. It disappeared from the Bavarian Alps back in the fifteenth century, and by the present century there were only a few small herds in the mountains of Italy and Spain. Italian ibex have been reintroduced into Switzerland, though, and are holding their own with protection from hunters.

Mountains

81 Dall or white sheep in Mt. McKinley
National Park, Alaska. (Ed Park)

82–85 High mountain animals must be sure-footed and alert: left, mountain goats of the South Dakota Black Hills (Ed Park); left below, domesticated alpacas of the Peruvian Andes (Carl Koford); right, the ibex (Schocher: Conzett and Huber); and below, the chamois of the Swiss alps (Feuerstein: Conzett and Huber).

With the present wild ibex, there is always a question of "purity." They inter-breed freely with domestic goats—and goats are everywhere around the Mediterranean. Perhaps the wild forms, instead of becoming extinct, have simply merged with the domestic stock. With the goat, as with most domestic animals, no one is sure which wild species formed the original domestic strains. But it is a curious paradox that with goats, as with horses, cattle, and dogs, the wild relatives of the domesticated species are unable to maintain themselves in the man-altered landscape.

The American Rocky Mountain goat, like its European relative, the chamois, seems in no immediate danger of extinction. This beautiful white animal is so incredibly skillful at clambering over rock surfaces that it easily outdoes wolves, pumas, bears, and other possible predators, including men. The Rocky Mountain goat lives for the most part above tree line, even through the winter, depending on its goatlike ability to eat almost anything; in this respect it differs from the chamois, which prefers to stay within the mountain forests.

North America also has mountain sheep—the bighorn and its close relative, the Dall. The bighorn sheep has not adapted at all well to advancing civilization. Once abundant all through the western mountains, it is now limited to carefully protected herds on mountain reservations. The Dall sheep, which has a more northern range than the bighorn, is smaller, has slenderer and less tightly curved horns, and is lighter colored, almost pure white in some parts of its range.

The habits of these two species of sheep are very similar. In the case of the Dall sheep, careful observations were made by Adolph Murie during the several years he studied the wolves and other animals of the Mount McKinley National Park in Alaska. The sheep feed chiefly on grasses, sedges, and woody plants like willow, cranberry, and sage. Mosses and lichens, important in the diet of other animals of high altitudes and the far north, are little eaten. Murie found that in the absence of hunting by men the sheep population of the reservation was holding its own nicely. The principle predators were wolves, but the chief hazard for the sheep was the occasional severe winter when a heavy snow cover resulted in many deaths from starvation.

Murie was able to watch wolves hunting sheep on several occasions. They would go after the lambs, and if they could maneuver so that the lambs were chased downhill, they had a good chance of getting their prey. But even the lambs were better than the wolves at running uphill over precipitous terrain. In fact, the sheep seemed hardly to mind wolves in the vicinity as long as they were above their enemy; sheep in flat country or valleys were much more timid and wary than those browsing on rugged slopes.

It is often thought that eagles are the chief enemies of mountain sheep and goats, but Murie found little evidence of this in the case of the Dall sheep. The newborn lambs stay very close to their mothers until they are a month or so old, by which time they are too big for an eagle to handle. To be sure, an eagle occasionally gets a lamb, but this seems to be quite rare. The idea of eagles as sheep predators may be based partly on the fact that eagles are often seen swooping down at sheep or other animals, but this may be sheer play. Murie once watched an eagle dive at a wolf eleven times in a row, each time just missing the jumping and snapping wolf. The eagle, at least, seemed to be enjoying the game.

There are no native caprines in South America, but the sheep niche in the

86 The "weeping woods": moss-carpeted cloud forest at 9,000 feet in the Congo. (Emil Schulthess)

Yaks, now usually domesticated, in the Himalayas (Detlef Hecker: Bavaria Verlag)

high Andes, from Peru southward, is occupied by the vicuña, a member of the camel family. There are four cameline species in South America: the llama, alpaca, guanaco, and vicuña. Llamas and alpacas are now known only as domesticated animals: the first as the pack animal of the Peruvian and Bolivian highlands, the second as a producer of abundant long wool. The wild llamalike guanacos range from sea level at the southern tip of Patagonia to the highest grasslands of the Andes, but the wild vicuñas are found only in the mountains, at elevations between twelve thousand and sixteen thousand feet—mostly above fourteen thousand feet.

An American ecologist, Carl Koford, spent nearly a year camping in various parts of the Peruvian highlands studying vicuña habits, and published his findings in some detail in a technical journal, *Ecological Monographs*. He found the vicuñas to be highly gregarious, living in two kinds of associations—*bands,* consisting of a single adult male with several females and their young, and *troupes* of unattached males, mostly yearlings or two-year-olds. The bands were strongly territorial, living throughout the year in a limited, well-defined area which the male vigorously defended. The troupes of unattached males showed no social cohesion in attack or defense, so that the proprietary family male was able to drive them off whenever they wandered into his territory.

Vicuña fighting, like that of most wild animals, is largely a matter of posturing, rarely involving actual physical contact. Like other camelines, vicuñas have a curious habit of spitting at each other, which, as Koford remarks, is an act that "shows 'displeasure' insufficient to merit a kick." The spitting is a "quick forceful expulsion of air, which incidentally sprays out saliva and small fragments of whatever masticated food is in the mouth." Spitting encounters were common between females within a particular band, between females and young, and between males in a troupe, but rare between adult males and females.

It has sometimes been thought that the vicuñas are in danger of extinction, but Koford found them to be holding their own, despite the inroads of men and dogs. It seems likely that this is because the Indians cannot afford efficient guns, and because the Indian dogs, living on the verge of starvation, "are neither cunning, agile, nor swift." The vicuñas generally have little difficulty outrunning the dogs. Pumas were probably the chief enemies of vicuñas in the past, but they do not appear to be common now in these open highlands. Condors may at times kill the newborn infants. In one case in which Koford watched a vicuña give birth, within twenty minutes fourteen condors had arrived to watch—standing at distances of twenty to sixty yards. The birds were chased by other females in the band, and within half an hour after the birth, all of the condors had left. But such great interest may well indicate that at times the condors have better luck.

Mountain Sanctuary

There are, then, many special mountain animals in the world: members of the goat tribe, sure-footedly adapted to precipices and rocky slopes; birds that nest on cliffs and crags; butterflies that live only in remote high valleys. But along with these there are many animals that are now found only in mountainous regions because these are still a sanctuary from advancing civilization. Steep slopes often are not worth cultivating or even lumbering, so that they have so far been let alone. In these remote places animals that once roamed the lowland forests and plains may still persist. In this respect, mountains are like the northern wilderness of the taiga.

Thus in the eastern United States, the Appalachians and the Adirondacks form

A comparison of latitude and altitude. Going up a mountain is like going north: vegetation changes with altitude much as it does with latitude.

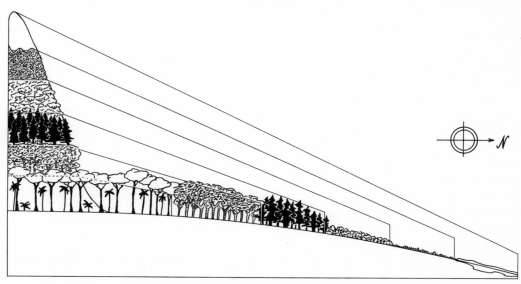

Ice and snow

Mosses and lichens

Low herbaceous growth

Coniferous forests

Deciduous forests

Tropical forests

a refuge for many animals, like the black bear and the fisher that once ranged widely through the deciduous forest. The Scandinavian mountains have similarly provided refuge for animals like the wolverine, and the Apennines and the Alps for the ibex.

But mountains are far from a safe refuge, as the grizzly bears in the United States have found. Man simply does not tolerate large carnivores. The last lions disappeared from Europe somewhere around A.D. 100, but they persisted in the mountains of North Africa until about 1922, when the last ones were shot in the Atlas range. The history of the chinchilla in the paramo of the Andes shows that mountains are no protection for a small and innocuous animal, if man wants it badly enough. Records of the customs office in the port of Coquimbo in Chile show that in 1905, for example, 18,153 dozen chinchilla pelts were sold, at an average price of $100 per dozen; next year the number sold was reduced by half, and by half again the following year. In 1909, 2328 dozen pelts were sold, and the price had risen to $500 per dozen. The instructions to European agents then were to purchase skins at any price, which served to finish off the wild chinchillas of the high altitudes.

Mountains also sometimes serve as refuges in a geological sense, as the habitat of "relic species" left over from animal groups that were once widespread. Thus, from fossil evidence, it seems that much of the evolution of the camel family took place in western North America and that in past ages camel-like animals were common in many parts of the world. But now only the guanaco and vicuña survive wild in the South American Andes, remotely separated from the other living camelines of the deserts of North Africa and Asia.

15

Island Life

Islands have a special fascination for many people. Perhaps it is because we like things to be clear and simple, or because there is something romantic about isolation from the outer world. And a small island in a genial climate can be "cosy." It may be difficult to come and go, but intrusion is also difficult, so that the human yearning for security, privacy, and protection gets some satisfaction. "Insularity," it is interesting to note, carries with it implications of smugness and conservatism—of self-satisfaction.

Of course there are all sorts of islands, ranging in size from isolated boulders to great land masses like New Guinea and Greenland. Australia and Antarctica are island continents. About all that these have in common are clear definition of boundaries in relation to the surrounding water, relative isolation from one another and from the main continental land masses, and a relatively high proportion of coastal conditions. But these few physical attributes have various biological consequences.

There are many biological analogies between islands and lakes. Both are discontinuous habitats—isolated patches of water on land or of land in water. The range in size, from puddles to inland seas, is similar to that of islands. Also, like ponds and lakes, islands are apt to have rather short geological histories; they become connected with continents or disappear under the sea in the course of geological change. Some islands, like some lakes, have had a long-isolated existence: in this respect, the Hawaiian and Galapagos Islands are comparable to lakes like Baikal and Tanganyika. Under such conditions special and peculiar local faunas evolve.

In general, the basic problem of island life—or of lake life—is dispersal: how to get from one favorable place to another through an alien environment. Of course every animal must have some means of getting about, no matter where it lives. Dispersal is a general problem for all living things, emphasized in island situations because of the special difficulties.

Island Hopping

Among land animals, the most dramatic means of dispersal is through flight. Sustained flight, as distinguished from gliding, has been developed independently by four different kinds of animals: insects, birds, bats, and the flying reptiles of the geological past. The powerful fliers could theoretically get almost anywhere on the planet, and a few of them have, even to the most remote islands of the seas. Yet, except for some of the oceanic birds, no species has achieved a world-wide distribution unaided by man. The ability to move often seems to be counteracted by a tendency to stay. It is curious how often migrating birds come back year after year to the same place to breed; they could fly anywhere, but they don't.

Many small organisms are dispersed passively by the currents of the atmosphere. This is especially true of the spores of microbes and of plants like ferns. But animals, too, get about this way. Many spiders float attached to a long strand of their silk; and spiders turn up in variety on the most remote islands. Experiments with sticky fly paper on airplanes have shown that small insects may often be carried by air currents—mosquitoes, for instance, have been found at a height of five thousand feet above the ground.

If the flying animals are the most mobile, the crawling and burrowing ones are the least. Land snails, especially, often have a very restricted distribution. Each little hummock in southern Florida had its peculiar variety of tree snail (*Liguus*) in the days before amateur collectors took to moving them about, and before real estate developments destroyed the hummocks. Yet animals like snails and earthworms do get about, though it is sometimes difficult to imagine how. On land, time gives distance even to the slowest movers; over a period of millions of years, an accident like a tree branch blown by a hurricane may bring new inhabitants to the remotest islands.

Many land animals are good swimmers, so that water is not necessarily a barrier to their dispersal. An East Indian species of crocodile has been known to swim five hundred miles, and many snakes are at home in the water. Among mammals, the hippopotamus easily swims the eighteen miles between Zanzibar and the African coast, and polar bears have been seen at sea equally far from the nearest resting place. Reindeer and other members of the deer family also swim well and are frequently seen crossing rivers or lakes.

An island in the Bahama a tight little environmen (Fritz Goro: *Life*)

A few animals get about by hitchhiking. Of course this is always true of parasites and symbionts, which get carried about by their hosts. Other animals have also been found taking free rides—tiny pseudoscorpions hanging onto flying insects, for instance. Wading birds frequently collect pellets of mud on their feet, and the seeds of plants as well as some mud-loving animals get transported in this way. In modern times, an immense number of animals have been carried all over the place by man; and some, like rats and lizards, get rides in his canoes and ships. Among lizards, the geckoes, which lay hard-shelled eggs attached to crevices in bark, may be transported not only by canoes but by drifting logs without any help from man.

Kinds of Islands

Land animals can get about, but some of them do so more easily than others, and this difference is reflected in the faunas of the various islands of the world. Alfred Russel Wallace, who published a book called *Island Life* in 1880, distinguished between *continental* and *oceanic* islands. The oceanic islands were those that had never had a connection with the continental land masses, so that the ancestors of

their inhabitants must have arrived somehow over water. He felt he could recognize such islands by the absence of mammals (except bats) and by the absence of amphibia (frogs and salamanders). Though some land mammals, such as deer and hippopotamuses, take to water readily and are good swimmers, none is known to undertake long ocean trips. Amphibia cannot long withstand exposure to water with a salt content like that of the ocean.

Neither land mammals nor amphibia occur in the faunas of such island groups as Hawaii, the Galapagos, or the Azores, which, from their volcanic structure, appear to have arisen directly from the ocean floor. Rats, of course, are everywhere, but it is quite clear that they have always come along with man, as have domesticated animals.

This division of continental and oceanic islands works well for extreme cases. The British islands clearly are a part of Europe and have been separated by the English channel only in the course of the retreat of the last glaciation, a matter of a few ten thousands of years. Trinidad is similarly a fragment rather recently separated from South America. Hawaii and Galapagos and many scattered small volcanic or coral islands are, on the other hand, clearly oceanic.

But there are other cases that are not so clear. The West Indies and the Philippines have terrestrial mammals and amphibia, but a very limited number of kinds; and it is hard to understand why other animals are not there if the islands once had land connections with the continents. It is easier to explain the inhabitants by the accidental transport that might happen over millions of years than it is to explain the absences. Then there are the islands of Madagascar and New Zealand, both of which clearly have very ancient separate histories. Madagascar was probably a part of the African continent a very long time ago, but whether New Zealand was ever connected with other land is debatable.

Of course islands differ greatly according to their size, location, structure, and climate. A small island cannot support as many different kinds of animals as a larger one, and islands in the mid-tropics offer different conditions from those in higher latitudes. In the Pacific, it is common to distinguish between "high" and "low" islands—those like Tahiti or Truk with hills or mountains, and the purely coral atolls that are almost awash. The Marshall Islands, with little rain, are "dry," while the Carolines, nearer the equator, are "wet."

But these differences will be clearer if we consider the conditions of animal life on a few different island groups.

The Strange Animals of the Galapagos

The Galapagos Islands have a special importance in the history of biology—and in the history of ideas—because it was there, in 1835, that Charles Darwin first consciously started to speculate about the origin of species. Why were almost all of the animals of the islands so very different from those of the mainland? Why was each island inhabited by a distinct species of such animals as the giant tortoises, the mocking thrushes, and the finches? In his book *The Voyage of the "Beagle"* Darwin set down all of the facts, but he refrained from speculation except to note that "one is astonished at the amount of creative force... displayed on these small, barren and rocky islands."

Many land animals, such as these reindeer, are good swimmers, so that water is not necessarily a barrier to their dispersal. (Walter Hege: Bavaria Verlag)

The Galapagos Archipelago lies astride the equator some 650 miles west of Ecuador, to which it belongs. There are a few fertile upland areas, but for the most part the islands are dry and stony, with a sparse vegetation of cactus and thorn scrub. Ecuador has used the islands chiefly as a penal colony, and while a few Europeans have gone there to live in much publicized efforts to escape it all, no one has pretended that the place was a South Seas paradise. The animals, though, are fascinating, and their habits have been carefully described by Irenaus Eibl-Eibesfeldt in a book called *Galapagos: The Noah's Ark of the Pacific*.

The giant tortoises are the most famous of the Galapagos animals. They are now all classed as a single species, but with distinct races on each of the larger islands. At one time they must have been extremely abundant. From the days of the first explorers and buccaneers, mariners in the Pacific regularly stopped at the islands to stow on board supplies of tortoises as a source of fresh meat. An American zoologist, studying the logbooks of whalers, found records of hundreds of thousands of tortoises put aboard. They soon became extinct on many of the islands, and it looked as though they would follow the way of the dodo and the great auk. They still persist in several places, however, even though the young often fall victim to the dogs and pigs that have gone wild on the islands.

The giant tortoises are different from anything now living elsewhere on earth, but their presence is not particularly puzzling; after all, members of the turtle tribe often are amphibious or aquatic, and they turn up fairly often in island faunas. There was a similar (but unrelated) giant tortoise on the Mascarene Islands of the Indian Ocean, but this became extinct along with its compatriot, the dodo, in the last century.

The newly hatched tortoises are tiny—weighing two or three ounces—but Eibl-Eibesfeldt found that they grow very rapidly. One that he took back to Germany increased twenty-five times in weight and tripled in length in two years. But it still would take a long time to reach the six hundred or so pounds of the adult.

To biologists, the most interesting of the Galapagos inhabitants are the birds, especially the group now known as Darwin's finches. There are thirteen species of these, different enough to be divided among three or four genera. Some of the species have slightly different subspecies or races on the main islands of the archipelago, so that a total of thirty-seven forms have been named. Yet all the birds look very much alike, and it is obvious that they have all descended from some common ancestor. The striking differences are in the shapes of the beaks, which reflect great differences in food habits. In the absence of competition in the Galapagos, these finches have come to fill niches occupied by a wide variety of birds in other parts of the world.

One often-mentioned species of Galapagos finch, for instance, has occupied the woodpecker niche—that of digging out insects from under bark and from holes and crevices. There are no woodpeckers on the islands, so this food supply of hidden insects was open for exploitation. The Galapagos finch has not developed the drilling beak and long, sticky tongue of woodpeckers, though he does have a good stout beak for opening up cracks. To dig out the hidden insects, he uses a cactus spine which, held point foremost in the beak, can be used as a probe. This is one of the most remarkable of the scattered cases of tool-using found in the animal kingdom—cases that make it impossible to say that man is unique because he uses tools. The uniqueness of man is only in shaping tools according to a predetermined design. Other finches have adopted the habits of flycatchers and warblers. Some are ground birds, others arboreal. Some eat insects, some eat seeds, and others are vegetarian.

There are a number of land birds on the islands besides the finches: a peculiar mockingbird, a pigeon, a hawk, two owls, a rail, a swallow, three flycatchers, and a warbler. There is a cuckoo no different from a species of the South American mainland, and barn swallows and bobolinks are regular visitors.

Darwin noticed long ago how tame the Galapagos birds were.

> "A gun is here almost superfluous; for with the muzzle I pushed a hawk off the branch of a tree. One day, whilst lying down, a mocking-thrush alighted on the edge of a pitcher, made of the shell of a tortoise, which I held in my hand, and began very quietly to sip the water; it allowed me to lift it from the ground whilst seated on the vessel... It would appear that the birds of this archipelago, not having as yet learnt that man is a more dangerous animal than the tortoise or the Amblyrhynchus [the land iguana], disregard him, in the same manner as in England shy birds, such as magpies, disregard the cows and horses grazing in our fields."

From the descriptions of Eibl-Eibesfeldt, it appears that the birds are still tame despite more than a hundred years of experience with man. This tameness is often characteristic of birds of oceanic islands, where there has been no need to develop instinctive fear of predatory mammals. This can be disastrous when man shows up, as is witnessed by the fate of the dodo and the great auk.

Birds of oceanic islands also sometimes lose the ability to fly—again perhaps because flight is not needed for escape from predators. None of the land birds of the

The marine iguanas of Galapagos live on rocky shores and feed on seaweeds they get by diving. (Alfred M. Bailey)

Galapagos is flightless, but there is a distinctive species of penguin and a curious flightless bird called Harris' cormorant.

Despite their vulnerability, these cormorants have so far managed to survive in a few remote spots, and Eibl-Eibesfeldt was able to make careful observations on two nesting pairs. He watched the hungry young induce the adults to regurgitate squid, and he noted the elaborate ceremonies between the adults in the ritual of changing places on the nest. The bird that emerged from the water always brought a bit of seaweed as a token gift for the brooding partner. Of course this sort of behavior is not unique to the Galapagos: birds everywhere have developed elaborate behavior patterns that are in many ways comparable to human rituals. But such observations have a special flavor when made on some rare species in a remote part of the world.

The Galapagos fauna also includes a number of lizards, including a land iguana, and a marine species with habits quite different from those of any other iguana. It lives on rocky shores and feeds on seaweed that it gets by diving. There are also several local species of snakes. Since these represent two distinct groups, it seems that snakes may somehow have arrived twice at the islands in the geological past— perfectly possible accidents in view of the swimming habits of snakes.

The Hawaiian Islands

The Hawaiian Islands are larger and more numerous than the Galapagos, and much more remote. They are over two thousand miles from the American coast,

Lemur-like primates have been found as fossils in many parts of the world, but only in Madagascar as living animals. Above: *Lemur macaco* or black lemur. Left: *Lepilemur mustelinus ruficandatus*. (J. J. Petter)

almost as far from the nearest other Pacific islands to the west, and much farther from continental land to the west. Lying just within the tropics, their rich volcanic soils, with high rainfall in many places, support a luxuriant and varied vegetation that offers a favorable environment for any animal that can get there. But few animals managed to do so, at least before man started purposefully and accidentally introducing them.

The native vertebrates include only birds and one species of bat; there are no fresh-water fishes, amphibians, reptiles, or land mammals. Not many insects reached the Hawaiian Islands, either. There is only one native species of butterfly, for instance. There were no mosquitoes in this paradise until Europeans started to arrive with sailing ships, bringing the yellow fever mosquito—but not the disease.

Insects that did get established in the geological past evolved into a respectable number of diversified species: as an example, there are more kinds of fruit flies (*Drosophila*) on these islands than anywhere else in the world.

The difference between the native fauna of Hawaii and that of the Galapagos illustrates what the distinguished paleontologist G. G. Simpson has called the "sweepstakes principle." This is simply that the farther out an island is from continental land masses, the less chance animals have of getting there in a given stretch of time. Of course, animals would have a better chance of reaching a large island than a small one, and a more diversified fauna could find places to live. But since oceanic islands generally are not large, this is a secondary consideration.

The Galapagos, six hundred miles from the mainland, drew turtles, snakes, various lizards, and a mouse (there is a small group of local species of mice belonging to the American genus *Oryzomys*). None of these kinds of creatures reached Hawaii, two thousand miles from the coast: among vertebrates, only birds and the one species of bat made the journey successfully.

But the birds that colonized Hawaii started on an evolutionary spree of their own even more remarkable than that of the Galapagos finches. They include one special family, the Hawaiian honey-creepers or Drepanididae, with seventeen genera and forty-three species and subspecies, all presumably evolved from a single colonization by some honey-creeper from America back in the geological past. Some of the Hawaiian birds continued the nectar-feeding habits of their ancestors, but others developed a variety of adaptations to exploit the rich food possibilities of the islands' forests, becoming insect-eaters, fruit-eaters, seed-eaters, and the like.

There are a number of other distinctive Hawaiian land birds aside from the honey-creepers: a crow, several thrushes and miller birds, and a number of others without distinctive English names. The Harvard ornithologist Ernst Mayr thinks that over millions of years different birds may have successfully become established on the islands on fourteen different occasions to give rise to the known fauna. Something like thirty species of forest birds have become extinct since civilization reached the islands, partly as a consequence of the destruction of the forests, partly because of introduced bird diseases. Great efforts are now being made to protect what is left of this very peculiar fauna.

New Zealand—a World unto Itself

New Zealand is, or was, a world unto itself. The two main islands have a combined area of over 100,000 square miles, with complex topography and a wide variety of animal habitats. Australia, the nearest continent, is a thousand miles away, and it is clear that there has been no land connection between the two for a very long time, if ever. There were no mammals of any sort (except two varieties of bat) before Polynesian man first arrived, probably about A.D. 750. There is a very ancient type of frog in New Zealand; and a lizard, *Sphenodon*, belonging to a group that lived at the time of the dinosaurs but that disappeared from the rest of the world a hundred million years ago. These may be left from some ancient land connection; but it is equally possible that in this vast stretch of time all of the New Zealand animals got there, somehow, over water.

The most striking of the aboriginal animals of New Zealand were the moas—

large, completely wingless birds. Remains have been found of twenty species, which have been classified into six different genera. All were grazing animals, living on grass and leaves; the largest, *Dinornis maximus,* stood ten or twelve feet tall, with a heavy, bulky body, and it may have required as much forage each day as an ox would. They must also have been very abundant; as many as eight hundred giant skeletons to an acre have been found, the bones being used for manufacturing fertilizer in modern times. Flocks of these grazing birds thus occupied the same sort of niches in the grasslands of New Zealand as do the grazing antelope of Africa or the kangaroos of Australia.

The moas, unused to mammal predators, formed an easy food supply for the first humans to arrive at the islands, and archeologists have been able to reconstruct a culture that lasted from about 750 until 1300 based almost entirely on the exploitation of these birds. When the Maoris arrived in the fourteenth century, bringing agriculture and a new way of life, the moas were probably already almost all gone.

Madagascar

Madagascar is a very large island, with an area of about 240,000 square miles, lying in the Indian Ocean about 260 miles from the nearest point of continental Africa. Much of the center of the island is a plateau, with elevations between three thousand and six thousand feet and with peaks rising to nine thousand feet, thus providing a considerable diversity of tropical habitats, including large areas of rain forest. Madagascar is geologically ancient—fossil dinosaurs have been found there—and whether it has ever been directly connected with the African mainland is a matter of zoogeographical debate. The present fauna is very distinctive, but for the most part it has African affinities.

As one thinks of moas in New Zealand, drepanid birds in Hawaii, and finches in the Galapagos, so with Madagascar lemurs at once come to mind. Lemur-like primates have been found as fossils in many parts of the world, but as living animals, only in Madagascar. The Madagascar forms, however, are very diverse. The living kinds are usually classified in three different families, with some ten genera and twenty species, and it is clear that various other species have become extinct within recent times. Some of these lemurs are arboreal, some are ground-living like the baboons; some are nocturnal, some diurnal. They have come, in short, to occupy a variety of niches in their isolated island home.

But lemurs are not the only mammals in Madagascar. There is a peculiar indigenous family of insectivores with about thirty species; there is a group of about twelve species of cricetine rats; and there are about twelve species of the mongoose family (Viverridae), all belonging to peculiar local genera. From the abundance of the fossils, it also appears that a pygmy hippopotamus, different from anything known from Africa, was common during Pleistocene times.

Madagascar also has a distinct bird fauna. There were at least two genera and several species of giant "elephant birds" there that were reminiscent of the New Zealand moas but were not related to them. They had become extinct before the first European arrived, but it seems likely that man was the destructive agent, here as elsewhere. Three species of flightless rail-like birds still survive, classed by ornithologists as a family by themselves (Mesoenatidae) and not clearly related to any

The dragon lizard of Komodo, which reaches a length of ten feet and a weight of 300 pounds, lives mainly on an East Indian island that is twenty miles long and twelve miles wide. (Sven Gillsater)

other known birds, although belonging in the same order with the cranes and rails.

There are about 150 species of frogs in Madagascar, which would seem to argue for a connection with the mainland at one time, but they are mostly endemic and may have evolved locally from a few arrivals. There are also many snakes, lizards, and turtles, some of them very peculiar. On the other hand, many groups of reptiles, important in other places, are absent: for instance, poisonous snakes.

The West Indies

One would expect the fauna of the West Indies to represent a sample of that of the American continents, just as the islands of the East Indies—especially Sumatra, Java, and Borneo—are representative of the Orient. Admittedly, most of the animals of the West Indies have relatives on the nearby continent, but it is astonishing how many groups are not represented on the islands. Cuba, for instance, is about the same size as Java (40,000 square miles, as opposed to 49,000). But Java has leopards, monkeys, and rhinoceroses, and until recent times it had elephants, antelopes, several species of wild cattle, and the like. Yet there are no large native mammals in Cuba or the other West Indian islands, and no evidence that any have ever lived there.

Cuba and Hispaniola are large, mountainous islands, with varied climate and vegetation; Puerto Rico and Jamaica are smaller but also varied. Aside from bats and rodents, the only living native West Indian mammal is a curious little insectivore called *Solenodon*, which is still occasionally found in remote spots in Cuba and Hispaniola and which is not closely related to any other living mammal. Among known fossils, there is another peculiar insectivore which became extinct in modern times; several species of ground sloths; and a fossil monkey in Jamaica. That is all—a remarkably small number.

Birds are numerous in the West Indies, but many families that seem typical of tropical America are absent—toucans, for instance, and tinamous, ovenbirds, ant birds, and manakins. Reptiles are also numerous, but they are mostly lizards. There are few snakes, and no poisonous ones except the fer-de-lance on some of the islands of the Lesser Antilles. It has been suggested that this was introduced by the early colonists to help keep slaves from running away, but this seems farfetched. The butterflies are also limited—striking tropical types like the glittering Morphos and the owl-like Caligos are absent.

The most likely explanation is that the West Indies have never had a land connection with either of the American continents: that they have acquired their animal inhabitants by the hazards of overwater transport in the course of many millions of years. The hardest thing to explain by this theory is *Peripatus*, a delicate, caterpillar-like, very ancient sort of animal that lives among the debris on the ground in the rain forests of both hemispheres. A peculiar species of this animal occurs in the forested mountains of Haiti, but how could it have got there over the sea? A tree frog, desperately clutching a branch, might ride a hurricane successfully once in a million years to colonize a new island. But *Peripatus?* Yet if *Peripatus* crawled to Haiti, why did so many other things stay behind? These are the puzzles of zoogeography.

Krakatoa

On August 27, 1883, the island of Krakatoa, in the Sunda Strait between Java and Sumatra, blew up. A cubic mile of earth was blown seventeen miles into the air, and the explosion was heard three thousand miles away. Much of the island disappeared, and the parts that were left had been so thoroughly burned and were so thickly covered with ash and pumice that no living thing could survive. This disaster gave scientists a fine chance to observe the slow process by which island populations become established. Since the nearest land not destroyed by the eruption, Sibesia Island, was about eleven miles away, anything that reached Krakatoa after 1883 must have crossed at least this much water.

Nine months after the explosion a scientist found only a few blades of grass and a single spider—small spiders manage to get about very well, floating in the wind

Island Life

87 Terns and other sea birds find security in such island refuges as this on Australia's Great Barrier Reef. (Fritz Goro: *Life*)

88 Left: A sea turtle returns to the water after leaving its eggs in the sands of the Great Barrier Reef. (Fritz Goro: *Life*)

89 Above: Black-footed albatross, powerful flyers, come to rest on Midway Island. (Alfred M. Bailey)

90 Right: This species of marine iguana (the pink one is in breeding condition) and the sleeping sea lion in the fore-ground are found only in the Galapagos Islands, but the "Sally Lightfoot" crabs occur in many places. (Robert I. Bowman)

on strands of silk. After six years, in 1889, there was a considerable list of insects
and spiders, and even one vertebrate, a lizard. In 1908, twenty-five years after the
eruption, 263 animal species were found—still mostly insects, but also 4 species of
land snails, 2 reptiles, and 16 birds. In 1920, 573 species of animals were found,
including a snake *(Python reticulatus),* 26 breeding birds, and 3 mammals (2 kinds
of bats and the ubiquitous rat). The lizards and rats may have come on driftwood
or on visiting boats, but the python probably got there by swimming; and the
vast majority of the species surely had arrived by "natural" means of dispersal.
After thirty-seven years, about 60 per cent of the original fauna had been replaced,
judging by comparison with the number of species found on islands of similar size
in the region.

Coral Islands

In addition to the major archipelagos and continental islands, there are numerous
small islands scattered over the vast stretches of the oceans—most abundantly in
the southern and western Pacific. These oceanic islands are either of volcanic or
limestone-reef origin. Among the most curious and interesting of these are the
atolls, described earlier in the chapter on coral reefs.

The atolls are necessarily oceanic: they have grown out of the sea. They do not have the geological permanence of dry land; with the changes of sea level due to the forming and melting of continental glaciers, they have sometimes been exposed and eroded, sometimes submerged. Atolls never have elevations of more than fifteen feet above sea level, the height to which boulders are piled by storms; and they have all probably been completely submerged at times during the past ten or twenty thousand years in the course of small fluctuations in sea level.

The conditions for land life on atolls are thus rather special. Their existence as islands has been too interrupted to allow for the evolution of special local species; they are separated from each other and from the continents by wide expanses of sea; they are small and often have no fresh water, though in regions of high rainfall, fresh water accumulates in the porous limestone rock, floating on the heavier sea water beneath, with the water level rising and falling according to the tides.

Any animal found on an atoll must have had some means of getting there either over or through the seas, which sets strict limits on the number and kinds of species. In the case of plants growing on the atoll of Ifaluk in the Caroline Islands, I calculated that about one-third of the species had arrived there by "natural" means; one-third had been brought purposely by man; and one-third were accidentally introduced through human agency. The calculation for animals would be more difficult, but all vertebrates (except birds and bats) must have come with man, and probably a great many of the insects had been accidentally introduced.

Crabs are always conspicuous on atolls; of course they get there easily enough through the marine larval stages. Hermit crabs are apt to be everywhere on land, awkwardly carrying their shells and fulfilling the scavenging functions that would belong to more efficient land animals in other situations. There is also that curious

A New Zealand kiwi ventures from its burrow at nightfall.
(National Publicity Studi of New Zealand)

The giant moa, once a grazing bird of New Zealand, now extinct.

giant relative of the hermit crabs, the coconut crab. It hides in burrows or hollows during the day and comes out at night to scavenge. It is perfectly capable of opening a coconut; it loosens the fibers by scratching the husk with its pincers and pulls off the strips, opening the nut itself by inserting one finger of the claw into the eye. Needless to say, the claws of coconut crabs are extremely powerful. The crabs are capable of climbing to the tops of the palms, but it is doubtful whether they actually cut down the nuts.

Insects on an atoll may be very abundant—flies and mosquitoes are sometimes great pests—but there are few species. On most Pacific atolls, for instance, there are only two species of butterflies, both powerful fliers that have managed to span the distances from island to island. Of reptiles, skinks and geckoes are everywhere, eating the insects, but it is fairly certain that these arrived with men and canoes, as did the rats.

The islands form fine nesting places for hosts of sea birds of many kinds. The birds have no transport problems in reaching the islands, and except where man is around they have few enemies. But man is almost everywhere; the Micronesians and Polynesians moved out to these Pacific islands perhaps two thousand years ago, and the island ecology can now be understood only in terms of human activities. The influence of man on the landscape is not limited to Pacific islands, however; it is apparent almost everywhere.

16

The Human Animal

If we take an airplane from New York to Chicago, from London to Berlin, or from Canton to Peiping, much of the landscape that unfolds below us is quite different from anything we have so far described in this book. The earth appears as a patchwork of sharply marked fields across which are drawn the firm lines of highways and railways, connecting the scattered splotches that are recognizable as villages, towns, and cities. These patterns on the earth are the consequence not of varying rainfall and temperature but of the activities of a particular animal, the human species. The list of landscape types, from rain forest to tundra, makes no allowance for fields, orchards, and towns; but nowadays these form the most extensive of the animal worlds on land, and it would be ridiculous to ignore this man-altered landscape.

What a curious creature this human animal is! He is an animal, without any doubt. The great apes—gorilla, chimpanzee, and orangutan—are most like man, and zoologists class them together as a group called the Anthropoidea, a superfamily of the order of primates in the class of mammals. Man differs from the apes in many ways: in the upright posture, with legs longer than arms, and with feet not much good for grasping things; in the lobed, protruding ears, prominent nose, and everted lips; in the scarcity and odd distribution of hair covering; and in the much enlarged brain. But a zoologist from Mars, examining pickled specimens of men and apes, would probably not be greatly impressed by the differences. Luckily, the classifications are made by men, who are greatly impressed with themselves; consequently, men are placed in one family, the Hominidae; and the apes in another, the Pongidae. All living men are classed as a single species, *Homo sapiens,* because the criterion for a species is the presence or absence of physiological or behavioral barriers to breeding, and it is obvious that the many varieties of men breed together easily enough when they come in contact.

As an animal man thus seems ordinary enough: the extraordinary thing is not the physical creature but his activities and accomplishments. Other animals modify landscapes: beavers making ponds, grazing herds maintaining grasslands, prairie dogs controlling the vegetation around their towns. But these activities are trivial compared with those of man, who has become a sort of geological force modifying the whole land surface of the planet. How did *Homo sapiens* get into this position?

Probably the primates ancestral to man were social carnivores. The carnivorous habit is rare among living primates: most of them are vegetarian or omniv-

Humans have long been ingenious fishermen: here the Wagenia tribe of the Congo brings in a haul in rapids above Stanleyville. (Emil Schulthess)

orous, eating whatever they can get in the way of insects, bird eggs, and the like. None of them is truly predatory in the sense that lions are, or wolves. But with man there is indirect evidence of long meat-eating habits, in that he can digest a variety of raw meat, from oysters to beefsteak; but without fire for cooking his vegetable diet is quite limited. There is also direct evidence of predation from the animal bones found associated with the earliest of the hominid fossils.

In his book *Adventures with the Missing Link*, Raymond Dart has tried to reconstruct the habits of the South African ape men. Dart studied 7159 fragments of bones, tooth, and horn that these creatures had left in their cave at Makapansgat. They must have had considerable skill in hunting, for these fragments represented the remains of at least 39 large bucks of kudu and roan antelope size, 126 medium-sized, wildebeest-type antelopes, 100 small gazelle-like animals, and 29 tiny duiker-like specimens. In addition, there were remains of 4 horses of extinct species, 6 chalicotheres (an extinct type of tree-browsing creatures), 6 giraffes also of extinct species, 5 rhinoceroses, a lone hippopotamus, 20 wart hogs, and 45 baboons.

Dart believes that these particular bones had generally been brought to the cave to be used as tools. Many anthropologists disagree with this interpretation, and the case for tool-using by the South African ape men is far from clear. But the bones do demonstrate considerable hunting skill—unless these creatures were purely scavengers.

These pre-men were undoubtedly social. The cave findings indicate larger-than-family groups, and the hunting of large game would require cooperating bands, perhaps of males only or of both sexes. A solitary human without weapons is a pretty feeble animal, not able to cope with anything but the smallest game and liable to fall victim to any passing lion or tiger. The social organization may well have been similar to that of the wolf pack—and the wolf is also a social carnivore. The size of the band was probably governed by the nature of the prey; a small group would not be able to get large or swift animals. But if the group became too large, there would be great problems in assuring a constant and adequate meat supply. Therefore the average band may have consisted of thirty or forty individuals.

The Australian aborigines—still a Stone Age culture—are successful kangaroo hunters. (Alfred M. Bailey)

The role of these pre-men in the biological community must have been similar to that of wolves; they were "higher-order consumers," in the ecological vocabulary. But with the development of tools and weapons they started diverging many thousands of years ago from the wolf pattern. This probably soon made them more efficient than any other predator, but it hardly changed the basic nature of their relations with the biological community. When these pre-men or early men learned to control fire, however, they did enter into an entirely new relationship with nature.

It will probably never be known with any certainty when, how, or where man first learned to use fire. Certainly it was a long time ago. Charred materials in the cave at Choukoutien in China, where the bones of Peking man were found, show that he already had fire, though he was a pretty low-browed sort of creature living perhaps half a million years ago. The earlier South African ape men probably did not have fire; at least no evidence has been found in their caves. With fire, man became an agent of ecological change. He could—and undoubtedly did—set fires in forests and grasslands to herd game and open up the landscape. Forest fires and grass fires antedate human activity: far back in the geological record there is evidence of fires, presumably started by lightning. But with man, fires became much more common and widespread, much more influential in altering the landscape.

Ten or twelve thousand years ago—just this morning as geological time is reckoned—another great change occurred in man's relations with nature because of the discovery of agriculture and animal domestication. Anthropologists call this the "Neolithic Revolution" because it marks the shift from the Old Stone Age to the New. But let us examine more closely man as a hunter and gatherer before considering the changes brought about by the discovery of agriculture.

Hunters and Gatherers

The Australian aborigines and various other peoples in different parts of the world still have a technical culture like that of the Old Stone Age, and we can learn a great deal by studying their methods of hunting and fishing. There are also considerable numbers of tools that have survived from the past, but these are almost always stone or bone. Wooden clubs and traps, fiber nets, and things of that sort have not survived, though they must have had a long history. One can find tantalizing glimpses of late Stone Age hunting methods in the cave paintings of southern Europe and in rock and cave drawings in other parts of the world. Mostly, though, man's knowledge in this field comes from a collection of clues on which we can speculate. From these clues and from the study of contemporary primitive people, it is clear that Stone Age man exercised great ingenuity in getting his animal food. Snares, traps, and pitfalls have a long history, as do clubs and spears. There are also a number of special inventions, like the boomerang of the Australians and the bola of the Patagonian Indians.

We know that the bow was in use at least in the late Stone Age because it appears in cave drawings of that time. How did man get this idea? It can be regarded as the first case in which man learned to store power, pulling back the bowstring for sudden release of the accumulated potential. It is difficult to imagine how this was discovered, but then it is difficult to imagine how many of the discoveries of human prehistory were made. Man today is apt to think that he is pretty clever, but in many things he has improved little on the techniques of his preliterate ancestors. This is particularly striking in fishing methods—the designs of fishhooks, nets, traps, harpoons, and spears go way back into prehistory, as do methods of fish poisoning.

For hunting on land, we have rifles and shotguns, which greatly increase our power of destruction—and our ability to make noise. We can make traps of steel. Yet the most remarkable thing is not our progress, but the amount that Stone Age man learned, not only about hunting but about the usefulness of all sorts of animals and plants in his environment. To be sure, knowledge went hand in hand with superstition—it still does—but both were effective in the sense that Stone Age man achieved a working relationship with his surroundings. Slowly he began to multiply in numbers and to dominate the other animals among which he lived. One important and curious symbiotic relationship that started some time back in the Stone Age was that between man and dog.

Transport is one of man's uses of animal muscle. (Annan Photo Features)

Man and Dog

There is general agreement that the dog was the first animal to be domesticated by man, but that is about the only point on which students of the subject agree. According to one theory, the dog is descended from some wolflike species now extinct; according to another, the ancestor of the dog is the present Eurasian wolf; and a third idea is that the modern dog represents a blend of several wild canine species. Curiously, this uncertainty about origins characterizes many of the anciently domesticated animals.

Men and dogs supplement each other nicely in hunting: the dog has the nose, man the eyes; the dog greater speed and more efficient teeth, man greater intelligence—though both can be cunning. The two animals have an unusual ability to understand and respond to each other. Dogs react quickly to changes in tone of voice or attitude, and cringe, obey, or show excited pleasure; and man, too, can interpret the emotions and actions of his dogs. Both have had a long evolution as social hunting animals, requiring intergroup cooperation and coordination, and it is interesting to speculate that this shared background in the evolution of their behavior accounts for their mutual understanding.

Dogs often tend to be scavengers, and it has been suggested that this habit led them to adopt men, rather than vice versa. According to this theory, dogs may have discovered the scavenging advantages of lurking around human kills and camps, and men may have seen the advantages of the dog's barking alarm and tracking skill. It is a nice idea but difficult to support with evidence. But of course, there is no direct evidence for any theory about how the man-dog association got started.

Among contemporary primitive people, dogs serve chiefly as scavengers around camp sites; lean and hungry native dogs can be remarkably efficient garbage collectors. Dogs are eaten in many parts of the world, and in some cases special breeds are raised as food. This has been true in parts of Africa and Asia, including

China, and among American Indians; and certain types of dogs were considered great delicacies in the Graeco-Roman world. It seems unlikely, however, that dogs were first domesticated because of their possibilities as food, though the planned use of dogs in hunting is characteristic of rather sophisticated cultures and may be a rather late development.

Our first direct evidence of the use of dogs comes from early Egyptian tomb paintings, when man had already reached the stage we call civilization. In ancient Egypt, there were even a number of special breeds of dogs, some developed for hunting, others for guarding flocks. From then on, hunting dogs appear frequently on the monuments of the various Mediterranean civilizations, but this does not prove anything about the possible beginnings of such use.

Creative Man

The man-dog association did not lead to any basic change in man's relations with the rest of nature. But with the development of agriculture, man shifted from being a simple consumer into being a new kind of producer: the anthropologists say he shifted from a food-gathering to a food-producing culture. He learned to clear away vegetation he could not use or did not want, replacing it with plants he could use directly or with plants that would serve as food for his domesticated animals. Man's action as an agent of ecological change thus became greatly intensified: he started the process of creating the man-altered landscape that has gone on at an accelerating pace to the present day.

There are many theories about how plant cultivation began and about the possible sequence of events in the course of the Neolithic Revolution. It seems likely that village life came before agriculture, and that plant cultivation antedated animal domestication. Settled village life is perfectly possible in the vicinity of an assured food supply such as a lake or estuary rich in fish—and village life provides the leisure necessary for experimenting with new kinds of tools, with planting, and with the taming of animals. The planting would then strengthen the security of the village, and the security of the man-dominated system would in turn reinforce its separation from the biological community.

It seems clear that animal domestication started independently in the New World and the Old; it is likely that there were two separate centers in the Old World, one in the Near East and the other in southeast Asia. In each case, man started to become not only an agent of ecological change but also an agent of evolutionary change. The animals and plants that he took under his care quite rapidly became modified, assuming different characteristics from those of the ancestral wild species. With protection from enemies and an assured food supply, natural selection gave way to artificial selection; the whims of man rather than the rigors of nature determined whether or not a new variation would survive and reproduce. Naturalists tend to regard man as a destructive force in the animal kingdom, and it is true that he often has destroyed species and habitats. But in the process of domestication he has also been a creative force, making new kinds of animals and new kinds of relationships, and building a new sort of biological community.

We may never solve the puzzle of how this cycle of domestication got started, but it is nonetheless interesting to speculate. One theory is that domestication developed from primitive peoples' widespread habit of keeping pets. Another theory is that it had a religious basis, that animals were first kept for sacrifice or worship or divination and that their practical usefulness was a later discovery. Certainly animals take a prominent place in a great variety of religious practices, and perhaps it would be interesting to examine some of these before considering domestication.

Kikuyu children driving cattle in Kenya. (Weldon King)

Animal Worship

Primitive man did not distinguish sharply between himself and his kind and other animals. One indication of this is the widespread idea of totemism: the close association between a group of people, tribe, or clan and a particular kind of animal (or sometimes plant or inanimate object). "Totem" is a word from the language of the Ojibway Indians of North America, but the phenomenon is world-wide, reaching its most elaborate development among the tribes of Australia.

All sorts of animals, from insects to lions and leopards, serve as totems. There is generally a belief in some kind of kinship between the totem animal and the clan—frequently the animal is regarded as ancestral to the clan. Therefore the totemic animal usually cannot be killed or eaten. Sometimes, however, the totem is ceremonially killed in sacrificial rites, and sometimes there is no tabu on killing or eating; in this case the totem serves merely as a badge or emblem for the clan.

It is tempting to wonder whether this carries over to the later use of animals as emblems, as in the armorial bearings of medieval knights and in the symbols of modern nations—the British lion and the American eagle. Even the football teams of American universities often have animal nicknames—lions, tigers, wolverines, falcons, and the like—and each state of the United States has an official bird.

Animal worship, as distinct from totemism, takes many forms. It reached its greatest complexity in ancient Egypt, where the gods had animal forms and where different animals, in various parts of the kingdom, were sacred to one deity or another. Cattle were among the most important deities in Egypt: the bull god Mnevis of Heliopolis, the bull god Apis of Memphis, and the cow goddess Hathor of Momemphis are obvious examples. The sacred bull and the sacred cow are recur-

rent themes in Mediterranean religions, and in our own day, cattle worship reaches its most extreme form in India.

The cattle of Hinduism are truly sacred beasts. In some places they are bathed, anointed with oil, colored with dyes, garlanded with flowers, and fed dainty food as an important part of the rites of worship. In most parts of India, the slaughter of a cow causes more outcry and horror than the murder of a man.

There are many other attitudes toward animals among the varied sects of Hinduism and other Eastern religions. In some cases animals in India and in other parts of the world are protected because of a belief in the transmigration of souls. In the general Hindu tradition, the horror of eating any kind of meat is comparable to the attitude toward eating dog flesh in the Western world.

In the Buddhist tradition, animals are protected not because they are specifically sacred, but out of a general aversion to cruelty in any form and from a deep feeling for the harmony of nature. In the words of an edict of King Asoka (250 B.C.), "Not to injure living things is good." The grounds of Buddhist monasteries in southeast Asia have come to function almost as wildlife reservations. This belief reaches an extreme in Jainism; the Jaina monk carries a broom to sweep insects from his path and wears a veil to sift them from his mouth.

But philosophies like that of Jainism can hardly have been involved in the process of domestication—the Jains, in fact, cannot be farmers because of their

principle of noninterference. They can exist only if someone else does interfere with nature, and our purpose is to trace the course of this interference.

The majority of the species of domesticated animals can be traced to one or another of three regions: southeast Asia, the Near East, and the New World. The first is the source of what have been called the "household animals"; the second of the grazing animals; while the third, the New World, is remarkable because even the high Mayan and Incan civilizations developed with little dependence on animals for either food or transport. Only the Incan llama was truly important.

The Household Animals

Many students of the subject maintain that the dog, pig, fowl, duck, and goose were all first domesticated in southeast Asia. The evidence is clearest about fowl, which are derived from the jungle fowl of the Burmese and Malayan forests. The domestic and wild forms interbreed easily, and Burmese villagers still occasionally deliberately cross their domestic birds with wild ones.

Again there is the puzzling phenomenon of the relationship between domesticated animals and religion and ritual. Much information on this subject has been assembled by an American geographer, Frederick Simoons, in a book entitled *Eat Not This Flesh*. Simoons points out that today the cock is a sacred animal with

276

many Burmese tribes. In ancient Persia "the cock was a herald of the dawn who ushered in the new day with his crowing and dispelled the evil spirits of the night." In ancient Greece the cock was sacred to the goddess Maia, and initiates in her mysteries did not eat chicken; the cock was also important in the Eleusinian mysteries and in the rites of other Mediterranean and Near Eastern religions.

It has long been suspected that chickens were first domesticated not for food but for divination, which is still practiced by many Asiatic peoples. The intestines or liver may be used, but more often the future is determined from the angle of bamboo splinters inserted into the fine perforations of the thighbones. The widespread practice of cockfighting may also have magical origins, though Simoons notes that the people who use cocks for divination do not use them for fighting. Cockfighting now is largely a sport of "civilized" cultures, while divination is practiced by "primitive" tribes.

Pigs and pork, of course, have long been involved with religion. There are evidences of pig cults in many parts of the ancient world, and pigs or boars have been favorite sacrificial animals. Avoidance of pork, which figures so prominently in the Hebrew and Moslem religions, may have started as a rejection of heathen practices rather than as a sanitary measure. Modern people who view either pork or chicken with horror often cite the unclean habits of the animals as the reason; but outside of some Hindu or Buddhist sects, the same people rarely reject both pork and chicken, though the two animals have equally "unclean" habits.

Grazing Animals

In the Old World, man has domesticated eleven species of grazing mammals: common cattle, zebu, water buffalo, yak, goat, sheep, dromedary, Bactrian camel, horse, ass, and reindeer. This is a curious list, and one cannot help wondering why these particular animals were chosen out of all of the possibilities; further, why the list has not been added to over a period of history when man's technical accomplishments have been so great. From the tomb paintings, it would seem that the Egyptians experimented with the domestication of a variety of animals, including antelopes and gazelles. Perhaps other animals turned out to be less useful, but the reasons for man's actions are often so devious that one suspects that practicality may not have been paramount here.

The most dangerous and difficult animal known to European hunters up to the time it became extinct in the seventeenth century was *Bos primigenius,* the ancestor of domestic cattle. The wild cattle of India, the gaur, ancestors of the zebu races, are notoriously fierce, and wild buffalo are considered the most dangerous of surviving game animals. Then why did man domesticate these and not the bison? The American bison has turned out to be easily tamed, and valuable for meat, hide, and wool; a similar bison was common in Europe in early times, yet it seems never to have been domesticated.

All of these grazing animals have been used, at one time or another, for milk. How the idea of milking got started remains mysterious, although if we drink a human mother's milk it seems a logical step to trying an animal's. Long ago the German geographer Eduard Hahn suggested that milking may have had its origin in connection with the widespread worship of the mother-goddess in the ancient

Llamas and sheep are herded together in the highlands of Ecuador. The llamas once provided the basic transport of the Incan empire. (Annan Photo Features)

world, that the first domestication may have had ritualistic rather than practical motives.

But the usefulness of these animals to man is clear, and perhaps anthropologists and geographers have searched too hard for indirect motives for domestication. The use of reindeer is an interesting example. Though reindeer and men have been associated closely for a very long time in northern Europe and Asia, one can argue equally plausibly that the reindeer is one of the oldest, or one of the most recent, of man's domesticates. The reindeer are fond of human urine, which gives them salt and minerals, and particular groups of men and animals may have drifted into a mutualistic association. Tame reindeer are used as decoys for getting wild ones—which provides another possible general theory of the origin of domestication. In the case of reindeer, it is clear that in cultures where the animals are milked (as among the Lapps) it is in imitation of the practice of other peoples with different animals. The use of the animals for sled-pulling or carrying packs is also imitative.

New World Domesticates

The New World cultures grew a considerable variety of plants, and some of the most important crops of the modern world come from them (maize, potatoes, tomatoes, and chocolate, for example). But they domesticated remarkably few animals. The Aztecs kept elaborate menageries, and pet animals are common with many tropical Indian tribes, but this did not lead to domestication. Dogs were present, presumably brought from the Old World, but they seem to have been used chiefly for food.

The llama of the high Andes was the most important of the American domesticates; with hundreds of thousands of the animals in use, it provided the basic transport system of the Incan empire. A llama can carry a cargo of from 22 to 130 pounds, depending on its strength, and can cover six to eighteen miles daily for as long as twenty days in a row. Like camels, llamas are notoriously intractable, and if overloaded, it is said that they simply lie down and refuse to move.

Llama wool is used, but it is coarser than that of the related alpaca and vicuña. In Incan times, the animal was the chief source of meat for the people, but nowadays the meat of sheep is preferred. Llama hides were also used by the Incas, and the dung is a common fuel in the high, treeless paramo country. Llamas were never milked—no American mammals were—and they were not used for pulling vehicles because the Americans did not have the wheel.

Llamas were also important in religious ceremonies, and it is said that a white llama was sacrificed every morning in the principal temple of Cuzco—stabbed in the heart with a stone knife. At large festivals, a thousand or more llamas were sometimes sacrificed.

The Andean people also domesticated the guinea pig, which lived about the household on scraps of food, and was used chiefly for meat, though it also served for religious sacrifices. The so-called Muscovy duck was also a household animal in many parts of tropical America, and the Mexicans domesticated the turkey. But considering the rich American fauna, what a small list this is!

Animals at Work

Before leaving this subject of animal domestication, we might glance at the variety of ways in which man has used his animal associates. Religion and ritual have been stressed here, and they are curiously important in all of man's activities. Animals as pets have been mentioned, but further exploration of this would be more appropriate in a later chapter about natural history in cities, that most drastically modified of man-altered environments.

Food, fiber, and transport are the most important of the practical uses of animals, and these have been discussed briefly, though with little indication of the variety of use. Nothing has been said about domesticated insects; yet the honeybee has long been important as a source of food and the silkworm as a producer of fiber. Man started robbing honey from wild bees way back in the Stone Age, as is shown by some of the cave drawings, and by the dawn of civilization he had learned to keep bees in special hives. Whether these should be called "domesticated" or not is a matter of definition, but they were certainly useful in producing a highly prized sweet.

By any definition the silkworm is domesticated. The wild ancestor is completely unknown and was probably some species now extinct. Female silkworms have lost the ability to fly, and the animals are now completely dependent on human care for their survival. But the origins of silkworm culture are lost in the dim prehistory of China.

Transport is one example of man's use of animal muscle—so often stronger and more enduring than his own. He has used a wide variety of the domesticates for plowing, carrying packs, or pulling sledges and carts. One thinks of horses first in this connection, but their great importance as a source of power is rather recent. Iron horseshoes, which increase pulling power by giving an effective grip, were not invented until the ninth century, and the modern harness, in which the pull is at the shoulder instead of at the neck, was developed only in the tenth century.

Man has also used other animals in a variety of ways as aids in hunting. The ferret may be as anciently domesticated as the cat; certainly it was used in classical times and throughout the Middle Ages for hunting rabbits and controlling vermin. Then there is the whole elaborate development of falconry in the ancient and medieval worlds, as well as various special cases like the use of cormorants in fishing by the Japanese and other Asiatic peoples.

Again in the case of these animals the degree of domestication, of modification through human handling, can be disputed. Perhaps the most interesting borderline example is the elephant. Long ago man learned to use the powerful muscles and great bulk of this animal in the Orient, but he has always depended on the periodic capture and taming of these wild individuals. The elephant has probably not been modified at all, in the genetic sense, by the association with man; yet he has been

Camels pulling plows in Israel. (Anna Riwkin-Brik)

Although man has long used the elephant as a domesticated animal, he must rely for his supply on taming wild ones. (Ylla: Rapho-Guillumette)

very useful in human enterprises. It appears that the African elephant is just as adaptable as the Indian kind, but except for very recent experiments in the Congo, the African species has not been used in modern times. The famous elephants of Hannibal's expedition against Rome indicate that in the past they were tamed, but the art was lost with the extinction of the North African variety.

Effects of Domestication

With the elephant, man has learned to use the natural animal as he found it, and one can find every gradation between this and the highly specialized breeds of cattle, swine, and poultry found on modern farms, animals that are so modified that they could hardly survive without man to look after them. The most highly modified animals are clearly the consequence of deliberate selection for egg or milk production, meat, muscle power, or some other trait prized by the breeder. But there are also changes that are the consequence not of artificial selection but of release from the pressures of natural selection. That is, by providing an assured food supply for his domesticated animals, and protection from predators, man insures that all sorts of variations survive that would be quickly eliminated in the natural community.

It has been argued that man himself can be regarded as a "self-domesticated animal." He has been able to provide food and protection for himself as well as for his domesticates. This may explain the wide variety of human physique, from pygmy to tall Nilotic Negro or squat Eskimo; the range of human skin color and hair form, similar in extent to that of the animals he cares for; and man's continuous sexuality which has become divorced from the usual rhythm of the seasons.

But domestication is only one aspect of man's relationship with nature. The man-altered landscape presents a whole series of special problems for the animals living there; it is a new world for all of its inhabitants.

17

Getting Along
with Man

As of 1960, it was estimated that there were about 2.9 billion individuals of one species of mammal, *Homo sapiens,* living on the surface of this planet. About 270,000 new ones are born every day and about 142,000 die, leaving a daily surplus of 128,000—equivalent to the population of a fair-sized city. This adds up to about 47 million annually, which means that in effect the world gains the population of a new Chicago every month. Such is the "population problem" which increasingly worries thoughtful people. But it is a problem not for men only, but for all of the rest of the animal kingdom as well. Whether an animal species will survive or become extinct depends more and more on whether it can get along with man; the human species has become the major environmental force on the land surface of the planet. So far the seas have largely escaped, except for coastal waters, but perhaps not for long, especially if we start dumping atomic wastes in the depths.

For this reason we cannot write about animal worlds and ignore this man-altered world. The great deciduous forests of Europe and China disappeared long ago; those of North America, more recently. Deserts are irrigated and grasslands are ploughed. The Amazon forest is still hardly touched, but roads are pushing into it, cities are forming, and its doom can be predicted with some confidence. The rain forests of Africa and the East Indies are being transformed more rapidly, and man is felt as a force even in the northern wilderness, in the taiga and tundra.

This raises all sorts of questions. Has man any "right" to push the rest of nature around, deliberately exterminating animals he doesn't like, accidentally causing the extinction of others by destroying their habitat? The answer is likely to take some form of the argument that "might makes right." We have the need and the power, and our own interests are paramount. But how can we justify an ethic of "might makes right" between men and animals, and at the same time deny that ethic between men and men? The argument that men have the right to destroy wolves because they are inconvenient is parallel to Nazi reasoning about Jews—and in the past bounties have been paid for American Indian scalps as well as for wolf hides. Aside from the ethical question, is it to the best interests of man to live in a completely artificial environment, with cement in place of grass, walls in place of trees? Since we are capable of self-awareness and of self-evaluation, we surely incur responsibilities for the consequences of our actions.

Swallows assemble on
telephone wires for their
journey south.
(Marc Foucault: Rapho-
Guillumette)

Yet the subject of this chapter is not with what ought to be, but with what is—
with the actual characteristics of this man-altered world and with the various
ways in which animals have adapted, or failed to adapt, to it.

The Man-Altered Biome

Cultivated fields are as similar on all of the continents as are, say, deserts or rain
forests. To be sure there are geographical and climatic differences; rice paddies and

wheat fields are different, and so are household gardens in Kansas and Polynesia. If a world survey of agricultural practices were made, the local differences would be impressive. But if we compare gardens, fields, and orchards with "natural" biomes, the similarities that result from human action in different parts of the world are striking, so that we may be justified in considering the man-altered landscape as a single major biome type.

The basic human action is to clear away unwanted vegetation, replacing it with useful plants—crops. The most general form of this clearing is the "slash-and-burn" type of agriculture found in many parts of the tropics today. The trees are felled or girdled and, when they are dry enough, set on fire; crops are planted in the ashes amid the trunks and stumps. Sometimes the field is left to the weeds after one crop has been harvested, or several crops may be planted before the land is abandoned. In any case, the weeds presently take over and a process of "succession" starts. After perhaps twenty years—the length of the cycle varies—forest has become established again, ready to be cut and burned for another crop.

The growth in these abandoned fields rapidly becomes a wild tangle of vegetation—truly "jungle," though I prefer "boondocks," a word much used by Americans in the Pacific during the Second World War and since. A new world is created for the local animals. Since at first there are no trees, there is no place for the numerous arboreal animals of the original forest. But there are rich opportunities for ground-living species because, instead of the more or less open forest floor, there is a lush growth of weedy plants with tender roots and stems and often fruits. The common plants of these clearings are rarely found in the original forest because they are limited to places where the fall of some giant tree has made a temporary opening, or to new land like that of river sand bars.

Just as plants rare in the forest become common in this "open habitat," so do all of the animals associated with them find new opportunities. The weed-eating insects multiply, and the lizards and birds that eat the insects move in. Rats, mice, and other rodents find a rich food supply—and so do the animals like snakes and hawks that eat the rodents. Thus a whole biotic community is built up with a species composition quite different from that of the original forest. But it is only a temporary community. As tree seedlings grow, the ground becomes more shaded again and the sun-loving weeds die out; slowly the stable conditions of the primeval forest are again established until man with axe and fire comes along once more.

One might call the animals and plants that move into such clearings "opportunists." Certainly man isn't trying to give them an opportunity, but he is unwittingly providing a favorable environment. When the clearings are maintained under continuous cultivation, as happens with the development of civilization, many of these opportunists find permanent places as weeds or pests, or in hedgerows, or around the margins of woodlots, and in similar bits of uncared-for land. The animals of the forest—or prairie or desert, as the case may be—that cannot adapt to these conditions then tend to disappear.

One could develop a complex classification of the subdivisions of this man-altered biome. There are the wholly cultivated fields of grains or vegetables which give little opportunity for any animals except the insect pests of the particular crop, and perhaps the predators and parasites of the pests. Orchards, with some weeds always growing among the trees, give somewhat more varied conditions for animal life, and of course tropical crops that are grown under shade trees, like coffee and cacao, provide an even wider range of possibilities for different kinds of animals. The pastures that man maintains for his herd animals become home also for many smaller creatures of the grasslands, and since man kills off the bigger predators, animals like rabbits, mice, ground squirrels, pheasants, and quail often thrive.

Household gardens are apt to be less rigidly maintained than commercial farms, and many small mammals, birds, lizards, and the like manage to make their home there. Nowadays the move to the suburbs, the tendency of city people to search for a pseudo-rural life, has created a whole new kind of habitat—the "suburban forest." It has a variety of trees, shrubs, lawns, garden plots, and occasional untidy corners, where many animals find a satisfactory environment, sometimes unobtrusively, sometimes—like the songbirds—with human encouragement. Then there are the many kinds of parks and recreation areas, from wildlife reserves to picnic grounds and golf courses, all offering some sort of special condition for animal life.

The rights-of-way of highways, railways, power transmission lines, and so on provide another interesting and little appreciated aspect of the man-altered biome. The amount of land thus occupied is astonishingly large. Frank Egler, an ecologist who has interested himself in this question, estimates that in the United States the rights-of-way of the utility companies alone cover an acreage greater than the area of all six New England states combined. Reliable figures are hard to come by, but it has been estimated that the highways in the United States are about equivalent in area to the state of Georgia.

In England and on the European continent there is a long tradition of leaving hedgerows along roads and the margins of fields, and these hedgerows provide sanctuary for a variety of animals. According to the English Nature Conservancy these animals cause no demonstrable harm to human enterprises. In fact the hedgerows help to preserve the "balance of nature," in sheltering predators that live off the pests of the fields and orchards. But this does not take into consideration the value of maintaining some natural diversity in the human environment.

Extinct and Vanishing Species

As we know, some animals manage to get along easily enough with man—with or without encouragement. Others that at present have a hard time probably could get along if man would modify his habits somewhat. But others have failed completely to adapt to the man-altered environment and have disappeared. Their numbers will inevitably increase as the area of wilderness left in the world becomes smaller. Of mammals, 106 forms are known to have become extinct in the last two thousand years; the same fate has overtaken 87 kinds of birds, and 19 more are listed as "probably extinct." Not as much attention has been paid to reptiles, amphibians, and insects, so there are no statistics.

The rate of extinction has increased in recent years, and in the present century an average of one kind of mammal and one bird has disappeared each year. Conservationists have made a list of some 600 species of mammals that are currently in danger and of 78 birds that are on the verge of extinction. Increasing efforts are being made to protect these threatened species, and in some cases preservation seems relatively assured. But in others, the habits of men and the habits of the animals just cannot be reconciled, and man is likely to win.

Civilization and wildness are hardly compatible, and in cultivated regions man cannot tolerate direct competitors like the big predators. There is no room for packs of wolves near great cities, nor for lions in peaceful country lanes. As we have pointed out, lions disappeared from Europe in Roman times, though they managed better in North Africa. The last lions in Tunisia and Algeria were killed in 1891, but a few survived in the Atlas Mountains of Morocco until 1922. The cougar or puma, once common over most of North America, has disappeared from the eastern seaboard and the central states, though lingering in the wilder parts of Florida. The various types of grizzly bears that once ranged over North America from the great plains to the Pacific coast, living mostly off the herds of bison, are now extinct except for a few forms that still persist in remote mountains, in the Canadian northwest, and in Alaska.

The dodo has come to be the classic example of extinction as a consequence of human action. But this illustrates a quite different circumstance: the special vulnerability of animals that have evolved on remote islands. The dodos of Mauritius as well as the solitaires of the neighboring islands of Reunion and Rodriguez were large, flightless relatives of the pigeons. Presumably their ancestors got to these remote volcanic islands of the Indian Ocean by flying and then, in a protected environment with ample food and no enemies, evolved into the curious creatures that were discovered by the first European visitors.

Mauritius and the other Mascarene Islands were uninhabited when they were first discovered by the Portuguese in 1505, and they were not greatly disturbed by human occupancy until the French took them over after 1700. But they were frequently visited by ships in the preceeding two centuries, and the trusting, giant birds were used for provisions. The dodo weighed between forty and fifty pounds; it had a fat, dumpy body covered with soft gray feathers; small useless wings; and a long bill, strongly hooked at the tip. It was said that three or four birds would provide a meal for the whole ship's crew, though the meat was also said to be quite tough except for the breast.

There are no reports of dodos being seen on Mauritius after 1680. Before this several of the birds were taken alive to Europe to be exhibited to the curious, but none ended intact in any museum. Oxford has a head and a foot, the British Museum has another head, and there is another foot in the museum at Copenhagen—and this is all that is left of the dodo except for numerous bones that have been found preserved in a marsh.

Our knowledge of the habits of these birds is understandably fragmentary, but it is said that they laid only one egg, which was incubated on a mat of leaves in deep forest. Thus their reproductive rate must have been very low, but even so, it seems unlikely that passing sailors could kill off a large population. Soon after their discovery the Portuguese freed macaque monkeys on the islands as well as pigs, and rats from the passing ships soon established themselves. Macaque monkeys are notoriously fond of eggs, and wild pigs are always a great danger to ground-nesting birds; these, as well as the sailors, were probably responsible for the disappearance of the dodo.

The very similar solitaires of Reunion and Rodriguez lasted a little longer—on Reunion until about 1750, and on Rodriguez until about 1800.

Monkeys, rats, and pigs, as well as men, were responsible for the extinction of the dodos and the solitaires. In the case of the great auk of the North Atlantic islands, man alone seems to have been directly responsible for the final disappearance of the bird. The great auk was a large, flightless, penguin-like bird (though no relative) that, from the plentiful remains, must have been quite common on northern European and American shores in prehistoric times (the bones turn up commonly in the refuse left by Stone Age men). The birds were apparently both curious and unafraid of any animal on land, inquisitively coming to the shore in large numbers when a ship appeared, and standing around while the sailors clobbered them one by one. The flesh was said not to have been very good, but the eggs were prized and the bodies were used for oil and fat. The last known specimens (a pair) were killed on Eldey Rock off the coast of Iceland on June 3, 1844.

Animals on islands are particularly vulnerable to human aggression or to the indirect effects of occupation by man, but the great continents are not immune. Historically, the greatest losses have been in North America, with Australia and Africa not far behind. Oddly enough, the fauna of Europe has suffered least. One can argue that the most susceptible European animals disappeared before records were possible; or that the animals of Europe have had a longer time to adapt to the changing conditions brought with civilization; or that the European tradition of great estates and parks has provided refuges. Probably all three explanations are involved to some extent. Whatever the reason, *not one* European bird is known to have become extinct in the last two thousand years, and the mammal list is limited to the lion, wild horse, aurochs, the Caucasian bison, and two forms of ibex.

The abrupt impact of European man on the North American continent resulted in a drastic and recorded change in the whole natural history of the area. Even so, it is not often easy to decide on the exact cause of the extinction of a particular species. This is true, for instance, in the two famous cases of the passenger pigeon and the Carolina parakeet.

The Carolina parakeet was found commonly in deciduous forest of North America from Virginia to Florida and westward as far as the river forests extended in Texas, Oklahoma, and Kansas. With settlement, the birds retreated westward. They were last seen in Ohio in 1856, in Kentucky in 1878, in Louisiana in 1881. They survived longest in the wilder parts of Florida; a specimen was collected there in 1901, and small flocks were sighted by ornithologists as late as 1920.

The settlers had no love for the parakeets, which had the habit of raiding orchards and gardens. In 1810 Alexander Wilson wrote, "I have known a flock of these birds to alight on an apple tree, and have myself seen them twist off the fruit, one by one, strewing it in every direction around the tree, without observing that any of the depredators descended to pick them up." In Florida they destroyed oranges and peaches, though their chief food was seeds of the cypress, maple, elm, and the like. Their habit of hovering over the bodies of fallen birds made it easy to kill large numbers, and since the species disappeared rather faster than the forests did, it is probable that man directly was the primary agent of extinction. The parakeets lived in the same kind of forests as the ivory-billed woodpeckers, yet a few of the latter survived until 1950 and they may still persist.

Passenger pigeons were slaughtered in untold millions, but one wonders whether they would have survived even if none had been shot. They nested in vast communal flocks that covered miles of the virgin beech forests of the North American wilderness. The forests are now gone, and the pigeon could have survived only if it had adopted different feeding, flocking, and nesting habits; it could have survived, in other words, only by adapting to the man-altered environment. Since masses of the birds were slaughtered, and since the forests also disappeared, we will never know whether some sort of adaptation might have occurred. Probably it would not.

In a few cases there is careful documentation of the process of extinction. This is true, for instance, of the heath hen, which finally died out on Martha's Vineyard under full ornithological supervision. In the nineteenth century it was an important game bird, known to range from New Hampshire to Chesapeake Bay. By 1870, however, it had become restricted to the island of Martha's Vineyard. By 1907 the total population had been reduced to 77 individuals, and sustained efforts were started to avert its becoming extinct. In 1916 there were 2000 or so birds, but in that year a combination of fire, gales, a hard winter, and an invasion of hawks reduced the number to about 100. The birds held on for a while, reaching a high of 314 in 1920, but declining fairly steadily after that—117, 100, 28, 54, 25, 35, 13—until 1928, when only one bird was found. This last survivor disappeared in 1931. The heath hen just couldn't get along in the man-altered environment, even when it was completely protected from direct destruction by humans.

The case of a zebra-like horse of South Africa called the quagga is interesting. In the eighteenth century this was a common animal on the plains of the Cape region, forming troops of thirty to fifty individuals, with the habit of traveling in single file and, when startled, of wheeling in unison like a troop of cavalry. They would run with the horses of the Boer farmers, and from the accounts it would seem that they might perfectly well have been made into useful domesticated animals. Specimens sent to European zoological gardens became very tame, and on various occasions they were broken to harness. It is said that a certain Mr. Sheriff Perkins drove a pair in London, and was often seen in Hyde Park riding a phaeton behind them in the early years of the nineteenth century.

But to the Boers, the quaggas were pests, of no interest or value compared with their prized horses. They were shot in great numbers to get meat for workers, and wagon-loads of hides were sent down to the coast where they were especially prized for making grain sacks. The efficient Boers had probably slaughtered the last of the quaggas in the Cape region by 1850, and the species is not known to have survived anywhere after 1878. The last known living specimen was one that died in the Berlin Zoological Garden in 1875.

In discussing extinction by human agency, there is a tendency to stress mammals and birds and a few conspicuous reptiles like the giant tortoises of Mauritius and the Galapagos. Man's activities have certainly resulted in great changes in the numbers of other kinds of animals, but it is hard to get precise data. One exception is the case of butterflies in the British Isles, since the Britishers have been ardent butterfly collectors for a long time and worry about the preservation of their fauna. Several British butterflies have become extinct in modern times, mostly because their habitats were destroyed by draining or clearing. In one case, however, that of the large copper *(Lycaena dispar)*, the species was apparently finished off by collectors of specimens. The effects of human greed, it appears, extend even to insects.

Of course there is nothing new about extinction. Dinosaurs disappeared many millions of years ago, without any help from men. Their disappearance more or less coincided with the beginning of the evolution of mammals. One's first thought is that perhaps the mammals were too much for the dinosaurs—maybe they were "more efficient" and "better adapted" and so replaced them. The trouble with

Animals Used by Man

Examples of domestication:
93 Right: In Tunisia,
camels are still employed
in husking grain by treading
on it. (Weldon King)

94 Below: A herd of sheep
on the high plains of
Bolivia. (Carl Frank)

Getting Along with Man

95 Above: This deer mouse, like many other small animals, finds man a convenient neighbor. (Jack Dermid)

96 Right: Buildings provide spiders with good locations for webs. (Jack Novak: Coleman and Hayward)

97–98 Shrews (right)
and hedgehogs (below)
have made themselves at
home in English gardens.
(John Markham)

99–100 Barn swallows have come to depend on man for housing, and our attics provide artificial caves for bats. (Above, Eliot Porter; right, Jane Burton: Coleman and Hayward)

this theory is that the geological record seems to show clearly that mammals did not undergo any great development until some time after the dinosaurs had become extinct. The mammals that lived with the dinosaurs were small, unobtrusive animals that would hardly seem a threat to anything.

We really have very little understanding of the causes of extinction in the geological past. About all that can be said is that one type of animal disappeared but another survived. Dinosaurs and other ancient reptile types faded out, but turtles and crocodiles, almost equally ancient forms, have survived in a changing world. Why and how? We really don't know.

Extinction can be regarded as an inevitable consequence of evolution, just as death for the individual is an inevitable consequence of reproduction. If new kinds of animals are to appear, some of the old ones must disappear, just as old individuals must die to make way for new. It can be argued, then, that the effect of human action in contributing to the extinction of other animals is "natural" and need not concern us. But the rate of change through human action is much faster than anything in the geological past. And only a single species is responsible for the elimination of these hundreds of others. Nor are they being replaced in the biological community by newly evolving forms. Man is acting purely as an agent of destruction, and destructiveness is not a value esteemed in any system of human ethics, however common it may be in human practice.

Man has sealed the doom of a rather impressive list of animals, but he has also given other animals new opportunities, either accidentally or on purpose, by carrying them to new regions of the world. Sometimes this has worked well, but more often it has been disastrous to both the local fauna and to man's own interests.

Man as an Agent of Dispersal

From the very beginning men, like other animals, have carried their parasites—their lice and intestinal worms—around with them. Free transportation is one of the benefits of the parasitic way of life. After the man-dog association developed, dogs also moved with men. Presumably this was how the dingo got to Australia. The early cultivators also carried their domesticated plants and animals with them wherever they could, and after man developed ocean-going canoes, animals like rats and lizards managed to get rides to new countries as uninvited passengers. But this movement of animals with men was relatively trivial until modern times, when ships and airplanes have broken down the barriers among the continents for many of the smaller creatures.

Man has carried his domesticated animals with him for obvious reasons. The first Spanish settlers in America brought horses, cattle, goats, pigs, and chickens with them, and this pattern was followed by Europeans everywhere in the course of their settlement. In most cases, these animals have remained domesticated, a part of the immediate human entourage; they have become too dependent on man's care to be able to get along by themselves. Goats are an outstanding exception; they often manage to do very well without human help—and with disastrous consequences for the landscape. Horses and pigs have also become wild again in some places. And on oceanic islands, where there is no competition from native mammals, pigs, dogs, cats and goats often flourish without the help of man.

Settlers, nostalgic in strange lands, have frequently tried to introduce well-remembered birds and mammals to give a feeling of "home." For the most part, such attempts at introduction have failed; it is not easy for an animal to become established in a new environment. Sometimes, however, the attempts have been more than successful. Starlings and English sparrows are America's heritage from the days of sentimental animal importation, but many other attempted introductions failed. As a matter of fact, all attempts to get starlings established failed until 1891, when about eighty birds were released in Central Park in New York and several pairs among these started to breed. Progress was slow at first, and the bird did not get beyond the Allegheny Mountains until after 1916; but by the middle of the century it had spread all over the United States, and in 1953 a starling was seen in Alaska!

Introduction of alien fauna has been most successful on oceanic islands where the local animals offer at most limited competition. New Zealand, isolated from the rest of the world since before the age of mammals, and with diversified climates and vegetation, has become a sort of gigantic laboratory for experimental introductions. Yet even in these open and varied environments, it is not easy for new species to become established. There are records of attempts to introduce 130 species of birds into New Zealand, but of these only 24 were successful. About half of the attempts to introduce mammals have failed, but in many cases it is clear that too few animals were released at the same time.

Residents of the Hawaiian Islands have also been much addicted to introducing birds and mammals from North America and the Orient. Again some of the introductions have been altogether too successful, while others, quite inexplicably, have failed. There are records of introductions of ninety-four species of birds; of these, thirty-one have become established on one island or another. Like those of New Zealand, the Hawaiian introductions were partly from sentiment and partly for purposes of sport or insect control. The native birds did not supply these needs, and for the most part the introduced species have moved into otherwise unoccupied niches. Many native species have become rare or extinct, but this seems to be not so much because of the competition of the new introductions as because of the destruction of the native forests. Among the most disastrous of the introductions into Hawaii, someone has remarked, were the proliferating bulldozers. The Brazilian cardinals add a touch of color to Hawaiian gardens, and the triple alliance of mynah birds, Chinese doves, and English sparrows occupy a niche in Honolulu streets and parks that no native bird could fill.

But the consequences of animal introduction have often been harmful. It is doubtful whether anyone in the United States loves starlings; or in Australia, rabbits. The mongoose now has no friends on tropical islands, though it was introduced with purely practical motives. This animal was first brought from India to Trinidad in 1870 for the purpose of controlling the rats in the sugar-cane fields, and at first it was a very successful operation. Four males and five females were brought from Trinidad to Jamaica in 1872; ten years later it was estimated that the animals had saved the sugar planters at least 40,000 pounds sterling annually. From Jamaica they were introduced to other Caribbean islands, and then to Hawaii.

There was no way, however, of insuring that the mongoose would stay on a rat diet. As the rats became scarce and the mongooses multiplied, they took to other food. Ground-living birds (including chickens), lizards, and the like were

Ducks hobnob with ocean liners in the St. Lawrence Seaway. (Marcel Cognac Annan Photo Features)

ready victims, and soon the animal became primarily responsible for the extinction of a number of island species. Furthermore, the rats presently became as abundant as ever, through a change in habit; they took to nesting high off the ground, out of the reach of the mongoose. A sort of biological balance was thus established.

Apparently in some cases a balance has also been established between the mongoose and native animals. It was thought, for instance, that the ground-nesting bridled quail dove of the Virgin Islands had been exterminated by the mongoose, but the birds have recently been seen again. Somehow they managed to live through the mongoose episode. But the species that manage to adjust are exceptional.

The animals man has introduced by accident have also often had disastrous consequences. Most of the accidental introductions are insects, and the damage most frequently is to man's own enterprises. Of the major insect pests in the United States, which cost farmers many millions of dollars a year in lost crops and in control measures, at least half are species that have been accidentally introduced from abroad. Statistics are hard to assemble, but the same would probably be true for most parts of the world. We have, for instance, given Europe the Colorado potato beetle, and in return got the European corn borer.

Insects in a new environment often increase enormously in numbers because the parasites and predators that keep them in control in their native land have been left behind. A logical way of dealing with this would seem to be to introduce such parasites and predators deliberately, and the agricultural departments of various governments have developed elaborate programs for such controls. There have been many failures, but sometimes the efforts have been spectacularly successful.

An outstanding case of successful introduction for biological control involved not insects, but rabbits and virus in Australia. The introduced rabbits had become a tremendous pest there, ruining large areas of pasture. Efforts to decimate them by bringing in predators like ferrets and weasels had no effect. Then a virus disease, myxomytosis, was tried. This was first discovered many years ago as an apparently unimportant disease of rabbits in Brazil. Somehow it was brought accidentally into Europe, where it caused considerable havoc in the rabbit populations. Purposely introduced into Australia, it spread rapidly and almost eliminated the pestiferous rabbits. Almost—but survivors are resistant to the virus, and perhaps soon the resistant rabbit strain will become well established, so that the Australians will be faced with the same old problem over again.

The prickly pear cactus, which was brought from America to Australian gardens, escaped to occupy vast stretches of landscape. But the plant was finally brought under control by the introduction of an insect borer from Mexico. The pretty flowering lantana, which escaped from Hawaiian gardens to crowd other vegetation off the hillsides, was also finally reduced to manageable proportions by insect enemies brought in from its Mexican homeland. But for each such success there are many failures, and we are still a long way from learning how to manage nature, or even how to repair our own blunders in moving organisms around.

Adapting to Man

It is easy to stress the damage caused by human activities in the biological community—and the damage certainly is real enough, and often unnecessary. But this neglects another side of the picture, the remarkable ability of many animals to adapt their habits to the man-altered environment. This is especially true in the outskirts of cities and in small towns, where the tree-shaded streets and yards of the suburban forest provide varied habitats.

The late Frank Lutz, curator of insects in the American Museum of Natural History in New York, set out some years ago to see how many different species of insects he could find on his suburban lot, which measured 75 by 200 feet. He found a total of 1402 species, and wrote a book about them, with the title *A Lot of Insects*. Friends remarked that his garden must be a mess with so many bugs around, to which he replied that his garden had won prizes in a contest held by a New York newspaper in each of the four years during which he was carrying out the study.

Among mammals, squirrels have taken to the suburban forest with obvious enthusiasm. Raccoons have learned how to raid garbage pails, and skunks seem to thrive nicely among at least some of the humans in New York suburbs. Opossums now are spreading farther north than ever before, becoming common around New York and in southern New England. One theory is that they are extending northward because of the gradually warming climate, but it may also be that they find suburbia a more favorable habitat than the earlier primeval forest.

The record of the passenger pigeon, Carolina parakeet, and heath hen, which failed to adapt to civilization, can be counterbalanced by that of the many birds that find human alterations of the habitat advantageous. The barn owl is a good case. A very "successful" species, it has managed to get almost everywhere around the earth, even to remote spots like the Galapagos Islands, and it has taken the

Barn owls increasingly prefer buildings to hollow trees for their nests. (Ronald Thompson: Coleman and Hayward)

advent of man in its stride. Every year in the United States more and more of these owls are found nesting in buildings, both in the country and in cities, instead of in their natural habitat of hollow trees. Curiously, they started the barn-nesting habit back in colonial times, when they were regarded as birds of ill omen and shot on sight; some animals just aren't easily discouraged.

The late Ludlow Griscom, one of America's chief authorities on bird habits, remarked that he had not heard of a barn swallow nesting anywhere except in buildings for many decades. He also noted that the cliff swallow might better be called the eave swallow. Both birds have become completely dependent on man to provide habitations. Chimney swifts are now almost never found nesting anywhere except in chimneys, though there are still many trees around with hollows that would seem appropriate nesting sites.

In some ways the rough-winged swallows are even more remarkable: many of them have taken to nesting in railway culverts, apparently quite undisturbed by the noisy trains rushing overhead. And the killdeer has discovered that the gravel of freight yards makes a fine place to nest.

Crows have taken to city and suburban life around Boston, even riding on the tops of the trolley cars of other days; but the New York crows remain less urbanized. Griscom also reported that at least twenty-fife species of birds nested within the city of Cambridge. Of course, men have adapted to the birds as well as the birds to men; the habit of providing feeding stations and special nesting places is now widespread, especially among suburbanites.

Above, left to right: Among mammals, squirrels have taken to the suburban woods, and raccoons have learned to raid garbage pails. (R. B. Fischer: National Audubon Society)

A house sparrow finds a use for ticker tape. (FPG)

A wren at home in a discarded jacket. (William S. Paton: Coleman and Hayward)

The great tits and other English birds have learned to open milk bottles. (Ronald Thompson: Annan Photo Features)

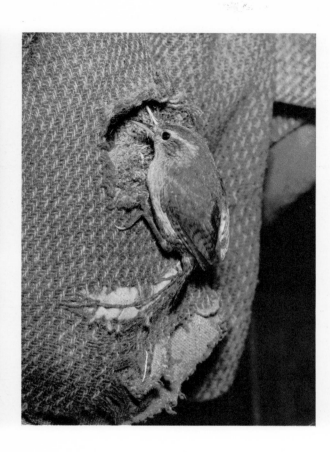

In England, back around 1921, some birds discovered the possibility of getting food by puncturing or removing the caps on milk bottles. Apparently this was started by the great tits or blue tits, but other species learned; and now sparrows, blackbirds, starlings, and others have acquired the habit. The knowledge has spread gradually over an ever-widening area, with no encouragement whatsoever from its human victims.

But we have chiefly been discussing suburbia, which is still fairly natural. The newest and most extreme of the subdivisions of the man-altered environment is the city itself, and a remarkably diverse collection of animals has learned to adapt even to this city world.

18

Natural History in Cities

Cities have been in existence now for about five thousand years. This covers all of human history based on written records, because cities and writing developed at about the same time. Though this span is hardly a moment in terms of the history of life, the development of the city created an entirely new kind of animal world and quite a few animals have moved in. Some of these man brought in purposely, as pets or to work for him; others found splendid scavenging opportunities and have been tolerated; and still others have flourished despite all efforts to keep them out.

In the city, the earth itself is covered with cement and asphalt; cliffs are built of steel, glass, bricks, and wood. The very nature of the air is changed by smoke, and nowadays by the exhaust fumes of motor cars. Though the streets are sometimes lined with trees, only a limited number of species can tolerate the polluted air and the cemented earth. There may be small gardens even in the very center of the city, and there are usually parks, but they, like everything else, are a part of the city planning, designed and arranged for purely human purposes.

Man dominates his environment completely in the city. Like an ant hill or a beehive, it is an aggregation of a single kind of animal along with a few specially adapted hangers-on. Also like the ant hill or beehive, the city is dependent on the outside world for support. No city is ever self-contained; it must live off the surrounding countryside. In fact, the city was not possible until foods had been found that could easily be carried and stored; cities—civilizations—have depended on the development of the cereal crops like wheat, rice, and maize that had these properties. Root crops like the potato, the manihot of Brazil, and the taro of the Pacific can support just as many people per cultivated area as the cereals; but in cultures based on the such tubers the population is dispersed in small villages, probably because the transport and storage problems were insuperable, at least until modern times.

Present-day cities draw on widely separated parts of the world for their materials. Trade, of course, long antedates city formation, but the first trade was in ornaments like shells, or in tools or metals. Except for salt, food was hardly an article of trade until the cities had come to depend on importations, first from the surrounding countryside, then from ever more remote areas. Athenian olives, Egyptian beer, and Roman sausages were among the articles of bulk trade in classical times. Thus, from the beginning the history of the city has been a chronicle of man's increasing withdrawal from the food network of a particular ecosystem.

A sacred cow eats serenely in the streets of Hardwar, India. (Calogero Cascio: Rapho-Guillumette)

Usually there is almost nothing remaining in a city to indicate the nature of the biotic community that once occupied its site. There are many differences among cities, but they reflect economics or national culture rather than biology. To be sure, the shade trees used in tropical cities are different from those used in regions subject to winter cold. But the animals are curiously similar, even in cities with very different climates: rats, mice, houseflies, fleas, lice, dogs, cats, horses, and those most urban of birds, pigeons.

Pigeons

City animals can be divided into two classes: those that man brought in on purpose, and those that moved in without any help or encouragement. Difficulties always turn up in making such distinctions. Take pigeons, for instance. These now live happily and successfully in many cities of the world, but they were always first brought in deliberately as domesticated animals, and the "wild" city populations are descendants of individuals that escaped from direct human supervision. Once they have escaped, they get along very well. They may be fed in the parks by many people, but they are heartily disliked by at least as many other people; the pigeons, however, seem to take both friends and enemies in their stride.

Pigeons were first domesticated in prehistoric times. They are pictured on the monuments of the first Egyptian dynasties, and their virtues both as food and as carriers of messages have long been appreciated. The domestic birds are clearly descendants of the common rock pigeon or rock dove of Europe and Asia, though over the centuries breeders have developed many fantastic variations on this original type. There are something like two hundred domestic varieties of pigeon, and Charles Darwin, among others, became fascinated by this case of evolution under domestication.

Pigeons certainly have escaped easily from human control in the city environment in modern times. Curiously, they do not get along so well by themselves in the country. In the United States, however, they have established themselves on cliffs in various places in the West. They are cliff dwellers in their Eurasian homeland, and they take easily to man-made cliffs—that is, buildings. In his book on *London's Natural History,* R. S. R. Fitter notes that pigeons were known to be established in London by 1385 and that they have been thriving ever since. He complains that "the London pigeon has been most unfairly and cavalierly treated by most writers on the birds of London...just because it happens to be descended from birds escaped from captivity."

Whether in Venice, London, Copenhagen, or New York, city pigeons thrive in the most completely built-up areas. Only rarely are they seen perched in trees; they prefer the steep cliffs of buildings and, to quote Fitter again, "nest in small colonies in all sorts of holes and crannies in buildings, usually high up and inaccessible, just as their wild rock relatives will seek the remotest crevices for their nesting places."

Duck hawks or peregrine falcons are frequently seen chasing pigeons in New York, but they nest mostly in the cliffs of the Palisades across the river. One pair of duck hawks successfully raised a family just under the roof of a Brooklyn office building, and another pair attempted to establish a nest on the roof of the St. Regis Hotel but was discouraged by the management because of their tendency to attack people living in the penthouse.

City Pets

Pigeons can sometimes be classed as pets, sometimes as nuisances, but most city animals are more easily sorted into one class or the other. The variety of pets that can be bought in pet shops or found in city apartments is considerable; it seems to reflect some deep urge in man to have other animals around him in this cemented world. In the city world one cannot argue that pets are kept for utility. The dogs are not needed to guard the house, and there are easier ways of catching mice than by keeping cats. Horses may once have been needed for transport, but this is no longer true of New York's Central Park or London's Hyde Park. And no one has ever claimed any utility for canaries, parrots, monkeys, and tropical fish.

In some cases dogs do have a residual utility; they are good at giving alarm in thief-infested environments. Macy's department store in New York some time ago discovered that the most effective way of dealing with thieves who hid in the store to loot it after it was closed at night was to loose police dogs in the building. Then there are the guide dogs of the blind, and the police horses who still have a special function in managing crowds. But these are rather trivial exceptions among the total population of pets.

The census does not take pets into account in its enumeration of city populations, so there are no statistics for most animals. John Kieran reports that 276,119 dogs were licensed in a recent year in New York, and that in the same year the Humane Society destroyed 59,413 unlicensed stray dogs. This gives a ratio of properly kept dogs to strays of 4.5 to 1. In that particular year, 133,436 stray cats were picked up and destroyed. If the ratio of pets to strays is the same with dogs and with cats, this would give the city a total cat population of some 600,000. But Kieran points out that cats breed faster than dogs, and that kittens are more often unwanted than puppies, so this figure is probably too high.

Westerners are apt to feel superior to the Hindu attitude toward cattle—Western man tends to think of himself as more practical. But a visitor from Mars might well be justified in thinking that our household pets were sacred animals. How else can all the fuss and care, the special foods, the veterinarians, the vigilance against possible cruelty be explained? In addition, pet species are strictly taboo as food.

Pet-keeping is certainly not limited to cities, and it long antedates cities as a human characteristic. South American Indians, African tribesmen, and Australian aborigines all often bring home the young of wild animals to be raised within the family as pets. Young mammals are sometimes suckled by foster human mothers along with their own babies; and as they grow up, such animals are not regarded as possible food, even though wild members of the same species are regularly hunted.

In our own culture, pets are probably commoner on farms or in villages than in cities, if only because they are more easily managed in a rural than in an urban environment. The curious thing is that city people have any pets at all, considering the difficulties that have to be surmounted.

One can argue at length about whether the human impulse to keep pets had anything to do with the origins of domestication. Probably not, because the essence of the idea of "pet" is uselessness, whereas of domesticated animals the criterion is usefulness. When a domesticated animal is turned into a pet, its utility is often lost or impaired—many a pet lamb or chicken has thus escaped the dinner table. Of course hunting dogs and riding horses, both serving as companions and helpers, would be exceptions to this rule. Cats and dogs, the commonest city pets, both have a long history of human association. In the case of cats, it is debatable whether they should be included in the list of truly domesticated species, or whether they should simply be catalogued as having a certain tolerance for the idiosyncrasies of human beings.

There are doubts about the wild ancestry of the modern cat, just as there are doubts about the ancestry of most of the animals presently associated with man. The ancient Egyptians clearly thought highly of cats, as proved by the numerous statues, drawings, and mummies. The Egyptian sacred cat was the same as the wild *Felis lybica* of North Africa, and the species turned up early in towns in other parts of the Mediterranean (leaving their bones as evidence) and probably crossed with the European wild species. At any rate, the cat has been aloofly associated—mostly as a noble, sacred animal—with the activities of Western man since the beginning of his civilization. Superstitions about cats are still with us, and they were rife in the Middle Ages, when cats and witches made an obvious alliance. It is chiefly in modern times that cats have been defended as being "useful" in keeping rats and mice under control.

The independent-minded cats have not so easily been bred into diverse strains as have dogs and other domesticated animals. Possibly geographical varieties like the Persian and the Siamese developed through hybridizing with local wild species, and these types can be maintained in our cities. But they also go wild with the greatest of ease. Altogether the cat is a most curious animal, equally adapted to parlors, back alleys, and island jungles.

Aquaria

Nowadays the balanced aquarium with gaudy tropical fish is everywhere; while the goldfish bowl has a long history, the more elaborate aquarium is a relatively new development and a hobby of growing importance.

The beginning of goldfish culture is lost in the mists of ancient Chinese history. The ancestral fish, a small, nondescript, brownish, carplike species of the Orient *(Carassius auratus)*, would seem to lack any feature that would attract attention for cultivation. But it seems unlikely that the golden varieties started in the wild; it is more likely that they turned up among fish kept in protected ponds. Wherever goldfish have become again established in the wild (as in the Potomac River near Washington) they have rapidly reverted to their original dull coloration.

However the golden variety got started, it has long been prized in China and Japan, and many odd forms have been developed by breeders, sometimes commanding fantastic prices. The Japanese cult of the goldfish is reminiscent of the Dutch cult of the tulip: neither can be explained except in terms of local fashion.

Goldfish are still the commonest of household fish, but they have been made inconspicuous by the hosts of small, bright, tropical fresh-water fishes that aquarists have imported and bred. The tropics of both hemispheres have been combed for suitable species, and great ingenuity has gone into developing methods of breeding. Many species have been hybridized to produce new types, and strange mutations have been carefully preserved. Guppies, originally from Trinidad, and some other species are now almost as completely domesticated as the goldfish, and this evolution has occurred right under our noses instead of over thousands of years.

The city apartment has thus become a very special and curious world with its tropical rain forest plants like philodendron, its big aquarium with bright fishes from South American and African streams, its cat observing the scene with all of the disdain inherited from ancestors of the days of the Pharaohs, and its dog trained to keep to cemented curbs instead of to hunting in the woods. All of these depend on man. Only the cat might be able to get along if man did not come home to provide food. What leads the human species to support this strange entourage? Why fish in the living room? Is it the same as pictures on the wall, or does it fulfill man's need to have something else alive in his otherwise dead city?

Pigeons are famous for living contentedly in the heart of man's biggest cities. (George Holton: Photo Researchers)

Zoological Gardens

Nowadays almost every large city has a zoo. The idea of a collection of wild animals goes far back in history, though less as a public amusement than as a private one for kings and nobles. In about 1100 B.C., the first emperor of the Chou dynasty in China maintained an animal collection which apparently had educational and scientific purposes, and the ancient Aztecs of Mexico also had extensive menageries and aviaries. Perhaps the same impulse that led so many different primitive peoples to keep pets led to the development of zoos at a more complex and sophisticated stage.

But there is no continuity in the history of zoos; they are far from universal. Alexander collected animals for Aristotle, but otherwise the Greeks seem to have cared little for strange creatures. The Romans, to be sure, kept lions, leopards, elephants, rhinos, crocodiles—a wide variety of animals—but chiefly for the purpose of slaughter in the gladiatorial games. Various monarchs in medieval Europe had menageries; a few strange animals, for instance, were kept at the Tower of London until the beginning of the last century, when the gardens of the Zoological Society of London were established in Regent's Park. But such collections were trivial and sporadic.

The zoo as we know it is a development of the nineteenth century; the Paris zoo was founded in 1793, London's in 1826, Antwerp's in 1843. Many of the early zoos were operated by private companies for profit, and exhibiting animals to tourists is still a common enterprise in many places. This aspect of the zoo seems to be related to the circus, which has long depended not only on acrobatic acts and the like but also on the exhibition of spectacular animals.

The great zoos of modern cities are generally supported at least in part by the municipality as a public duty; and they are visited by throngs of people who come to see the animals. Is there some deep meaning in this? In his book *The City in History*, Lewis Mumford has remarked: "The playful antics of the monkey, the imperturbability of the hippopotamus, the gay sleek motions of the seals—all these examples of nature's inexhaustible creativity, if they did not bring the city dweller into contact with nature, at least had a relaxing effect upon the overstrained urban ego."

It is during the present century, as men have congregated in cities in ever-increasing numbers and as the wilderness has retreated with ever-increasing speed, that the zoos have grown into great institutions and have developed ingenious methods of exhibiting the animals in "natural" settings and with a maximum freedom of action. Along with the development of the zoological garden has come a great increase in the popularity of aquaria open to the public, and in the discovery of methods of maintaining oceanic fishes in huge tanks where they can be watched. As men find greater difficulty in getting out into animal worlds, they have shown increasing ingenuity in bringing fragments of those worlds into their cities.

Uninvited Guests

The animal world of the city includes not only the invited guests—pets—but a whole collection of animals that have moved in without any encouragement from man. These include rats and mice and quite a number of insects like silverfish, cockroaches, bedbugs, clothes moths, house crickets, and houseflies. Of course every building doesn't have all of these, though some have quite a few more species. But together, these animals form a group that has shown a remarkable ability to adapt to the conditions of human life.

There is a whole series of different kinds of insects, especially beetles, that have become adapted to life in ant nests. Some of these are encouraged by the ants, but others get along comfortably in the nest environment by managing somehow to escape from ant house-cleaning activities. These "ant guests" have long been called *inquilines* by entomologists, and it would seem to be a good word also for the animals that have adapted to human habitations. Of course, in the list above, the bedbugs could be classed as parasites, along with lice, fleas, ticks, and the like, since they get their food directly from the human body. But the others are not

English sparrows are America's heritage from the days when animals were imported for sentimental reasons. (Frank H. Bauer: Rapho-Guillumette)

direct parasites in the biological sense; they are simply hangers-on—human inquilines.

The cockroaches are interesting in this respect. Among the most ancient of insect types, they were flourishing way back in the Carboniferous period when the coal beds were laid down, 300 million years ago. There are something like five thousand species living in the world today, the great majority of them inhabitants of tropical forests. They are mostly scavengers, living off the debris of the biological community—a way of life that has served them well for many millions of years.

If you build a shelter in a remote tropical forest, some of the local roaches promptly move in on you. They undoubtedly moved in on primitive man as soon as he started making shelters, and some species have stayed with him ever since. They were well known in classical times—in Latin they were called *lucifuga,* because of their habit of avoiding the light. In England they are commonly called "black beetles," though they are not proper beetles at all. They have never been popular guests in human households. It is said that the north Germans call them *Schwaben,* while the Schwabs call them, in turn, *Preussen*. In east Germany they have been called *Russen* and in west Germany *Franzosen*. In New York a common small roach has been called the "Croton bug" because people associated it with the development of the Croton aqueduct bringing water into that city.

The cockroaches thrive, despite the disapproval of their hosts. They are certainly messy, dirty guests. Their fondness for the starch used in the cloth binding of books makes them hated by librarians and bibliophiles as well as by housewives. But they are a nuisance rather than a danger, since they have not been implicated as carriers of any human disease and do not attack man directly.

Along with the roaches there are the houseflies. When or where *Musca domestica* first took up with man, no one is sure. Many kinds of flies of this type are found in various parts of the world, and often are annoyances locally, but *domestica* has got everywhere. It is most abundant where there are horse droppings to breed in, and with the decline of the horse it has become less common in cities. But it is still very much around, for it can breed in almost any kind of garbage. Curiously, no one is quite sure how the fly gets through the winter in northern regions; probably small populations persist in favorable places like cow barns, to multiply explosively with the onset of spring.

The little fruit flies, *Drosophila*, are also now universally associated with man. They are present whenever bananas or grapes or other fruits get overripe, and one wonders how they survived in places and times when fruit-eating was not habitual all year round. *Drosophila* species have long been the favorite animals of the geneticists, since they can easily be raised on bits of banana in small bottles and can pass through a generation in nine days or so. Since hundreds of different pedigreed genetic strains are now cultivated in laboratories around the world, fruit flies must be listed among our important "domesticated animals."

Actually, all of these inquilines have proven useful to biologists. The animals that have moved in on man understandably also turn out to be animals that are easily maintained under cage conditions. Thus cockroaches and houseflies, as well as fruit flies, are frequently used for laboratory studies. Like them, mice and rats—the most widely used laboratory animals of all—adopted man before he turned the tables on them for the purposes of science.

Mice and Rats

Among the rodents, man's closest associates are the house mouse, the black rat, and the brown rat. That mice have been with us for a long time is shown by the history of the word: the English mouse is related to the Anglo-Saxon (and Latin) *mus*, the Hindu *musa*, and so forth. Housewives may get annoyed with mice, but in general our feelings about them are quite different from those we have about rats— think of the difference between the two words when applied to fellow humans. The mouse is a symbol of timidity, and the Latin diminutive, *musculus*, was even a term of endearment. Mouse strains in the laboratory have been of great use to mankind in medical and biological experiments. So have rat strains, for that matter, but our attitude toward rats remains quite different.

Curiously, there is no direct evidence of the existence of rats in classical Greece and Rome, and it has been suggested that the black rat did not get to Europe until the time of the Crusades. Yet remains of rats have been found in the ancient house sites of the lake dwellers of Switzerland and in other Stone Age locations. Possibly classical writers did not distinguish between mice and rats, calling them both *mus*. At any rate, from the late Middle Ages on, rats played an important role in European history because of the great plagues of typhus that swept the continent. They also began to appear in legends, like that of the Pied Piper of Hamlin. Rat-catching became a special profession, often mentioned, but not held in high honor, to judge from Mercutio's use of the label in the third act of *Romeo and Juliet*.

The secure position of the black rat on the European continent was upset about two hundred years ago by the inroads of another species, the brown rat (given the scientific name *Rattus norvegicus* from a mistaken idea of its origin). It was reported from Germany in 1750, Paris in 1753, Spain in 1800. It is particularly adapted to seaports; it appeared in Copenhagen in 1716, London in 1728, and had reached the ports of the United States by 1775.

The brown rat is more aquatic and more subterranean than the black rat, but the latter is a better climber. The black rat thus manages to survive in drier inland situations, especially in the tropics. In a few cases the two species have been reported getting along in the same building—brown rats in the cellar and black rats in the attic—but over much of Europe and the United States the black rats have been completely defeated.

Many varieties of these rats have been described. One, a variety of the black rat called *Rattus rattus alexandrinus* and otherwise known as the "roof rat," is the common tropical form. The rat that accompanied the Polynesians on their island voyages and became established on the Pacific islands is also distinguished as a special "race," but in most places, it has given way to its more aggressive cousins from Europe.

The late Hans Zinsser, in his delightful and informative book *Rats, Lice and History,* makes much of the similarities between rats and people. Both can eat almost anything; both breed rapidly and carelessly and at any time of year; both have managed to establish themselves all over the world, even in rather improbable places; and both live in close association if not in harmony. And, though Zinsser did not stress this, both appear to be addicted to racial conflict, as is shown by the conflicts between the black and brown species of rats.

Parasites

Along with the inquilines, living indirectly off man, there is a group of parasites that use man directly as food. These are often divided into internal and external kinds, depending on whether they live inside the body or outside. The city provides ideal conditions for many species of both sorts because of the large number of people crowded together—the parasite has no trouble in finding new hosts. For this reason cities have long had the reputation of being unhealthy, and it is only recently that we have learned enough about the habits of the parasites, and of methods of sanitation and control, to manage the urban environment. Even so, in the cleanest and fairest of cities, there are still areas of blight that are rich hunting grounds for the parasites of man.

Most of the parasites causing diseases are microbes, and the microbial world has not been discussed in this book. But the whole collection of intestinal worms and all of the external parasites are "animals" by any definition. Some of the worms that infest the human species have complicated life histories involving other hosts—the liver flukes, for instance, must pass from man to man by way of certain snails—and such species cannot spread in the urban environment unless their alternate host also lives there. Others, like hookworm, are easily controlled by rudimentary sanitation. But a few, like the pinworms of children, get along splendidly even in the most sanitary of cities.

Of the external parasites, lice have been with men everywhere from the beginning; there is evidence of this from specimens found on the mummies of ancient Egypt and ancient Peru. Bedbugs, too, persist, as travelers to out-of-the-way places can testify, even though they are easily controlled by modern chemicals.

Most curious, though, is the way two types of mosquitoes have adopted man. One of these is the yellow fever mosquito, *Aedes aegypti*. Quite clearly it was originally an African insect. There it is found in towns, and also in the forest, breeding in rot holes in trees. In towns, the larvae live in all sorts of water containers—vases, pots, rain barrels, and cans. The mosquito spread all over the world in the days of sailing ships, breeding happily in the water butts of the ships, and it managed to establish itself in all of the seaports of the warm regions of the earth and to spread to inland towns. (The Hawaiian Islands had no mosquitoes until the first sailing ships arrived.) But outside of tropical Africa it is never found except in close association with man. The forests of tropical Asia and America have plenty of suitable rot holes in trees in which the mosquitoes could breed. But they don't; the larvae are found only in the household and garden water containers of towns and cities.

When Walter Reed and his associates discovered that *Aedes aegypti* transmitted the virus causing yellow fever, its urban habits made control relatively easy—it was necessary only to develop a thorough house-to-house inspection of water containers, without worrying about the more complex aquatic habitats of forests and meadows. With modern chemicals and thorough inspection, it has been possible to exterminate the mosquito in many cities, thus removing permanently the possibility of a yellow fever epidemic.

The other type of domestic mosquito is a puzzle to students of evolution and animal classification. It breeds in puddles and sewers as well as rain barrels, and in the country as well as in towns. It is interesting that there seem to be several different species or races. Specimens from the tropics and bordering regions are slightly different from those in the northern and southern temperate zones. The tropical type is called *Culex fatigans* and the high-latitude type *Culex pipiens*. But it develops that there are different forms of *pipiens* that cannot be distinguished by appearance. One form must have blood to develop eggs, while the other can develop eggs if fed only fruit juices. In most cases the two forms, found breeding in the same city sewers, will not cross—they act like two separate species.

A further complication is the discovery that sometimes mosquitoes of a given type from one city, say Budapest, will not cross with specimens from another city, London, for instance (the two cities involved in the first experiments). Perhaps this is a case of evolution in action, of species being formed under our noses; but we are far from understanding everything about the matter. Needless to say, the fact that all of these mosquitoes look alike doesn't make experimenting any easier! Moreover, with the *Culex* mosquitoes, as with so many other of the animals associated

The monkeys of India take advantage of the protection given them by Hindu belief. (George Daniell: Photo Researchers)

with man, it is not known where their original home may have been, or what their habits were before the human species created a special niche into which they could move. Maybe their differences have developed since man came along, or perhaps, like those between the brown and black rats, they antedate the association with man.

Man and Nature

Mosquitoes like *Aedes* and *Culex,* then, have learned very well how to get along with man, even in his cities. Or have they? Man has acquired a powerful destructive force with such new insecticides as DDT, and the World Health Organization has seriously undertaken the project of eradicating *Aedes aegypti* from the Western Hemisphere because of its potential threat in the spread of yellow fever. Man has come to regard this planet as his private property, with other inhabitants to be tolerated only at his convenience or pleasure.

This seems curiously presumptuous. The planet has been hurtling around the sun for something like five billion years. Life, we now think, got started somehow about two billion years ago, and there is a record of fossils for about half of this period. Manlike animals, capable of making tools, have been around for perhaps a million years, but for most of that period they were just one more kind of predator in the biological community—somewhat more efficient than wolves because of their tools, but not essentially different in their effect on other animals. Modern man, *Homo sapiens*—creatures we would clearly recognize as fellow humans—may have evolved no more than fifty or a hundred thousand years ago. But even *Homo sapiens* did not develop strikingly new relations with the rest of nature until the beginnings of agriculture, something like twelve thousand years ago. Since then, things have been changing at an accelerating pace, but civilization, urbanization, and industrialization occupy only a minute flash of time in the long history of the earth. Why, then, do we think it belongs to us?

One can argue that the long history of geology and evolution was all simply preparation for the appearance of man. This isn't necessarily a religious argument. We all like to think that man is the crowning glory of the evolutionary process, though we also all get qualms when we look at some kinds of human actions, whether toward fellow men or toward the rest of nature. And it does take a great deal of arrogance to believe that all of that preparation has meaning only in terms of human society. Man seems rather trivial when looked at in the perspective of the billions of years of geological time, or the millions of light-years of astronomical space.

As a matter of fact, one can equally well look at man, not as the crowning glory of anything, but as a sort of disease that has happened to afflict the planet earth. The wildly multiplying numbers of men are all too similar to the wildly multiplying cells of a cancerous growth that can gradually destroy an organism. If cancer cells could discuss the matter, they would very likely maintain that they were doing well in getting the upper hand over all of the other kinds of cells in the body. The cancerous growth, in destroying the system, ends by destroying itself.

A reasonable prediction concerning the future is impossible—the human experiment has been too brief and too explosive for its implications to be understood. No one has a reliable crystal ball, and people who have attempted to assess probabilities differ widely. The apparent trend, certainly, is for the man-altered landscape to replace all others, and bright views of the future anticipate vacation resorts even in Antarctica. If present human population growth continues, the whole land mass will be solidly cemented with urban development in a very few hundred years— standing room only.

Obviously the present rate of human population growth cannot continue indefinitely—the space on earth is limited and it is hardly likely that we will be able to shoot excess millions out into space annually. The human system, if it is to survive, has to come into some sort of equilibrium.

Biological communities, as we have seen, tend to be in equilibrium. With any given species, birth rates and death rates are in rough adjustment: oysters, facing many hazards, produce millions of young; while elephants, with few hazards, have few offspring. There may be cyclic fluctuations in population size, as with the Arctic lemmings; but this is most characteristic of relatively simple communities. The biological community also tends to be in equilibrium with the materials used by its members. Carbon, nitrogen, calcium—all of the chemicals used by organisms—pass through the system in endless cycles; they are used over and over again.

The man-dominated community is currently not in equilibrium. Human population growth is far out of balance. The materials used by man are constantly being dissipated in such a way that they cannot be used again. It is true that nothing is really lost from the planet (if we ignore nuclear reactions), but iron that has rusted and disintegrated into the soil is not again available for human purposes. In burning coal and oil, man is destroying quickly the accumulated reserves of those two billion years of life. In many ways our spectacular accomplishments are at the expense of the capital reserves of the biological system. We are not earning our way.

If civilization is to continue for any appreciable length of geological time, it will have to find some means of reaching balanced relations with the materials on which it depends. Surely this is possible, though none of the forecasts of the future made by science-fiction writers looks very attractive to me. But when man reaches the necessary equilibrium with the materials of nature, let us hope that somehow he manages also to preserve some of the diversity of nature. The natural history of cities can be fascinating—but the animal world of the wilderness is even more so.

Index

Numbers in parentheses indicate color plates; those in italics indicate pages on which black and white illustrations appear.

DESIGN BY ULRICH RUCHTI